MW00533932

WHY WE WILL
NEVER
WIN
THE WAR ON
AIDS

Bryan J. Ellison
and
Peter H. Duesberg

Secret

*Inside Story
Communications*

El Cerrito, California

Inside Story Communications
190 El Cerrito Plaza, Ste. 201
El Cerrito, CA 94530

Designed by Gary Walterscheid and Bryan J. Ellison

Manufactured in the United States of America

ISBN 0-9646475-0-8

Contents

Preface   v

Acknowledgements   ix

Chapter	1	Chasing Wild Geese	1
Chapter	2	The Great Bacteria Hunt	19
Chapter	3	Virus Hunting Takes Over	41
Chapter	4	A War on Cancer	62
Chapter	5	AIDS: The Virus Hunters Converge	93
Chapter	6	A Fabricated Epidemic	120
Chapter	7	Dissension in the Ranks	146
Chapter	8	So What Is AIDS?	173
Chapter	9	With Therapies Like This, Who Needs Disease?	197
Chapter	10	Marching Off to War	227
Chapter	11	Learning the Lessons	256

Selected Bibliography   271

Index   279

They said, "Come, let us build ourselves a city, and a tower whose top shall reach the sky. Let us make ourselves a name, so that we will not be scattered all over the face of the earth."

And G-d descended to see the city and the tower that the sons of man had built.

And G-d said, "They are a single people, all having one language, and this is the first thing they do! Now nothing they plan to do will be unattainable for them!"

— *Bereishit* (Genesis) 11:4-6

Preface

AIDS. The acquired immune deficiency syndrome. Mention the acronym, and you will immediately evoke deep-seated images in almost anyone. Few people can cite even the basic statistics—how many victims, how many dead, how many come from risk groups—yet everyone carries around powerful impressions drummed in by a decade of media coverage.

It all started in the early 1980s, in the wake of the sexual revolution. Young homosexual men began showing up in the major cities, wasting away as they slowly died from horrible opportunistic infections. This strange new disease that destroyed the immune system spread to intravenous drug users, through the blood supply to hemophiliacs, and through sex to the rest of the population. By 1984, scientists had discovered the virus, later named the human immunodeficiency virus, or HIV. The more we learned, the gloomier things looked. The virus would eventually kill almost everyone it infected, and a carrier could seem healthy for years while being able to infect large numbers of unsuspecting victims.

Science seemed to be paralyzed in the face of the most mysterious virus ever. No one could produce a vaccine or find a drug to treat AIDS. The only advice for preventing the disease ranged from the bizarre to the draconian: wear condoms if you have sex, use sterile syringes if you inject drugs, or perhaps we must quarantine the HIV carriers. It all seemed like *The Andromeda Strain* in slow motion.

The deepest emotional responses came from the stories of individual AIDS victims, people whose private lives we knew nothing about, yet who seemed to represent the great danger of AIDS facing the whole population. Rock Hudson. Ryan White, the teenage hemophiliac. Paul Gann, the crusading tax reformer. Kimberly Bergalis, the dental patient. "Magic" Johnson. Arthur Ashe.

This was the official doctrine of AIDS. It was promulgated by the federal government, from the President right down through the Surgeon General, the National Institutes of Health (NIH), and the Centers for Disease Control (CDC). The media echoed this party line, as did thousands of foundations and activist groups. Politicians, right or left, joined in the chorus. Scientists and physicians reinforced the official view with a consensus of expert opinion.

But now this myth is falling to pieces. Prophecies of universal doom have gradually vanished, while most Americans have never even *met* an AIDS victim. Though it never turned into one of the larger epidemics, AIDS has become a $25 billion medical disaster—probably the worst ever. The most technologically advanced research establishment in history has produced no cure, no real prevention, and scientific predictions that have proven to be little more than garbage. "Magic" Johnson stands as a symbol of the millions of HIV-infected people worldwide who remain alive and well, even after a decade. Indeed, only a minority of HIV-positives have ever developed AIDS. What is wrong with this picture?

There is another view of AIDS. Hundreds of scientists and medical doctors are now breaking ranks with the party line, questioning even the most fundamental science behind the War on AIDS. HIV may be just another harmless virus after all. AIDS itself may not be contagious, but merely an umbrella term for a variety of unrelated diseases in unrelated risk groups, conditions which have simply been renamed. The only new epidemic, among homosexual men and intravenous drug users, may be caused entirely by long-term abuse of hard drugs.

Since 1987, the main advocate for this startling alternative view has been Peter Duesberg, a professor of Molecular and Cell Biology at the University of California, Berkeley. For three decades, he has studied viruses, especially retroviruses—of which HIV is one example. For his groundbreaking work, Duesberg was elected into the prestigious National Academy of Sciences, and received an Outstanding Investigator Grant from the NIH. He has even been a top candidate for the Nobel Prize. But for asking questions about AIDS that his colleagues could not answer, they have retaliated against his funding, his ability to publish papers in top journals, and his status within the establishment that had once honored him.

I met Duesberg in February, 1989. I was a prospective graduate student visiting U.C. Berkeley, and he generously offered an hour to explain his reasons for doubting the HIV hypothesis of AIDS. His arguments resounded with clear logic, the sort one no longer hears even in the best college classes. Returning home to decide between graduate schools, I began digging into the scientific literature and raising the issue with biology professors at various universities. As I soon learned, scientists not only disagreed with Duesberg, they grew violently angry at any questions regarding HIV. None had bothered to read Duesberg's scientific papers on the subject, nor could any provide answers. The typical response, stated with the seriousness of a mortician, was "I don't think my colleagues would agree with that." No evidence, no logic, no independent decisions. Scientists had made their collective decision out of an all-pervasive fear of peer pressure.

How could Duesberg be right, but virtually all his colleagues wrong? Because science was no longer science. Something had changed radically in the research establishment, transforming it into a dishonest bureaucracy quite unlike the popular image of truth-seeking professionals.

Naturally, I chose to attend U.C. Berkeley. I spent nearly five years working in various research laboratories, doing cancer research with Harry Rubin and AIDS research with Duesberg. On the side, I also researched the recent history of science, and discovered the startling origins of the modern establishment. Bad science did not begin with AIDS; this has merely been the culmination of a century-long drive away from medical sanity.

AIDS is the product of an elite group within the research establishment—a club known as the "virus hunters." Their roots extend back to the nineteenth century, in the era of the bacteria hunters, when the brand new field of microbiology was generating armies of doctors eager to blame any disease on bacteria. They did—even noncontagious diseases, such as the vitamin deficiencies. The modern virus hunters emerged in the wake of the war on polio, which spent huge amounts of money training new scientists to study viruses. By the time these students graduated to begin their own research, the polio epidemic had disappeared. The virus hunters turned their sights on diseases ranging from multiple sclerosis to cancer, blaming each on harmless viruses. In so doing, the virus hunters collectively seized the reins of political power within the NIH-funded establishment. Among these, the *retrovirus* hunters, a small circle of perhaps one or two hundred key scientists, rose to the very top.

The virus hunters of the wars on polio and cancer became the architects of the War on AIDS. The movers and shakers included such names as Carleton Gajdusek, Hilary Koprowski, Howard Temin, David Baltimore, Myron "Max" Essex, J. Michael Bishop, Harold Varmus, Robert Weinberg, Robert Gallo, Harry Rubin, and Peter Duesberg. As a whole, this group cornered the Nobel Prizes, held editorial positions at the most influential scientific journals, and controlled the allocation of grant moneys. When the virus hunters blamed AIDS on a virus, only Rubin and Duesberg broke from this group to protest, and were thus ejected from the circle of power.

The virus hunters also had allies in the public health establishment. Officials at the CDC, such as Alexander Langmuir, Harold Jaffe, and Donald Francis, worked behind the scenes to help ensure that various epidemics, including AIDS, would be blamed on viruses. Working with the virus hunters in the NIH and the universities, these people created the War on AIDS.

I finally decided that this story should be told publicly, and have therefore written this book. Although Duesberg himself did not actually write it, his previous research on HIV and other viruses, and on AZT and other drugs, has been incorporated into parts of several chapters. Chapters 1 through 4 tell the story of the virus and bacteria hunters, and how they have come to dominate biomedical research. Chapter 5 shows how the virus hunters and public health activists hijacked AIDS research from the very day the first patients were reported. Chapter 6 explains the scientific evidence that HIV is a harmless virus. Chapter 7 profiles the main scientists dissenting against the HIV-AIDS dogma. Chapter 8 presents the evidence that recreational drugs and certain other health risk factors are the real causes of AIDS, while Chapter 9 reveals the true story behind AZT, the immune-destroying toxic drug used to "treat" AIDS. Chapter 10 exposes the hidden forces that engineered the War on AIDS and how the public has been manipulated, and Chapter 11 discusses the solutions to the bad science behind AIDS and other epidemics.

Not surprisingly, the controversial nature of this book has led it on a rocky road to publication. Among the top twenty New York-based publishing houses, most considered the book proposal fascinating but entirely too controversial for them to handle. The book was finally signed on by Addison-Wesley publishing, which placed it near the front of its catalogue and planned a heavy promotional campaign. Apparently, however, the editors never read the proposal, for only after we delivered nine chapters of the manuscript did they suddenly panic. The editor tried desperately to have us rewrite the book almost from scratch, deleting or softening the most controversial points. When they realized such radical editing would be impossible, they refused to accept delivery of the full manuscript.

The only major publisher still willing to take on the book was St. Martin's Press, which now received a complete manuscript before signing. But a few weeks after accepting it, they, too, suddenly had a change of heart. Again the book had to be rewritten entirely, deleting any information that would reflect poorly on the AIDS establishment or would show how drugs cause the epidemic. Then St. Martin's made clear the fact that they did not want to publish the book at all, and were merely backing out of the deal.

Thus I have finally decided to publish through Inside Story Communications. The book you hold is a complete, unadulterated edition. We tell the full truth behind the War on AIDS, pulling no punches. The lid has been forever removed from this controversy.

We believe this book may spark the beginning of a rebellion—a taxpayer's and citizen's protest against the medical research bureaucracy and the virus hunters who dominate it. The reader of this book will be shocked, enlightened, and angered at the deadly effects of politics on science and medicine. Most of all, the reader will never again trust scientific "experts" on blind faith; scientists will finally be held accountable for their proclamations.

— Bryan J. Ellison
May, 1994

Acknowledgements

We are extremely grateful to all the dissidents against the HIV-AIDS hypothesis, whether scientists, journalists, or public-spirited citizens, who have decided that the truth is more important than the comfort of compromise. Many people from around the world, too numerous to mention, have kept us abreast of the latest developments in the AIDS epidemic, or have helped inform the public at risk of their own careers and social status. This debate over AIDS has flourished only because of their courage and integrity.

For providing us with all manner of information for the background and content of our book, we especially thank Joan Shenton, Michael Verney-Elliott, and Hector Gildemeister of Meditel Productions, Ltd., in London; Phillip Johnson of U.C. Berkeley (for information as well as critical advice); Serge Lang of Yale University; Michael Ellner of HEAL in New York; Richard Strohman of U.C. Berkeley; Henry Palka of Hartford, Connecticut; Charles Ortleb of the *New York Native*; David Schryer of Hampton, Virginia; Felix Konotey-Ahulu of Cromwell Hospital in London; Ilse Lass of Berlin; Abraham Karpas of the University of Cambridge, England; Joel A. Schwartz of Santa Barbara, California; Bernhard Witkop of the National Institutes of Health; Gunther Stent of U.C. Berkeley; Harry Haverkos of the National Institute on Drug Abuse, in Rockville, Maryland; and Harry Rubin of U.C. Berkeley. We also appreciate Brian Davis of Berkeley, California, for helping catalog our AIDS files.

We are also indebted to those people who not only provided us with critical information, but who also consented to be interviewed for, or quoted in, our book. These include John Lauritsen of New York; Steve and Cheryl Nagel of Minneapolis, Minnesota; Frank Buianouckas of Bronx Community College, CUNY, in New York; William Bryan Coyle of Fairfax, California; Meny Bergel of the Institute of Leprological Investigation in Buenos Aires, Argentina; Etsuro Totsuka of London; Teresa Schmitz of Miami, Florida; Sue Threakall of Birmingham, England; and Stephen Caiazza of New York (now deceased).

This book would not have succeeded without the well-timed advice and experience of A. James Trabulse of San Francisco, who patiently helped us through the minefield of contract negotiations. Gary Walterscheid provided indispensable help in designing the title and cover, and in making the book truly marketable. William H. McIlhany, of Beverly Hills, California, served as an intellectual mentor to Bryan Ellison and recruited many important individuals to help us in the AIDS debate.

We are grateful to Janie Lowe of Pittsburg, California, Devron Byerly of Fullerton, California, Russel Schoch of U.C. Berkeley, and E. David Smith of New Orleans for editorial review. Their efforts helped strengthen the final manuscript.

Finally, we extend our gratitude to our most critical opponents in the AIDS debate, who have unwittingly provided us the great volume of evidence by which we have disproved the virus-AIDS hypothesis and exposed the political maneuverings behind the War on AIDS.

Chapter 1

Chasing Wild Geese

Losing the AIDS fight

By any measure, the war on AIDS has been a colossal failure so far. In the thirteen years since the first AIDS cases were diagnosed, our leading scientists and policymakers cannot demonstrate that their efforts have saved a single life. This dismal picture applies as much to the United States as to Europe and Africa.

No scientist or doctor has stepped forward to claim credit for discovering an AIDS vaccine, nor is any vaccine expected for several more years, at minimum. In contrast, the post-World War II polio epidemic was declared ended in barely over a decade, once the vaccines of Jonas Salk and Albert Sabin became widely available. Nor have any useful drugs against AIDS been produced. AIDS patients can only choose zidovudine (AZT) or, in certain cases, ddI, ddC, or d4T, all these drugs originally developed as cancer chemotherapies, and bringing with them all the usual effects: hair loss, muscle degeneration, anemia, nausea and vomiting—a severe price for benefits that cannot be measured. Such therapies do not save lives, prolong them, or enhance their quality. Physicians can do little more than comfort the dying patient, monitor his condition, and hope for the best.

Public health officials still cannot prove they have stopped anyone from contracting AIDS. Despite various preventive educational programs, in schools and in the community at large, as well as various official and unofficial efforts to distribute condoms or sterile hypodermic needles in Europe and the United States, no actual decrease in the number of new AIDS cases can be seen anywhere. On the contrary, each year brings a greater number of new AIDS patients. Perhaps more astoundingly, even the screening of the nation's blood supply has not led to any noticeable reduction in AIDS-type diseases (including pneumonia, candidiasis, and lymphoma) nor in death rates among blood transfusion recipients, including hemophiliacs.[1]

Worse yet, the experts have found their estimates and projections of the epidemic to be embarrassingly inaccurate. The latency period—the time between when a person is infected with HIV and develops AIDS—was originally calculated in 1981 to be under one year; almost every year since, this incubation period has been revised upward. Now it is placed at eleven years or longer. Even at the clinical level, doctors find the prognosis of any single infected patient frustratingly unpredictable. They cannot anticipate which disease manifestations the patient will develop—a yeast infection, a pneumonia, a cancer of the blood, dementia, or perhaps no sickness at all.

1

Estimating the spread of the virus has meanwhile led to another problem: officials have continually predicted the explosion of AIDS into the general population, striking males and females equally, as well as homosexuals and heterosexuals, followed by a corresponding swath of death. But the test for HIV, commonly known as the AIDS test, having first led officials to announce that one million Americans were already infected with the virus as of 1985, has not allowed that estimate to budge to this very day. In short, the virus does not seem to be spreading. AIDS itself has not yet affected larger numbers of women, nor entered the heterosexual population outside of drug addicts; nine of every ten AIDS patients is still male, and over ninety-five percent still fall into the same risk categories—homosexuals, heroin addicts, or, in a few cases, hemophiliacs. In Africa, six to eight million people said to be infected for over a decade have translated into a mere 250,000 AIDS victims, some three to four percent of the HIV-positive people. The Caribbean nation of Haiti, where six percent of the population was known to be infected by 1985, has meanwhile remained relatively untouched by the epidemic.[2]

How could the largest and most sophisticated scientific establishment in history have failed so miserably in saving lives, and even in forecasting the epidemic's toll? Certainly not for lack of resources. With an annual federal AIDS budget now over six billion dollars, AIDS has arguably become the best-funded epidemic of all time. Not only are tens of thousands of scientists employed in a permanent, round-the-clock race to unravel the syndrome's mysteries, but the researchers have access to the most sensitive medical technology in history. These techniques have now achieved the ability to detect and manipulate individual molecules, abilities unimaginable to the scientists who fought smallpox, tuberculosis, and polio. Nor have AIDS researchers suffered any lack of scientific data. With 77,000 papers having already been published on this one syndrome, AIDS has been surpassed only by the combined literature on all cancers generated throughout this century.

The answers to the epidemic do not lie in increased funding or efforts to make science more productive. The answers will instead be found by interpreting existing information. Science's most important task, much more than unearthing new data, is to make sense of it. Without going back to check its underlying assumptions, the AIDS establishment will never make sense of its mountains of raw data. Scientists took a wrong turn at some point by making one or more bad assumptions, upon which they have built a huge artifice of mistaken ideas.

The ultimate test of any medical hypothesis lies in the public health benefits it generates; current beliefs about AIDS have produced nothing. Faced with this medical debacle, scientists should re-open a simple but staggering question: What causes AIDS?

Any new disease or syndrome forces medical experts to search for the new agent, which they hope to bring under control. From the start, however, they have a responsibility to consider *both* possible causes for an epidemic: an infectious microbe, or some non-infectious cause, such as poor diet or some toxic substance present in an unusually large quantity. Lives depend on this determination; a contagious disease must be handled differently from a toxic syndrome, and the unnecessary public hysteria created by a misidentified cause can lead to tragic misery and death.

The search for the cause of AIDS, officially ended in 1984, should have examined both infectious and toxic hypotheses. But while minor lip service was initially paid to a chemical basis of the new syndrome, the tremendous weight of federal resources was diverted into a mad race to find a virus. The scientists directing this search, including Robert Gallo, David Baltimore, and Anthony Fauci, had previously risen to the top of the biomedical research establishment as experts on viruses or contagious disease. Such virus hunters had become soldiers without a war since the end of the polio epidemic, the last great infectious epidemic in the industrial world. Holding powerful positions within the scientific establishment, the virologists chose to employ their familiar tools, rather than dropping their old habits to meet new challenges. The appearance of AIDS in 1981 sparked these leading researchers to scramble for a new virus; by 1984, the National Institutes of Health's Dr. Robert Gallo had used his political influence to declare his newly discovered virus the cause at a press conference, not in a scientific forum.

Yet serious doubts are now resurfacing about HIV, the so-called "AIDS virus." Dozens of prominent scientists have begun to raise this question openly during the last seven years, and the controversy gains momentum with each passing week. The consensus on the virus hypothesis of AIDS is falling apart, with its advocates digging in their heels even as its opponents grow in number.

As with most disease today in the industrial world, AIDS appears not to be a contagious syndrome. The evidence exists in the scientific literature, but is widely neglected by researchers intent on viewing the data through the single lens of virology. If biomedical science has erred, if AIDS is not caused by a virus, then the entire medical and public health approach to the syndrome is misdirected. People are not being warned about the true risks for developing AIDS, doctors are using ineffective or dangerous treatments, and public fear is being exploited. Science can no longer ignore this question or sneer at dissenting researchers and physicians. Lives are at stake.

Such a disaster seems almost too fantastic to be true. But blaming non-infectious conditions on contagious microbes has occurred many times before, and as the research establishment becomes more centralized, bureaucratized, and fraught with commercial conflicts of interest, each such episode achieves more monstrous proportions.

Indeed, hidden in foreign-language materials and the footnotes of obscure sources lies the story of SMON, a frightening disease epidemic that struck Japan while the war on polio was accelerating in the 1950s. In many ways, SMON anticipated the later AIDS epidemic. For fifteen years the syndrome was mismanaged by the Japanese science establishment, where virtually all research efforts were controlled by virus hunters. Ignoring strong evidence to the contrary, researchers continued to assume the syndrome was contagious, and searched for one virus after another. Year after year the epidemic grew, despite public health measures to prevent the spread of an infectious agent. And in the end, medical doctors were forced to admit that their treatment had actually caused SMON in the first place.

Once the truth about SMON could no longer be ignored, the episode dissolved into lawsuits for the thousands of remaining victims. This story has remained untold outside of Japan, ignored as too embarrassing for the virus hunters. It deserves to be told in full here.

The SMON epidemic

Any previous skepticism dissolved once Reisaku Kono saw the patient. She was middle aged, suffering from a mysterious nerve disorder that had already paralyzed both her legs. Kono was there to observe the victim because of his work studying polio virus, which in a few infected individuals would break into the central nervous system, causing progressive paralysis and sometimes a miserably slow death. While the condition he examined that day in 1959 was not polio, it bore a certain resemblance. And the suspicion was growing that this, too, could be the result of some undiscovered virus, perhaps one similar to the polio virus.

Kono was visiting the patient at the hospital affiliated with Mie University's medical school. Hiroshi Takasaki, a Professor of medicine at the University, told Kono about a number of these cases he had recently seen at the hospital. They now realized they were facing an outbreak of something new, not just a minor mystery that doctors would catalog and forget. Just the previous year, medical Professor Kenzo Kusui had published a report of another such case in central Japan: the patient had suffered a similarly strange combination of intestinal problems, manifesting as internal bleeding and diarrhea, with symptoms of nerve degeneration. This sequence, stomach pains or diarrhea followed by nerve damage, had been noticed in a few isolated cases as early as 1955, but was now turning into a local epidemic.

More published reports began accumulating after Kono's visit to the hospital. The next five years saw seven major regional epidemics of the new polio-like syndrome, with the annual number of new cases increasing from several dozen in 1959 to 161 victims by 1964—an alarming rate for those small areas. Scientists jumped to conclusions, believing they had every reason to assume the disease was infectious. Just its sudden appearance was enough evidence to convince them. The disease also broke out around specific towns or cities; clusters of cases were sometimes seen within families, and the first person to develop the condition in each of these families was followed by a relative within several weeks; many outbreaks were centered around hospitals, places notorious for spreading disease; and the annual peak of new patients occurred in late summer, hinting at possible spread of the disease through insects. Those scientists who first thought the disease might be related to some non-contagious occupational hazard were quickly dissuaded once the data showed that the disease lacked the expected preferences. Farmers, for example, who would be more easily exposed to pesticides, had a lower than average incidence. Medical workers, on the other hand, had a rather high rate of this condition—further suggesting it was contagious.

Other evidence pointed in the opposite direction. The scientists investigating the epidemic did notice some important contradictions, but the momentum to look for a virus had been generated, and virtually no scientist was willing to risk his status pursuing some unpopular guesses about this horrible epidemic. Yet these puzzling anomalies never disappeared. For instance, the disease had an odd, amazingly consistent bias for striking middle-aged women, but was less common among men and could hardly be found among children, who normally transmit virtually any infectious disease. And careful medical inspection showed that the symptoms did not coincide with ones typically expected for an infection; blood and other bodily fluids, which usually circulate a virus throughout the body, showed no abnormalities, nor did the patients manifest any fevers, rashes, or other signs of fighting off some invading germ. These important pieces of evidence indicating a non-contagious disease, which should have raised doubts, continued to be ignored for several years.

The virus hunt pressed onward. Scientists were expecting to find a virus that primarily induced diarrhea, as was the case in polio. Looking back on this period, Kono has since become admirably frank about his early biases, shared at the time by his fellow virologists: "I was at that time engaged in poliovirus research, so I suspected such a virus to be the cause."[3] But despite years spent searching for the elusive virus, he never could isolate a single one from any patient. A uniquely honest man, Kono patiently reported his null results as he plodded forward.

Meanwhile the epidemic was growing, and the 1964 Olympic Games in Japan were fast approaching. Ninety-six new cases had been diagnosed the previous year, and the increased number of cases was being accompanied by new symptoms; some victims, for example, were now suffering debilitating blindness. In preparing to host tourists from around the world for the upcoming Olympics, the Japanese could ill afford to have an uncontrolled plague. To make matters worse, forty-six new patients suddenly appeared around the city of Toda, one of the locations for Olympic events. Embarrassingly dubbed the "Toda disease," this outbreak directly threatened Japan's reputation and tourism while focusing public fear on the epidemic. Etsuro Totsuka, later to become a lawyer for victims of the disease, summarized the public mood at the time: "Even I was quite worried at the time, as a university student studying physics. The general public, including me, was extremely worried; we didn't know how to prevent it, and there was no cure."[4]

In May of 1964, at the 61st General Meeting of the Japanese Society of Internal Medicine, the disease was raised as a formal topic. Kenzo Kusui, one of the first doctors to report patients stricken with this condition, chaired that session. The participating researchers gave the disease a formal name, Subacute Myelo-Optic Neuropathy (SMON), and they agreed on a standardized clinical diagnosis. With this kind of serious attention given SMON by medical doctors and scientists, the Japanese government could not afford to ignore the situation. The Ministry of Health and Welfare quickly provided a research grant, launching a formal commission to investigate the epidemic under the leadership of Magojiro Maekawa, a medical professor at Kyoto

University. Kono became one of several virologists named to the commission, thereby establishing its mandate as a formal search for a virus. As Totsuka has wryly commented, "Maekawa's group was a bunch of virus chasers."[5]

The same year brought the first sign of a possible breakthrough. Masahisa Shingu, a virologist at Kurume University and a fellow member of the commission, announced his discovery of a virus in excretions from SMON patients. The virus was classified as an "echovirus"—an acronym for *E*nteric *C*ytopathogenic *H*uman *O*rphan virus, called "orphans" because they had been discovered accidentally during polio research but caused no disease. Echoviruses were known for infecting the stomach or intestines, and Shingu found evidence of infection in various SMON sufferers. He excitedly drew the conclusion that this orphan virus had finally been matched with a disease. Perhaps, he speculated, this virus could also occasionally break into the nervous system, much like polio virus. He published the finding in 1965, unabashedly boasting he had isolated the syndrome's cause.

But Kono, knowing the potentially disastrous results of blaming the wrong microbe for the disease, took a more cautious attitude. In 1967, after three years of research trying to confirm Shingu's claims, Kono could only report to a SMON symposium that he had not isolated the virus from patients, nor could he find even indirect evidence that the patients had previously been infected. Kono's better judgment saved Japanese science from stampeding in the wrong direction. He was fully vindicated four years later when other researchers announced the same lack of evidence for Shingu's virus being harmful.

In the midst of this fruitless investigation, the Maekawa team stumbled across a surprising observation that was tragically brushed aside. According to surveys of hospitals, about half the SMON patients had previously been prescribed a diarrhea-fighting drug known by the brand name Enterovioform, and the other half had received a compound marketed under the name Emaform. Not only was this an unlikely coincidence, but both drugs were prescribed for problems of the digestive tract—the early symptom of SMON. The suspicion naturally arose that these drugs might play some role in the syndrome, but the commission bowed to the consensus view of SMON as being contagious and quickly dismissed this notion. Besides, they argued, two different drugs should not cause the same new disease. Had the commissioned researchers checked further, however, they would have discovered that the two drugs were merely different brand names applied to the same drug, a fact that did not surface for several years.

Faced with a disappointing lack of results, the SMON commission dissolved in 1967. The cumulative total of reported SMON cases had meanwhile reached nearly two thousand by the end of 1966, a respectable but not thoroughly frightening number. Except for the quiet growth of the disease epidemic, the floundering virus hunt might have killed public interest in SMON research altogether.

But almost immediately after the folding of the official commission, two rural areas in the Okayama province began reeling from a new explosive outbreak of the syndrome. Dozens of elderly women, and some men in their thirties, began filling the nearby hospitals, totalling almost three percent of the local population by 1971. Scientific attention was again focused on SMON, with the specter of a resurgent epidemic looming in the minds of government officials.

Again ignoring the evidence that SMON might not be infectious, ambitious virologists leapt to the opportunity. Two researchers issued reports in 1968 describing a new virus found in tissues of SMON patients, stirring a wave of excitement. The agent fell under the classification of "coxsackie" viruses, known to infect the digestive tract and originally discovered as a by-product of polio research. But this particular virus, to the dismay of its finders, ultimately proved to have been an accidental contamination in the laboratories. Nevertheless, this short-lived "discovery" helped reinvigorate the search for a SMON virus.

The Japanese Ministry of Health and Welfare, anxious about the expanding epidemic, again decided to form an official investigating body in 1969. Established with over ten times the funding of the old 1964 commission, the SMON Research Commission became the largest Japanese research program ever devoted to a single disease. Its first meeting was symbolically held in the heavily affected Okayama province in early September. The consensus view among Japanese scientists had completely settled on some unknown virus as the probable cause of the disease, and the naming of Kono as chairman symbolically established the new commission's priorities. Among Japanese virus hunters, he held the highest respect.

Yet after more than a decade of persistent research, the virologists had come up painfully empty-handed. With this in mind, and sensing the need to cover all possible avenues that might yield clues to SMON, Kono launched the commission's work by dividing it into four sections, each led by top Japanese medical officials. His colleague Itsuzo Shigematsu, head of the epidemiology department at the Institute of Public Health, was put in charge of conducting nationwide surveys on the extent, distribution, and associated risk factors of the disease; Kono himself, as Director of the Central Virus Diagnostic Laboratory at the National Institute of Health, headed the heavily favored virology group; autopsy results from SMON victims were gathered and analyzed under the leadership of the Head of the National Institute of Health's Pathology Department; and a Professor of Neurology at the University of Tokyo headed a thorough study of SMON symptoms. According to SMON-victim lawyer Etsuro Totsuka, Kono had "told us he presumed the cause was a virus, but he wanted to exclude all other possibilities scientifically."[6] Altogether, forty top scientists participated in the Commission during 1969. Although Kono had opened the door for alternative research directions, the virus hunt accelerated—albeit with some false starts. One scientist, for example, claimed in 1969 a single isolation of a new virus from a patient, but he gave no one else the chance to study it, and eventually retracted his discovery as mistaken.

During the very period SMON was impinging ever more dramatically on Japanese life, some key scientific claims by English and American virologists were beginning to have a profound impact on virus research worldwide, and particularly on SMON research in Japan. The first came in the early 1960s from virologist Carleton Gajdusek of the American National Institutes of Health, who reported finding evidence of the first "slow virus" in humans. He believed it to be the cause of kuru disease among New Guinea natives, but his methods were highly unusual by any scientific standards. He had never actually isolated a virus, but had instead ground up the diseased brains of dead kuru victims and injected these unpurified mixtures into the brains of living monkeys. When some of the monkeys showed deficits in motor skills, Gajdusek published his findings and was lauded by his fellow virologists. The second alleged discovery came from London's Middlesex Hospital in 1964, directly inspired by Gajdusek's claims. Two researchers found a virus that was believed to cause the childhood cancer, Burkitt's lymphoma—the first virus ever claimed to cause human cancer, and the first known human virus thought to have an incubation time between infection and disease measured in years, rather than days or weeks.

These bizarre discoveries were made by very large and respected research establishments; Kono could therefore not afford to ignore them. Other medical experts on the SMON commission warned him that the SMON symptoms did not resemble those of standard virus infections, suggesting the condition was not contagious. Kono, however, brushed aside this advice: "If such were the case, Dr. Gajdusek could not have established a slow virus etiology for kuru."[7] Awed by the large and powerful American research establishment, Kono truly believed that Gajdusek had proved the existence of "slow viruses." Imitating Gajdusek's methods, he injected unpurified fluids from SMON patients into the brains of experimental mice and monkeys, hoping to cause the disease and isolate the guilty virus. But over the course of an entire year, nothing happened to the animals. The experiment was abandoned. Frustrated, but not willing to give up, Kono decided the American researchers were better equipped to find such a virus. He mailed the same fluid samples directly to Gajdusek, who repeated the inoculations into the brains of his own chimpanzees; after three years, they, too, remained perfectly normal. With that, Kono finally abandoned the search for a "slow virus."

With their virus research faltering, a few of the investigators began looking for bacteria. One lab found that SMON patients had imbalanced levels of the beneficial bacteria normally growing in everyone's intestines, but could not isolate any new invading microbe. Two other researchers, as well as Kono's own lab, did notice unusually large amounts of a mycoplasma, one type of bacterial parasite, in disease victims; however, since mycoplasma are found in a large percentage of human populations and are usually known for being relatively harmless or causing some pneumonias, Kono and his fellow researchers decided against pursuing this further.

By 1970, one fact stood out more agonizingly than any other: twelve years of microbe research into the SMON epidemic had yielded nothing but dead ends. Yet the pressure continued to mount as the death toll rose. The year 1969 alone claimed almost two thousand new SMON victims, the worst ever. Kono and his Commission were running out of options.

Fortunately for the Japanese people, several researchers on the Commission were not virus hunters, and these scientists actually rediscovered the evidence for a toxin-SMON hypothesis.

The drug connection

While the race to find a SMON virus was capturing all the attention, other scientists were turning up some important clues to the mysterious syndrome. One pharmacologist, Dr. Beppu, in 1969 visited the hard-hit Okayama province to investigate the increasing outbreak, and independently discovered the same coincidence the Maekawa group had years earlier: that SMON victims had taken certain drugs to treat diarrhea. Upon investigation, all these drugs turned out to be different brand names for a substance known as clioquinol, a freely available medical drug used against some types of diarrhea and dysentery. Beppu fed the chemical to experimental mice, hoping to see nerve damage like that in SMON, but was disappointed when the mice merely died. He failed to understand the importance of that result, however. Clioquinol was sold because it was belived not to be absorbed into the body, instead remaining in the intestines to kill invading germs. The death of Beppu's animals, however, proved that the drug not only entered the body, but could kill many essential tissues in the animal. His oversight left the SMON Commission to rediscover this clioquinol connection the following year. "He later confessed to feeling stupid, because he gave up the experiment when the animals died," Totsuka explained of Beppu. "He wanted to prove a neurological disorder, but only proved the drug's severe toxicity."[8]

Meanwhile the SMON Commission's first priority lay in conducting a nationwide survey of SMON cases reported since 1967, gathered by sending questionnaires to doctors and hospitals throughout Japan. A follow-up survey continued the monitoring while the Commission analyzed the data. These studies were based on a revised clinical definition of SMON, in which the symptoms were spelled out in more accurate detail.

In the fall of 1969, shortly after the Commission began its work, the head of the clinical symptoms section came across several SMON patients with a strange green coating on their tongues. Until that time, doctors might have seen an occasional patient with such a strange symptom, dismissing it as an oddity. But now the growing number of SMON victims finally meant that any one physician could run across several such patients, and draw a connection. Still locked in the grip of the microbe-hunting mentality, however, the other researchers on the Commission raised the suspicion that this might be caused by Pseudomonas bacteria, known for their ability to release colorful blue and green pigments. One of the investigators did isolate such a bacterium from some patients but not from others, and the inexplicable symptom merely became a part of the revised SMON definition.

The green tongue observation achieved new importance in May of 1970, when one group of doctors encountered two SMON patients with greenish urine. Enough of the pigment could be extracted to perform chemical tests, and within a short time the substance turned out to be an altered form of clioquinol, the same drug previously found by the Maekawa Commission and by Beppu.

This raised two very troubling questions. Clioquinol had been marketed for years on the assumption that it only killed amoebae in the intestinal tract, and could not be absorbed into the body; its appearance on the tongue and in the urine now proved this belief wrong. Could the medicine therefore have unexpected side effects? And why would SMON patients manifest the drug by-products so much more obviously than the rest of the population? This latter question particularly bothered one neurology Professor at Niigata University, Tadao Tsubaki. Making an educated guess, he openly formulated the hypothesis abandoned by earlier investigators—that SMON might be the result of clioquinol consumption, not of a virus.

As expected, the interpretation of SMON as a non-contagious syndrome did not become popular among the virus hunters. And the suggestion that *clioquinol* might be guilty met even stronger resistance, for the drug was being used to treat the very abdominal symptoms found in SMON. Medical officials hardly wished to hear they were exacerbating these abdominal pains and adding the insult of nerve damage to the injury. According to Totsuka, "All doctors and scientists wanted to believe in a virus, because they prescribed clioquinol. One of the drug's main side effects was constipation and abdominal pain. Now because the drug caused pain, doctors again prescribed the drug."[9] Doctors, ignorant of clioquinol's side effects, assumed the stomach pains resulted from the primary sickness, and kept increasing the dose in a vicious cycle. Indeed, this new SMON hypothesis disturbed even the researchers who found green pigments on the tongues and in the urine of SMON patients, for these doctors had also prescribed the drug. Tsubaki, fortunately, had never given clioquinol to patients, and therefore felt free to suggest it as the cause.

Faced with strong opposition from the virus hunters, Tsubaki knew he had to gather strong evidence before they could shoot down the potentially important clioquinol hypothesis. Pulling together several associates, he arranged for a small study of SMON patients at seven hospitals. By July of 1970 he had already compiled enough data to draw several important conclusions: 96% of SMON victims had definitely taken clioquinol before the disease appeared, and those with the most most severe symptoms had taken the highest doses of the medication. The number of SMON cases throughout Japan, moreover, had risen and fallen with the sales of clioquinol.

This clioquinol hypothesis explained all the strangest features of the SMON syndrome, such as its preference for striking middle-aged women, its absence in children (who received fewer and smaller doses of the drug), and its symptomatic differences from typical viral infections. It also shed new light on the supposed evidence that SMON was infectious—its tendency to appear in hospital patients, to cluster in families, to afflict medical workers, and to break out more heavily in the summer. All of these reflected the patterns of clioquinol use. The epidemic itself had begun shortly after the 1953 approval for pharmaceutical companies to begin manufacturing the drug in Japan.

From thirty-seven cases in January of 1970, the syndrome had now risen to claim nearly sixty victims during the month of July. The Japanese Ministry of Health and Welfare decided not to wait any longer, and promptly released the information to the press. The news of Tsubaki's research reached the public in early August; the number of new SMON cases for that month dropped to under fifty, presumably as some doctors stopped prescribing clioquinol to their patients. On September 8th the Japanese government banned all sales of the drug, and the total new caseload for that month sank below twenty. The following year, 1971, saw only 36 cases. Three more cases were reported in 1972, and one in 1973. The epidemic was over.

For the next few years, the Commission's research focused on confirming the role of clioquinol. In 1975 it released a comprehensive report. Systematic epidemiological surveys matched use of the drug with outbreaks of the syndrome, and experiments were performed on animals ranging from mice to chimpanzees; as it turned out, the drug induced SMON-like symptoms most perfectly in dogs and cats. Meanwhile, the investigators began uncovering individual case reports of SMON symptoms from around the world, wherever clioquinol had been marketed. Totalling roughly one hundred cases, the published reports ranged from Argentina in the 1930s to Great Britain, Sweden, and Australia in more recent times, often with the doctor specifically pointing out the association with the use of clioquinol or similar compounds. Ciba-Geigy, the international producer of the drug, had received warnings of these incidents years before the Japanese epidemic, a fact that later became the basis of a major lawsuit against the pharmaceutical company.

Clioquinol, often marketed under the brand name Entero-vioform, has been available for decades throughout many countries in the world. But while doctors outside Japan have published a few reports of SMON-like conditions, no real epidemic of the disease has ever broken out in Europe, India, or other countries with widespread use of the drug. Much of the difference lies in the heavier consumption of clioquinol in Japan, where the stomach, rather than the heart, is considered the seat of the emotions. The general over-prescription of drugs in that country further worsens the problem, such that many SMON victims had histories of using not only clioquinol but also multiple other medications, often at the same time. Government health insurance policies have encouraged this over-medication, paying doctors for every drug prescribed to the patient. As a result, the proportion of the Japanese health insurance budget spent on pharmaceutical drugs grew from twenty-six percent in 1961 to forty percent in 1971, a level many times higher than in other nations. By the time the Japanese government decided to ban clioquinol, many of the hardest-hit SMON patients had each consumed hundreds of grams over the course of several months. And whereas the outside world mostly used clioquinol to prevent diarrhea when travelling abroad, the Japanese usually received the drug as hospital patients, having an already weakened condition.

"Why had research on the etiology of SMON not hit upon clioquinol until 1970?" asked Reisaku Kono years later, at a 1979 conference. The question has two answers, both pointed out by Kono himself:

> There were at least two occasions when physicians suspected that clioquinol might have something to do with SMON. I know of a certain professor rebuking one of his staff physicians for connecting clioquinol with SMON. In 1967 the study group of the National Hospitals on SMON reported as follows: Entero-vioform [clioquinol's brand name], mesaphylin, Emaform (home produce of clioquinol), chloromycetin and Ilosone were often prescribed to SMON patients, but no link was found between Entero-vioform and SMON. This report referred to Entero-vioform in particular so that clioquinol must have been suspected by someone in the study group. Dr. Tsugane, who was responsible for the survey, said that the survey was not thorough enough to unearth clioquinol as a causative agent. One of the reasons could have been that clioquinol had been used as a drug for the intestinal disorders of SMON, and it was hard to believe that clioquinol was toxic rather than a remedy.[10]

Referring here to the tentative fingering of clioquinol by the Maekawa group, Kono observed that too many medical doctors refused to recognize the possibility of an iatrogenic disease (one caused by the doctor's treatment). They understandably disliked the idea that a drug might cause some of the very symptoms for which it was prescribed in the first place.

Another, more fundamental, reason for overlooking clioquinol lay in the prevailing attitude of the virologists. As expressed by Kono, "We were still within grasp of the ghosts of Pasteur and Koch!".[11] SMON, a vaguely polio-like syndrome, had first appeared in the midst of a war against polio. The polio virologists, Kono included, were naturally inclined to search for a new virus as the cause of the new disease. The Japanese government, having funded polio virus research, simply kept up the momentum by funding the same virologists to study SMON. Thus the virus hunters received the lion's share of research monies and attention, and with that the power to direct the SMON research program. Had it not been for Kono's foresight in also appointing non-virologists onto the Commission, the epidemic might have lasted much longer.

At least the epidemic had ended, with the truth universally recognized. The virologists had learned their lesson, and the search for SMON viruses was over.

Or was it? Incredibly, against all evidence, the SMON virus hunt suddenly came back to life within weeks of the epidemic's end. The fight over the cause of the syndrome was to drag on for several more years, with the virus hunters simply ignoring the fact that SMON itself had disappeared after the ban on clioquinol.

The virus hunt revived

In February of 1970, while the SMON Research Commission was still scrambling to find the cause of the epidemic and a few researchers were just beginning to notice the greenish pigments in some patients, Assistant Professor Shigeyuki Inoue at Kyoto University's Institute for Virus Research claimed discovery of a virus in the spinal fluid and excretions of SMON patients. He added the extracts to laboratory culture dishes of hamster tumor cells, and found that the new agent killed the cells. With more experimentation, Inoue classified the microbe as a new herpes virus. He was able to isolate this particular virus from nearly all SMON patients he tested, over forty in all, and found antibodies against the virus in other victims.

Reisaku Kono moved promptly to test these new observations. He used Inoue's own virus isolate and cell cultures, and within three months of Inoue's first report found that the virus could kill some cells. These particular cells, however, were extremely sensitive, prone to spontaneous death even in the uninfected cultures. Kono began to suspect the virus was harmless. He also could not isolate the virus from any SMON patients, unlike Inoue's lab. Perhaps, he openly wondered, the alleged virus might not exist at all.

A number of careful scientists sided with Kono, insisting they could neither find the virus in SMON victims, nor could they cause cell death in culture dishes by adding virus samples from Inoue's lab. Nor could Inoue's extracts induce symptoms when injected into mice. Indeed, Kono and some of these other investigators could never even find the virus at all, reinforcing the growing question of whether it truly existed. The virus could not even be detected in the samples sent them from Inoue. An occasional mouse injected with Inoue's supposed virus would become sick, but the symptoms did not resemble those of SMON. Kono won allies among his peers when many of them could not reproduce Inoue's observations, a troubling problem for any scientific claim.

Nevertheless, Inoue had meanwhile rapidly achieved celebrity status for his "SMON virus" during 1970, before the clioquinol announcement that August. The Japanese news media had prematurely publicized his results, creating the widespread impression that the cause of SMON had been determined. Hysteria over the contagious plague swept through much of the country, causing frightened family members of SMON patients to avoid contact with their "infected" relatives, and leading many of the victims to commit suicide. "Patients were isolated, many committed suicide, and there was national panic," reflected Totsuka on the horror he witnessed. "I met families who lost relatives. I heard from most or all of my 900 clients; most of the patients said they very much feared and dreaded the disease. Everybody told me about that, about those sufferings. Once they found out about the drug, they were somewhat relieved, because it was not infectious."[12]

The new virus-SMON hypothesis had indeed achieved a life of its own, causing a few scientists to jump on the Inoue bandwagon; months *after* clioquinol had been banned and the epidemic had virtually disappeared, several labs excitedly issued reports claiming they could reproduce Inoue's findings. Inoue himself further insisted he had caused SMON-like symptoms in mice, including weight loss, paralysis, and nerve damage, either by injecting the virus into their brains or feeding the virus to other immune-suppressed mice unable to fight off the infection. Inoue and a collaborating scientist also both claimed to have photographed the virus directly with electron microscopes, although Inoue's colleague eventually retracted his own report as having been mistaken.

A meeting of the SMON Research Group was finally held in July of 1972 to resolve the controversy. Until that time, Inoue's results had received attention and concern equal to the clioquinol research. But based on the inability of many scientists to produce the same results, which must be done for any scientific hypothesis to be accepted, the members at the meeting decided not to focus any more research efforts on the Inoue virus. Samples were frozen for future study, and the Group thereafter devoted its resources to studying clioquinol.

Despite the absence of confirming evidence, and despite the disappearance of SMON following the ban on clioquinol, Inoue and his supporting colleagues continued to publish reports of evidence for the virus hypothesis, often in the pages of the *Lancet*, a prestigious British medical journal. This publicity carried the Inoue hypothesis overseas, leading the 1974 edition of a respected American textbook, the *Review of Medical Microbiology*, to incorporate the Inoue virus hypothesis of SMON.

Shocked and angered by the favorable publicity surrounding Inoue's hypothesis, Kono wrote a letter to the *Lancet*, published in August of 1975. The international popularity of virus research had whetted scientists' appetite for Inoue's hypothesis, but Kono also knew he was battling a nearly complete ignorance of the SMON episode outside Japan:

> Inoue et al. published several papers on SMON virus, and a standard textbook adopted Inoue's virus theory as confirmed. However, research in the laboratories of the SMON Research Commission in Japan failed to confirm Inoue's results. Unfortunately, this negative information has not been published in English...[13]

Despite this letter, the 1976 edition of the same textbook again supported the virus hypothesis of SMON, barely acknowledging that a controversy existed over the syndrome's cause.

The epidemic's toll had officially ended in 1973 with 11,007 victims, including hundreds of fatalities. Angered upon learning of Ciba-Geigy's calloused disregard of previously reported clioquinol toxicity, many of these patients filed a lawsuit in May of 1971 against the Japanese government, Ciba-Geigy of Japan and fifteen other distributors of the drug, and twenty-three doctors and hospitals. The ranks of the plaintiffs soon swelled to some 4500, with legal action initiated in twenty-three Japanese district courts. The largest group of SMON victims sued jointly through the Tokyo District Court; when frustrations mounted over the slow and indecisive actions of their lawyers, 900 of the plaintiffs broke away to form a second group. The aggressive investigations conducted by this new legal team reinvigorated the case, bolstering the positions of the plaintiffs in parallel lawsuits and forcing the defendants to use hardball tactics. Etsuro Totsuka, one of thirty members of this legal team, has described the fight:

We were the only team gathering information outside Japan, inviting foreign experts to testify in Japanese courts, discovering that the United States FDA had restricted clioquinol ten years before Japan, and waging an international campaign against Ciba-Geigy...

We found many foreign doctors who had reported clioquinol side effects before. They were contacted by Ciba-Geigy, and except in one or two instances were persuaded not to help us. By the time I saw the doctors, they had already been contacted by the other side. They had been invited on trips, some to Ciba-Geigy's headquarters... We felt they were already compensated, under the condition not to tell us anything.[14]

The two sides slugged it out for several years, but the testimony by members of Kono's SMON Research Commission proved devastating. Prepared to yield by mid-1976, the defendants finally proposed a settlement in the Tokyo Court. However, just as the battle seemed finished, one of the defendants made a surprise move. That October, Tanabe Seiyaku, Ltd., a leading Japanese producer of clioquinol, suddenly decided to switch its defense strategy—by insisting that SMON was caused by the Inoue virus after all. Despite having been thoroughly repudiated by the investigations of Kono's former research commission, the Inoue virus-SMON hypothesis had maintained a small but steady following among a few virus hunters. Now one of the defendants was reviving this hypothesis in order to cast a cloud of ambiguity on the issue.

The technique partly worked. Ignoring the dismal failures of the old SMON virus hunt, Tanabe withdrew from settlement offers in several courts and repeatedly filed challenges, motions, and appeals in a desperate legal gambit that lasted nearly two years. Most of these efforts were blocked, but Tanabe stunned plaintiffs in 1978 by winning a partial victory in one court decision. Pressured by the lawyers, the Kanazawa District Court issued the first ruling in the SMON lawsuits, favoring the plaintiffs but reducing the reward on the basis of Inoue's supposed "SMON virus." Careful fact-gathering by plaintiffs in the Tokyo Court, which issued the second judgment, prevented the virus hypothesis from gaining more ground, and a string of legal victories followed in the other courts.

Today most scientists and laymen outside Japan have never heard of the virus-SMON controversy, even in the face of the lawsuit against the distributors of clioquinol, television documentaries in Germany and England on clioquinol, and two conferences during the 1970s on iatrogenic (medically-caused) disease. The SMON disaster, a fifteen-year rampage that ignored the evidence of a toxic cause and sacrificed thousands of human casualties for obsessive microbe chasing, is simply too embarrassing to the virus-hunting establishment.

AIDS: SMON lessons forgotten

When Michael Gottlieb, at the medical center of the University of California, Los Angeles, observed five patients dying from bizarre diseases during the early months of 1981, he already suspected he was opening the curtain on a new epidemic. AIDS, like SMON, did grow dramatically over the next decade, although more widely—appearing with unnerving suddenness in major cities of the United States and Europe as well as in Africa and the Caribbean, where mystique-ridden stereotypes of these countries lent credibility to stories of widespread devastation.

Again following the pattern of SMON, AIDS circumstantially appeared to be contagious, with cases turning up among hemophiliacs and other recipients of blood transfusions, and with outbreaks of the syndrome found among mutual sex partners in the homosexual community. In other words, potential transmission routes for some unknown virus could be identified. But other evidence actually indicated both syndromes to be non-infectious: whereas SMON struck middle-aged women more than any other group, AIDS showed an extreme bias for young men in their twenties to their forties, mostly heroin addicts and homosexuals.

SMON, as it turned out, resulted from the use of a prescription drug for the early symptoms of SMON itself, a fact so horrifying to doctors that the possibility was repeatedly cast aside whenever the evidence would emerge. AIDS is also partly the product of a prescription medicine—AZT, the very one provided as a therapy for AIDS. Once again, that horrifying possibility is cast aside by scientists and doctors.

AIDS, too, became a centrally managed epidemic, with the U.S. National Institutes of Health directing most research and preventive education in this country. Special commissions were also set up by prestigious scientists and government officials, beginning in 1986, to focus all resources and efforts into a concerted War on AIDS.

And from literally the first week after Gottlieb reported his AIDS cases, the virus hunters began the search for an AIDS virus, dominating the research effort just as their Japanese counterparts had done with SMON. Once again, several viruses in turn were blamed, from the herpes-type cytomegalovirus to the retrovirus HTLV-I, until a consensus formed around another retrovirus, the Human Immunodeficiency Virus (HIV).

The SMON epidemic finally ended because Reisaku Kono and other Japanese scientists possessed the wisdom to direct some resources into non-virological research, and to listen when those other investigators found answers. But the officials and scientists driving our war on AIDS have had no such tolerance for alternatives, else they would probably have solved the problem years ago. Ignoring the lessons of SMON and other diseases, today's biomedical research establishment stubbornly blocks all research and questions that disagree with the consensus view of AIDS.

Despite this antagonism, an impressive and growing number of scientists are expressing doubts about the virus-AIDS hypothesis. The evidence argues that HIV is simply another harmless passenger virus. Rather than finding open doors and public debate, the dissenting scientists have suffered intimidation, lost research funding or consulting fees, found themselves blocked from publishing papers, and become socially isolated from the modern political structure that sustains, and can therefore equally well destroy, scientific careers at whim.

Where the war on SMON was a molehill of misdirected science, AIDS has become an unmoveable mountain. The difference lies in the respective sizes of the scientific establishments involved. Not only is the funding for AIDS research much greater than the amount spent on SMON, but the pre-existing structure—measured in numbers of scientists, size of departments, and sheer volume of published data—now far exceeds the combined size of all scientific endeavors in human history. Thus errors necessarily become magnified beyond any individual's control, making pragmatic opportunism far easier for the career-building scientist.

SMON and AIDS are even more intimately connected. Both have been episodes in a long series of miscalculations emanating from a single ongoing, self-propagating scientific program—microbe hunting. Microbiology certainly achieved many notable scientific discoveries, especially early in this century. But the polio epidemic marked the end of the infectious disease epidemics that once ravaged the industrial world. Microbe research has mostly outlived its usefulness, leaving virus and bacteria hunters with little to accomplish, yet they still dominate the increasingly well-funded science establishment. As a result, they have for three decades been misleading science and the public about medical conditions ranging from cervical cancer to Chronic Fatigue Syndrome, from Alzheimer's disease to hepatitis C, and many more. All these smaller programs are failing in their public health goals as they prescribe the wrong treatments and preventive measures, while generating unnecessary fear among the lay public. Ironically, in the very process of covering up bad assumptions with volumes of irrelevant data, the microbe-hunting establishment creates its best excuse for even more money, personnel, and power: They must have resources to find the answers.

SMON did not mark the first time microbe hunters falsely blamed viruses or other microbes for non-infectious diseases. "Pellagra is a classic example," Reisaku Kono emphasized in retrospect. "It was once believed to be a communicable disease and, as is well known, Goldberger swallowed fecal extracts of the patients to destroy this notion."[15]

Pellagra, the quintessential human tragedy representing the era of the bacteria hunters, has been too widely forgotten. Chapter Two tells the story of Goldberger and other scientists who fought the excesses of the first microbe-hunting establishment.

Chapter 1 Footnotes

[1] Duesberg, P.H., AIDS acquired by drug consumption and other noncontagious risk factors. *Pharmacology & Therapeutics* 55:201-277, 1992.

[2] Duesberg, P.H., Human immunodeficiency virus and acquired immunodeficiency syndrome: Correlation but not causation. *Proc. Nat. Acad. Sci.* 86:755-764, 1989.

[3] Soda, T. (ed.). *Drug-Induced Sufferings: Medical, Pharmaceutical, and Legal Aspects.* Excerpta Medica, Amsterdam, 1980, p. 11.

[4] Ellison, B. Interview with Etsuro Totsuka. May 1, 1992.

[5] Ibid.

[6] Ibid.

[7] Soda, Op cit., p. 12.

[8] Ellison, Op cit.

[9] Ibid.

[10] Soda, Op cit., p. 13.

[11] Ibid., p. 11.

[12] Ellison, Op cit.

[13] Kono, The SMON virus theory. *Lancet* II:370-371, 1975.

[14] Ellison, Op cit.

[15] Soda, Op cit., p. 11.

Chapter 2

The Great Bacteria Hunt

The leading killers in the industrial world today are the slow-developing conditions of older age, including heart disease and cancer. As our health and life expectancies increase, we ironically live long enough to die of these new diseases.

But people throughout the Third World and in our own past have faced deaths at much younger ages, and from a different cause: contagious disease. Pre-industrial societies are marked by frequent and deadly epidemics of every conceivable infectious illness, from flus and pneumonias to tuberculosis and malaria. Although infectious disease was commonplace, people were mystified by these strange conditions that could be passed from one individual to another. Thus during the many centuries in which infections dominated human mortality, myths ranging from possession by evil spirits to inhalation of miasmal airs were offered as explanations.

Not until the seventeenth century did the first person use lens-making technology to discover the existence of microbes. Antony Leeuwenhoek, a Dutch janitor with a penchant for constructing microscopes in his spare time, found immense numbers of the tiny one-celled organisms now known as bacteria. The tiny creatures existed not only in water, but within the bodies of humans and animals alike. Leeuwenhoek's discovery did attract the attention of established scientists at the time, but he never supposed that these bacteria might cause disease, considering them mere curiosities. Nor had he any reason to blame them for disease, as no logical rules yet existed for proving such an idea.

Two centuries later, Leeuwenhoek's discovery did give birth to the germ theory of disease. A French chemistry professor named Louis Pasteur was asked by local brewers to determine why some vats fermented and others did not. He learned through his experiments that yeast, a microbial type of fungus, was the organism making the alcohol, and that bacteria could prevent the fermentation as well as cause contaminated food to decompose. Physicians and scientists throughout Europe soon made the logical connection with disease, and the hypothesis that such germs might cause sickness became a widespread topic of discussion. Joseph Lister, for example, gained prominence as the doctor who popularized antiseptic surgical techniques in the wake of Pasteur's growing fame.

Still, no one had actually proven that a particular disease was caused by a corresponding bacterium. Many leading doctors, in fact, refused to believe that disease could result from transmissible microbes at all. Although they ultimately turned out to be mistaken, their healthy skepticism nonetheless played a critical scientific role, forcing the early microbe hunters to formulate objective standards for blaming any disease on a germ. The importance of such proof cannot be underestimated; many diseases are not infectious, yet a number have been falsely blamed on microbes throughout the nineteenth and twentieth centuries. Such mistakes can be easily avoided only when scientists carefully apply logical standards.

By 1840, Jakob Henle, a professor at Germany's Göttingen University, publicly suggested that infectious disease would be found the result of some invisible living organism that could be transmitted from person to person. The problem, as Henle observed, was that to prove this "contagion" caused a disease, it would have to be isolated and grown outside the human body. At the University of Prague, another German professor named Edwin Klebs carried this reasoning one step further during the 1870s. Not only should the microbe be cultured from the diseased body, but it should be able to cause the same disease when injected into another animal. To many European doctors, this proposal certainly made logical sense. But without any examples proven by such experiments, most doctors preferred to suspend judgment on the germ theory.

At this point a German medical doctor named Robert Koch entered the fray. He founded his research on the results of Casimir Joseph Davaine of France, who had demonstrated that blood from cows with anthrax could transfer the disease to newly injected cows. Studying the strain of bacterium found most easily in cattle with anthrax, Koch wanted to prove his suggestion that the microbes could form spores. He was therefore forced to find some way to grow them under his microscope. He developed a method of growing the bacteria in the eye fluid from slaughtered cattle, and quickly proved his point. Moving beyond these studies, Koch then inoculated mice with these bacterial cultures and discovered that they, too, became sick as their bodies filled with the deadly bacteria. Having initially planned to study bacteria merely for their own sake, he instead published a paper in 1876 boldly announcing he had proved this bacillus to be the cause of anthrax.

Koch thus became the first person to meet the criteria of Edwin Klebs. However, the anthrax bacteria were large and easy to isolate, and they usually caused disease in animals rather than humans. So he next followed his growing interest in the subject of human disease, and started his work with the study of open wound infections. Observing samples from various animals and people, he reported that bacteria could hardly be found in healthy organisms, while they were abundant in the blood of the diseased animals. Koch's results led him to add now a third and key condition to the others proposed by Klebs:

> In order to prove that bacteria are the cause of traumatic infective diseases, it would be absolutely necessary to show *that bacteria are present without exception and that their number and distribution are such that the symptoms of the disease are fully explained.* [italics in original][1]

In other words, a microbe cannot scientifically be proved guilty of causing a disease unless every diseased individual has large amounts of the germ growing in the damaged tissues of the body. A single exception would be enough to pronounce the microbe innocent of creating that disease.

One major problem with meeting such standards of proof lay in the difficulty of culturing pure preparations of any given bacterial species. Koch's 1878 book on his wound infection experiments described his attempts to purify the cultures so that contaminating bacteria could not be blamed for causing the disease, but only in 1881 did he finally publish a paper describing a new technique for pure culture of bacteria. The method used a dish, later improved and named the Petri plate after Koch's assistant, that allowed scientists easily to separate individual bacteria by growing them apart from one another. Finally the microbe-hunting tools, both experimental and logical, were in place.

Koch next focused his attention on tuberculosis, the leading infectious killer of humans at that time. Within months, he found, isolated, and cultured a bacterium from the patients. According to Koch:

> In all tissues in which the tuberculosis process has recently developed and is progressing most rapidly, these bacilli can be found in large numbers... As soon as the peak of the tubercle eruption has passed, the bacilli become rarer...[2]

Having met the first two conditions of proof, he went on to show that guinea pigs injected with the purified bacteria would now become sick with tuberculosis. The proof complete, Koch published his landmark 1882 paper describing the experiments.

He wrote another key paper on tuberculosis in 1884, in which he spelled out the three criteria for proving a microbe guilty of causing a disease. First, the germ must be found growing abundantly in every patient and every diseased tissue; second, the germ must be isolated and grown in the laboratory; and third, the purified germ must cause the disease again in another host. Together, these rules have become known as Koch's Postulates.

Fame quickly followed Koch's work, and scientists and doctors alike jumped on the bandwagon. During the next two decades, bacteria were found and proven guilty of inducing over a dozen major diseases, including diphtheria, tetanus, food poisoning, some types of pneumonia, and syphilis. But in the rush and popularity of the new microbe hunting, a scientific sloppiness led many researchers to blame newly discovered bacteria prematurely, without having satisfied the universally accepted postulates of Koch. Even Koch himself was partly guilty, for he too maintained an over-enthusiastic ambition to find bacteria in almost every disease. In his study of cholera, for example, he isolated the correct bacterium, but could not find an animal that would become sick when injected with the microbe. He nevertheless declared it the cause of cholera using statistical correlations, rather than testing other animal species to meet the third postulate. At this same time, microbe hunters were just beginning to understand how vaccination works, but Koch never used this as a reverse means of conducting the test. As it turns out, scientists have since produced cholera in rabbits, dogs, and guinea pigs, though often under special conditions. While Koch was lucky on that score, he and others soon made numerous mistakes in identifying disease-causing bacteria.

But the successes did lead to a variety of developments in medical technologies, including the discovery of antibiotics for killing bacteria, the development of new vaccines against various microbes, and an increased emphasis on hygiene. Governments began enforcing public sanitation and vaccination measures—mostly after Koch's appointment to the Imperial Health Office of Germany—policies that soon spread throughout the industrializing world. Nutrition, and standards of living, also improved among industrial nations during the same time period. While controversy exists over the importance of each condition in stopping particular epidemics, the epidemics as such have largely disappeared, and medical intervention against the microbes is widely credited for this. Indeed, no other medical discovery has ever achieved as much acclaim.

Naturally, then, scientists have since kept an ambitious eye out for new microbes, hoping to find the causes of unexplained diseases—often the ticket to fame and fortune. But when scientific standards such as Koch's postulates have been pushed aside in the race for recognition, medical disasters have usually struck. Humans and animals, whether healthy or sick, are host to many hundreds of microbes, the great majority of which cause no harm whatsoever. Some can even be beneficial, such as the E. *coli* bacteria that populate the intestines and aid digestion. Without the rigor of the scientific method, researchers can easily isolate one of these harmless microbes and blame it for a disease, even if the illness is non-infectious.

Plagues of Malnutrition

As we know today, scurvy is a disease caused by a lack of vitamin C in the diet. It begins with such characterisitic symptoms as bleeding gums, progresses to swollen legs and brain-destroying dementia, and ultimately leads to death. Long before vitamin C was chemically identified and isolated in the 1930s, various observant individuals had noticed that scurvy could be cured, even in its latest stages, by some "antiscorbutic factor" found in such foods as citrus fruits, potatoes, milk, and fresh meat. But the historic preoccupation with contagious disease often obscured this discovery, each time delaying public knowledge of the health benefits of such foods for many more years.

Fear of contagion predates Robert Koch's discovery of disease-causing bacteria. During the mid-sixteenth century, roughly 100 years before Leeuwenhoek first saw microbes in his primitive microscope, scurvy was given its first description by physicians that included Ronsseus, an advocate of a dietary hypothesis of the disease. His contemporary Echthius, on the other hand, watched outbreaks of scurvy among monks in a single monastery and concluded the disease was infectious.

This latter opinion proved influential for centuries, despite an early proof of diet as the cause. Sir Richard Hawkins, British admiral, confronted scurvy among his sailors on a long voyage in 1593. Upon reaching Brazil, he discovered that eating oranges and lemons would cure the condition. Nevertheless, even he felt obligated partly to blame unsanitary shipboard conditions, and following his death the British Navy completely lost all memory of the citrus fruit cure.

While Hawkins still lived, a Frenchman named Francois Pyrard described an expedition to the East Indies. Unaware of Hawkins' findings, he ascribed scurvy to a "want of cleanliness" and insisted that "it is very contagious even by approaching or breathing another's breath."[3] Yet Pyrard ironically had also discovered the curative power of citrus fruits. His independent dietary discovery was forgotten, as was Hawkins', and the infectious view continued to prevail.

An outbreak of scurvy occurred on a 1734 voyage of a British ship, affecting one sailor especially severely. Anxious to prevent spread of what he believed to be a contagious disease, the captain marooned the hardest-hit sailor on the nearest island. Fortunately for the sailor, he ate grass, and later shellfish, from which he received enough vitamin C to recover. A passing ship found him, and upon reaching England he astonished many by the very fact he lived. This was one of the events that stimulated James Lind, British naval surgeon, to begin his experimentation in curing scurvy. After several years of research, he concluded that the key to the cure and prevention of scurvy was some factor found in citrus fruits but missing from sailors' diets. This proof he published as a book in 1753, but he was roundly rejected by the British medical establishment for some forty years. Only in 1795 was lemon juice finally provided to naval sailors (at that time often called "lime" juice, thus originating the nickname "limeys" for sailors). During this period the English captain James Cook also discovered, on his 1769 voyage, that fresh vegetables and citrus fruits worked, despite apparently no knowledge of Lind's work. But he too insisted on hygienic practices and fresh air, which he believed to be as important as diet in preventing scurvy, thereby helping confuse the significance of his results.

By the turn of the nineteenth century, the point seemingly should have been settled. However, the role of diet had never been fully accepted outside of England, and even British doctors gradually reduced their emphasis on it as the century progressed. This negligence, combined with the rise of bacteria hunting in the later 1800s, led too many scientists to forget or ignore the earlier discoveries. One could more easily isolate a new bacterium than a new vitamin.

Jean-Antoine Villemin provided one prominent example. A member of the Paris Academy of Medicine, he was the first to demonstrate that tuberculosis was an infectious disease; Robert Koch had based his search for the tuberculosis bacillus on this work. Villemin became a passionate advocate of the germ theory for disease in general, and in 1874 began debating the still widely accepted view that bad diet was somehow responsible for scurvy. In one paraphrased version he states

> Scurvy is a contagious miasm, comparable to typhus, which occurs in epidemic form when people are closely congregated in large groups as in prisons, naval vessels and sieges... We have many examples of well-fed sailors and soldiers going down with scurvy, while others less well fed do

not. Also, we have positive evidence of the spread of the disease by contagion—for example, the introduction of scurvy into French military hospitals
by veterans returning from the Crimea, and the rapid spread of scurvy from
one sailor to another in naval vessels.[4]

Villemin, of course, was using a poor argument that nonetheless is still
repeated today by top scientists for other diseases. Outbreaks of a disease do
not really argue for an infectious cause, merely for a factor common to the
group in which the disease appears. Another member of the Academy of
Medicine responded to Villemin by arguing that some diet common to the afflicted was indeed the reason for those scurvy epidemics. Further, he pointed
out the danger of falsely blaming a disease on infection: medical authorities
would justifiably see the need to quarantine patients to protect the public.

The growing popularity of the germ theory, and its clear successes, soon
gripped medicine so tightly that it began redirecting research on scurvy. In
1899, British explorer Frederick Jackson teamed up with a professor at
London University to perform experiments on the disease in animals. Jackson
decided that fresh meat did not contain a vitamin, but rather that older meat
was contaminated with bacteria that spoiled it and produced "ptomaines,"
poisons that would cause scurvy. Joseph Lister, the surgeon inspired by
Pasteur's discoveries enough to popularize antiseptic surgery to avoid infections, had by this time become President of the Royal Society of London and
was only too happy to provide funding for Jackson's research. As he himself
put it, he wished to see new research on scurvy in light of the recent microbe
discoveries. The two researchers chose monkeys for their experiment, feeding
them various diets to see whether diet itself or food contamination would induce scurvy. But since vitamin C had not yet been isolated, the diets were not
well controlled for the postulated food factor, and the results showed that
monkeys fed tainted meat became sick more often. The President of the
Royal Society endorsed and promoted the experimental report, and microbe
hunters—believing scurvy to result from digestive tract infection, and intent
on finding a guilty bacterium—seized on the report in an attempt to to silence
diet-minded critics.

The obsession with microbe hunting not only distracted scientists from
finding vitamin C, but actually helped *cause* epidemics of scurvy. For instance, Louis Pasteur's technique of sterilizing milk by heating it had spread
throughout Europe and America, becoming popular because the microbe
hunters had convinced the public of hygiene's primary importance. The pasteurization process unfortunately also tended to destroy the vitamin C in milk,
which led to hundreds of new scurvy cases among young children each year.
Unwilling to admit their mistake or to read the available history of the disease, the American Pediatric Association issued a report on childhood scurvy
in 1898, concluding that bacteria-produced ptomaine poisoning, not the heating of milk, was the real cause of the epidemic. Thus the deadly illness continued to haunt the population, remaining needlessly mysterious.

Researchers simply would not let go of the germ theory in their scurvy
research. The highly respected 1907 textbook *Osler's Modern Medicine*,

while recognizing some dietary role in the disease, insisted that an unidentified microbe contaminating the food must infect the unsuspecting victim and cause the sickness. Another contemporary view held the disease to be a type of inherited syphilis, itself a genuine bacterial disease. One French scientist actually found a new strain of bacteria in a scorbutic baby and proposed it to be the cause, although other scientists examining the blood of other patients could not find the bacterium. During World War I, another group of scientists isolated a different bacterium from scorbutic guinea pigs and still another from an adult human. The bacillus found in the animals was then injected into healthy guinea pigs, some of which developed certain symptoms vaguely resembling scurvy. But the bacteria could never be found in the blood of these newly infected animals, and blood from a sick animal would not make another animal sick when injected. Still, the researchers argued they had the scurvy-causing germ. Another report at that time proposed that scurvy could be transmitted through lice. Many or most doctors in Russia meanwhile believed bacteria to be the cause, as did various surgeons in other European armies. And at least one German doctor, sent in 1916 to examine Russian soldiers suffering from scurvy, largely blamed their unsanitary conditions. Of course, all of the germs blamed for scurvy failed to meet Koch's postulates, standards that could have prevented much of the wasted effort, but scientists were busier trying to emulate Koch's success than his rigorous logic.

Fortunately, the microbe hunting craze did not permanently derail the search for vitamin C, which was finally purified by the 1930s. C. P. Stewart, Professor of Clinical Chemistry at the University of Edinburgh, in 1953 summarized the chronic scurvy disaster:

> One factor which undoubtedly held up the development of the concept of deficiency diseases was the discovery of bacteria in the nineteenth century and the consequent preoccupation of scientists and doctors with positive infective agents in disease. So strong was the impetus provided by bacteriology that many diseases which we now know to be due to nutritional or endocrine deficiencies were, as late as 1910, thought to be 'toxemias'; in default of any evidence of an active infecting micro-organism they were ascribed to the remote effects of imaginary toxins elaborated by bacteria.[5]

Beriberi is another fatal condition, brought on by a dietary lack of vitamin B$_1$ (thiamin). The nervous system degenerates, creating paralysis, swelling, and often heart attacks. Though it has primarily plagued Asia throughout history, it appeared with a vengeance in the West after the French Revolution, when the French population rejected the dark bread of peasantry in favor of the royal milled white bread from which the thiamin had been unknowingly removed. Bread processing soon swept throughout Europe and the United States, and beriberi followed closely.

The first person to discover the basic cause of the condition was Kanehiro Takaki, a medical doctor and later Surgeon General for the Japanese Navy. Concerned about the beriberi epidemic rampant in the Japanese military and in the cities, he carefully studied its characteristics and during the 1880s performed an experiment. By experimenting with the diets of sailors in different ships, he found he could cure and even prevent the disease. The military, responding decisively, altered the official diet for sailors and thereby ended the epidemic in 1885. Takaki then published his persuasive results in a prestigious British medical journal, the *Lancet*, in 1887. Instead of acknowledging poor nutrition as the cause of beriberi, the scientific community wantonly disregarded it. The report had arrived during the height of the bacteria-hunting craze, five years after Robert Koch had found the tuberculosis bacillus, and microbe hunters were eager to find new germs. Even in Japan, microbe hunters strongly influenced by Koch and his contemporaries sniped at Takaki, insisting that beriberi was truly infectious and had been cured by better sanitation, not by better diet. These same critics did not bother testing their own idea, blinded by the promise of bacteria hunting.

Christiaan Eijkman, a Dutch army doctor, had meanwhile observed first-hand an epidemic of beriberi among the Dutch soldiers in Java. Although the disease mysteriously left the natives alone while ravaging the conscientiously hygienic Dutch, Eijkman's infection-biased medical training led him to assume some germ must cause the disease. He therefore decided to advance his skills in finding bacteria, and spent a few months (1885-1886) working in Robert Koch's laboratory in Berlin. Having become desperate, the Dutch Colonial Administration in the meantime formed a team of scientists under Dr. Pekelharing to study the disease. Pekelharing also assumed the condition was infectious, and, after consulting Koch, recruited Eijkman onto the team.

In Java, Pekelharing isolated a bacterium that he promptly blamed for beriberi. He left shortly thereafter, turning over his work to the enthusiastic microbe hunter Eijkman. But Eijkman, unable to find the microbe in all the sick patients, tried at least to transmit the disease to chickens through blood from patients. At first nothing happened, then all the chickens developed a sickness like beriberi—including those not having received any blood. Confused, he performed several other experiments until he discovered that the sickness was caused by eating polished rice, which had temporarily been fed to the chickens instead of their usual unprocessed rice. This explained the human disease: the Dutch all ate polished rice, while the Javan natives did not. Eijkman convinced the Dutch prison warden in Java to test the idea by feeding unrefined rice to the prisoners. Their beriberi soon disappeared.

Upon presenting his results to his supervisor, Eijkman received only rejection. His superior even went so far as to publish an attack on the chicken and prison studies, and when Eijkman published his own paper in 1890, colleagues criticized him. The Dutch commission to which Eijkman belonged officially concluded that, although blame could not be fixed on the Pekelharing bacillus, the epidemic must be caused by an undiscovered germ. Eijkman himself was so under the hypnotic spell of the germ theory that he continued for at least eight more years to refer to beriberi as a contagious disease caused by microbes, despite his own results.

The peer pressure of scientific consensus must also have intimidated him. At least two dozen of his colleagues continued to find and blame the sickness on a dizzying variety of microbes, ranging from bacteria to worms. Scientists isolated bacteria from the digestive system, the blood, and the urine of beriberi patients. One group found three types of bacteria and blamed them all; another investigative team discovered four types simultaneously. Three groups blamed protozoa, organisms similar to the one causing malaria, and at least two scientists decided fungi growing on moldy rice were the culprits. And even a virus was reported found and falsely convicted in 1900.

No single one of these microbes remained popular for long, however, largely because a fair number of scientists failed in trying to find each germ in all beriberi patients, and were willing to publish their negative results. Robert Koch himself ironically held high hopes of finding the beriberi bacillus, but was unsuccessful during his research on a trip to New Guinea. Koch's careful commitment to logical scientific standards overrode his enthusiasm, and he openly published his lack of results in 1900. Nevertheless, reports of beriberi-causing microbes actually continued into the 1910s, and the predominant infectious view of the disease led doctors to "treat" it with such compounds as quinine, arsenic, and strychnine. The question of beriberi's cause was finally settled, even for the microbe hunters, only when vitamin B_1 was isolated in 1911 and again in 1926. The vitamin is now added back to white bread, and beriberi has become a rare disease.

Robert Williams, one of the scientists who pioneered the discovery of vitamin B_1, later commented on the dangerous influence of the microbe hunters in emulating Pasteur and Koch too carelessly:

> Because of [the work of Pasteur and Koch] and other dramatic successes bacteriology had advanced, within twenty years after its birth, to become the chief cornerstone of medical education. All young physicians were so imbued with the idea of infection as the cause of disease that it presently came to be accepted as almost axiomatic that disease could have no other cause.
>
> This preoccupation of physicians with infection as a cause of disease was doubtless responsible for many digressions from attention to food as the causal factor of beriberi.[6]

The Pellagra Plague

In terms of the number of people affected, pellagra has probably been the most devastating vitamin deficiency epidemic of all. It manifests itself most visibly by the rough and peeling skin with splotches of reddish pigmentation, followed by nerve disorders and dementia, wasting syndrome and diarrhea, and finally death. Unsurprisingly, the name "pellagra" derives from the Italian for "rough skin." As was discovered earlier in this century, niacin deficiency is the cause. Because corn lacks niacin, and various populations have turned to corn as a nearly complete substitute for other vegetables, pellagra has usually appeared wherever corn has become a dietary mainstay. First described in the eighteenth century, the disease soon grew into an epidemic in Italy, and spread throughout the Mediterranean area during the nineteenth century.

Doctors who wrote the early descriptions of the disease clearly noticed the association with corn diets and poverty. Beginning in the early 1800s, a series of prominent physicians formulated several closely related hypotheses about this connection, speculating either that corn itself caused pellagra or that the fungus on moldy corn produced some sort of poison. Some prescient observers even correctly guessed that corn was not nutritious enough as a complete diet. But most European doctors originally agreed that the syndrome could not be contagious, since it never seriously spread out of the impoverished corn-eating subpopulations. And as early as the 1790s an occasional doctor observed that pellagrins (pellagra patients) could be cured with more balanced eating habits.

Despite the clear inability of the disease to spread beyond the risk groups, some doctors unfamiliar with the disease still proposed it to be contagious. Already in the 1700s several physicians blamed the disease on "miasms," or bad airs, and the German doctor Titius, himself far removed from epidemic areas, in 1791 simply called it infectious. Prominent French doctor Jean-Marie Hameau, in his 1853 doctoral thesis, decided that since pellagra strikes people living near sheep, and because sheep have an infectious disease with some symptoms resembling pellagra, that the disease was transmitted from sheep. Barring this unlikely possibility, Hameau conceded the infection might come from contaminated corn. Although most doctors did not agree with Hameau's view, a typical approach to treating pellagra was nevertheless based on fighting infection, which included artificial bleeding, quinine, and arsenic. The latter, in particular, was the treatment pioneered by one of the early Italian microbe hunters, who believed the common fungus on moldy corn caused the disease.

As the successes of Pasteur and Koch became widely popular, scientists and doctors began flocking into bacteriology. No longer required to invent hypothetical infections, they could use the increasingly simple tools for isolating real bacteria and blaming them. Many wanted to have Koch's success, but few were willing to apply the acid test of Koch's postulates, nor even to ask whether the disease in question was truly contagious, as evidenced by spreading out of its initial risk groups.

Thus bacteria hunting turned to pellagra with a vengeance. In 1881, the Italian doctor Majocchi was first to isolate a bacterium from both spoiled corn and the blood of patients. Several more scientists discovered that this microbe was the same as a previously identified bacterium found in potatoes, and that the rotten mass of corn contaminated by this germ could cause diarrhea in dogs, though not in other animals. However, unlike Majocchi, they could not find the bacterium in the blood of pellagrins, instead finding it growing in the intestines of all humans, including those without disease. So ended Majocchi's bacterium.

Another bacterium blamed in the 1880s was later found only in some pellagrins, as well as in some people without the condition, and so was forgotten. A third bacterium reported in 1896 by Carraroli was also soon abandoned.

Then, for several years after the turn of the century, an Italian researcher named Ceni generated a remarkable number of scientific papers claiming that a corn fungus excreted by chickens—regardless of whether the fowl had eaten fresh or spoiled corn—also caused the disease in humans. Ceni and his co-workers found these fungal spores in most, but not all, people who had died of pellagra, and tested a variety of animals to show that large amounts of this fungus would make the animals sick, especially when injected into the blood. Ceni soon expanded his list to two, and then four, separate fungi that he thought would all cause pellagra. Even though these fungi could not grow in the body, Ceni insisted they could still release poisons. During these years Carraroli, who had previously isolated a bacterium from pellagrins, now jumped on the fungus bandwagon, alleging that one of Ceni's fungi could be isolated from the fecal matter, urine, blood, saliva, and affected skin of patients. By injecting the fungus into experimental animals, he even produced symptoms he thought resembled pellagra. In fact, Carraroli was so caught up in admiring this microbe that he simultaneously accused it of causing syphilis.

Another researcher inspired by Ceni reported in 1904 two new candidate bacteria for causing pellagra, based on their presence in corn and resistance to the heat of cooking. One of these could cause intestinal sickness when injected into animals. The other was similar to the intestinal bacterium present in all humans that helps digest food, so he decided it released poisons that could act as co-factors, or enhancers, in helping Ceni's fungi cause pellagra.

The sheer volume of Ceni's ongoing research forced a number of scientists to spend a great deal of effort refuting his results. The fungal spores, as it turned out, neither caused pellagra nor any other disease in animals, nor could they be found in patients having died of the disease. And the full-grown fungi were often simply natural parasites of dead humans.

Yet the microbe hunt continued. Tizzoni, a prominent Italian researcher and doctor, began reporting from 1906 onward for several years his experiments on two strains of bacteria, both blamed by him for pellagra. Having found the germs in pellagrins, he and other scientists were able to cause some sort of sickness in monkeys and guinea pigs injected with the bacteria. Thus, he brazenly declared, "It would seem to be settled that pellagra is a bacterial disease."[7] However, a number of scientists never could isolate these bacteria from people with pellagra, leaving Tizzoni's work with little impact among European doctors stymied in trying to cure the disease.

The chances of finding a cure, as well as the opportunities for microbe hunters, multiplied dramatically once the pellagra epidemic appeared in the United States. A few cases had passed unnoticed before the twentieth century, but the first recognized instance appeared in Georgia, when a single farmer was diagnosed by his doctor with the disease in 1902. Four years passed without the medical establishment paying any attention. Then an outbreak suddenly appeared at a hospital for the insane in Alabama. Eighty-eight patients became severely ill, most of whom died. Soon dozens of cases began appearing in hospitals throughout Southern states and even in Illinois. Facing a now-unnerving epidemic, the head of a hospital for the insane in South

Carolina visited Italy in 1908 and decisively concluded that the American epidemic was indeed pellagra.

Hundreds of cases had by then occurred in over a dozen states. By mid-1909 the Public Health Service, a branch of the federal government that still exists today, established a small laboratory for pellagra research in South Carolina. Their man in charge, Claude Lavinder, pursued three lines of activity: experiments, therapy, and public relations. Having no other serious model to follow, he searched for a microbial cause of the disease by injecting various types of animals with bodily fluids from pellagrins, though to no avail; none of the animals became sick. Lavinder's treatments fared no better, for he used the widely popular arsenic as well as mercury. But his propaganda efforts proved more effective, for the media soon mobilized to convince Americans they were facing a disease that could spread out of control, and that would affect everyone, rich and poor alike.

The growing epidemic activated the concern of many medical doctors, who held a National Conference on Pellagra in 1909, also in South Carolina. As in Europe, the evidence of pellagra's association with corn-based diets was clearly recognized at the meeting, as was the fact that it struck exclusively poor communities (soon thereafter blacks were recognized as the major risk group), both facts indicating a non-contagious epidemic. But the age of microbe hunting was still in full swing, and although many scientists began investigating the corn connection, the conference also set in motion a revived hunt for a pellagra microbe.

The following year Lavinder was replaced at the pellagra lab by John D. Long, who believed the disease was brought on through a lack of hygiene. He discovered an amoebal microbe in the intestines of most of his pellagra patients, and fingered this germ as the cause in his 1910 report. Long, as it turned out, had followed the lead of Louis Sambon, a well-known British doctor who in 1905 had announced after a brief visit to Italy that he believed pellagra to be an infectious disease. Building on his own work on malaria, Sambon declared to the press in 1910 that the disease was transmitted by insects, either flies or buffalo gnats. He failed to notice that unlike malaria, pellagra did not spread out of its risk groups; even in epidemic areas, only very poor farmers were affected. Sambon did realize that an infectious disease should spread at least somewhat, and therefore argued erroneously that children were primary targets of the disease.

Because of his own reputation, and the fact that he had assembled an official commission of top British doctors, Sambon's hypothesis caught on and quickly spread to the United States. One scientist, convinced of the Sambon hypothesis, published evidence in 1912 that airborne insects crowded the areas near water during the seasons pellagra was most prevalent, implying malaria-like spread of pellagra. Another research team created a complex hypothesis of insect transmission in Kentucky, reasoning that insects picked up the deadly microbe from horses, transferred it to blackbirds that flew to other areas, where more insects now carried the germ to unsuspecting humans. Meanwhile at least two other prominent doctors actually isolated protozoa from many, but not all, pellagrins, and published these as either causes or cofactors. Even the Department of Agriculture sent a special team of entomologists to study insects in South Carolina in 1912. Potential transmission routes ranging from contaminated drinking water to mosquitoes, even houseflies and bedbugs, were suspected as vectors carrying pellagra, and newspaper articles served to fan public fears as the epidemic grew.

The consequences of this contagion mania were serious, striking eerie parallels to our modern response to the AIDS epidemic:

> So great was the horror of the disease that a diagnosis of pellagra was synonymous with a sentence of ostracism. A severe case of eczema was enough to start a stampede in a community, and pellagrins sometimes covered their hands with gloves or salve, hoping to conceal their condition.
>
> Many hospitals refused admission to pellagra patients. One in Atlanta did so on the grounds that it was an incurable disease. At another hospital in the same city, student nurses went on strike when they were required to nurse pellagrins. Physicians and nurses at Johns Hopkins Hospital in Baltimore were forbidden even to discuss pellagra cases which might be there. Fear of the disease spread to schools and hotels, too...
>
> ... Tennessee began to isolate all its pellagra patients. The state board of health declared pellagra to be a transmissible disease and required physicians to report all cases...
>
> ... Exhibits on pellagra were prepared for the public, creating fear of the disease along with interest in it...
>
> ... There was pressure for a quarantine in Kentucky, and pellagra patients at the Western Kentucky Asylum for the Insane were isolated...
>
> Isolation did not prevent spread of pellagra but instead heightened panic over it.[8]

A second National Conference on Pellagra was organized in South Carolina in 1912, and this time the clear momentum of scientific and medical thought had turned in favor of finding pellagra germs. Earlier that same year, an official federal government commission, the Thompson-McFadden Commission, was created and began studies in the South. One of its three leaders was an Army Medical Corps man who had previously served on Louis Sambon's pellagra commission in England. Naturally, the commission showed a complete bias for infectious causes. Quickly and casually dismissing dietary connections, the commission turned its attention to studies of sewage, insect transmission, bacteria, fungi, and even the suggestion that Italian immigrants had brought the disease with them. Ultimately the stablefly was officially blamed by the commission for spreading the deadly contagion.

The prestige of this federal commission spurred the Public Health Service to renew its own effort at finding the pellagra microbe in 1913. Lavinder was reassigned to head a group that once again tried repeatedly to give monkeys the disease from injections of human blood. They failed miserably. Yet even then Lavinder could not completely let go of the infection hypothesis, and eventually gave up pellagra research altogether.

Finally, as the epidemic reached the 200,000-victim mark during 1914, and while the Thompson-McFadden Commission continued to issue its reports, the Public Health Service replaced Lavinder with an obscure officer named Dr. Joseph Goldberger as head of their team. This was the turning point in the epidemic.

Within weeks of arriving in the South, Goldberger saw the obvious that the entire medical establishment and its experts, gripped in the madness of microbe hunting, refused to notice: venturing both into rural areas and insane asylums to see the victims firsthand, he was astonished to find that even where many patients were concentrated, their doctors and nurses did not catch pellagra. He also observed the different diets of the two groups, the doctors eating meat and vegetables and the farmers their customary corn diets. Goldberger drew the inescapable conclusion. Some nutritional deficiency was the cause. After publicly stating his hypothesis in 1914, he was attacked by doctors who insisted the disease was contagious. He also stirred up excited debate and opposition at that year's conference of the Southern Medical Association.

Gathering the proof for his notion through a series of experiments in which he completely cured pellagra by changing diets in orphanages, hospitals, and prisons, Goldberger announced his findings in 1915. *The New York Times* carried the story, though buried inside its pages. At another medical conference, where the leaders of the Thompson-McFadden Commission presented further findings on infection, Goldberger stirred up intense anger and controversy by critiquing the commission's latest study. When he then presented his own results, the effect was electrifying. Two leading advocates of the contagion view backed down, one of them a leader of the Thompson-McFadden Commission, the other withdrawing his own paper from submission.

But when the news media began giving Goldberger's results favorable publicity, pellagra microbe hunters reacted with alarm and anger. Prominent doctors joined in a growing chorus of protest against the supposedly dangerous nutrition hypothesis, arguing that the public was now being misled. One such doctor at a medical conference "drew applause when he described as 'pernicious' the newspaper publicity that told people there was no danger of pellagra except from poor food and cooking."[9]

The Thompson-McFadden Commission struck back especially hard in 1916, in the pages of medical journals as much as in *The New York Times*. They reiterated their conclusions, including the dangers of insects. Goldberger patiently confronted his critics and answered their objections, but finally reached a point of exasperation. He decided to perform a new experiment to prove the disease non-infectious. He, his wife, and fourteen coworkers injected themselves with samples of blood, feces, mucus, and other bodily fluids from pellagra patients. As he expected, none contracted pellagra. Even this experiment had little effect on medical opinion. Opponents continued to attack or ignore him for several more years, their ranks only gradually thinning with time. Part of the problem lay in pellagra's increasing human toll until the early 1930s, when diets finally began changing to include greater variety. Goldberger continued studying the disease until his death in 1929, and niacin, the vitamin missing in pellagrin diets, was isolated in the mid-1930s.

Return of the Bacteria Hunters

By the 1930s, the bacteria hunting era was rapidly drawing to a close. This change, however, arose neither from the consistent application of Koch's postulates nor from lessons learned in the vitamin deficiency disasters. Medical scientists, it seems, have learned little, if anything, from these mistakes. Social and economic changes, not lessons learned, caused the temporary decline of microbe hunting. Nutritional and genuinely infectious epidemics steadily declined until after World War II, when they reached bottom. Today infectious disease constitutes only about one percent of all causes of death in the industrial world, the consequence of improving nutrition and other factors over the last couple of centuries. Public fear of contagion evaporated along with the epidemics, and the microbe hunters were forced into relative obscurity for a time.

But today the bacteria hunt is enjoying a modest revival, largely in the wake of the virus hunting era that currently dominates biomedical research. A few erroneous bacteria-disease hypotheses have survived as holdovers from the old microbe hunt a century ago, and are still widely believed; others have been newly invented in the last few years, and are gaining ground in the fashions of scientific opinion.

Leprosy is one example. The modern disease has two types, neither connected with the biblical disease of the same name: the tuberculoid form is somewhat more benign and involves lesions on skin and damage to nerves, but is relatively contained in small areas of the body, while the lepromatous form causes the well-known grotesquely large lesions on different parts of the body. The disease can create numbness and paralysis, and can appear so horrible that popular myth mistakenly believes limbs even fall off. Several million cases exist today, almost entirely in the Third World.

The disease has long been thought to be contagious, and in 1872, as microbe hunting was just getting off the ground, Gerhard Armauer Hansen discovered a bacterium in lepers that he blamed for their condition. The bacillus has proved difficult to grow in culture, and can be hard to distinguish from the tuberculosis bacillus. Although leprosy is admittedly extremely hard to transmit between people, scientists defend their notion of the disease as being infectious on three grounds—it slowly declines over time in countries where lepers are quarantined, children living in families with lepers are more likely to get the disease than other children, and the Hansen bacillus can be found in most or all patients with this sickness.

Regarding the first point, leprosy has actually declined in various nations, including the Western world during the Middle Ages, whether or not large-scale quarantine or increased sanitation takes place, so some other factor must cause its disappearance. On the latter point, the little-known truth is that in Third World areas most affected by leprosy, infection by the Hansen bacillus is extremely widespread in the healthy population, suggesting its presence in lepers is pure coincidence. Indeed, over ninety percent of the bacillus-infected population never develop leprosy.

As for the spread of the disease, it does not behave in any way like an infectious epidemic. Doctors and nurses caring for lepers are notoriously immune to catching the disease, even though half of them become infected with the bacterium. Nor do breastfed babies or young children get the disease from their leper mothers, despite becoming infected during the first year of life. Nor can transmission of the disease be documented between married partners or through open wounds and blood contact. Defenders of the Hansen hypothesis can only hide behind "practical difficulties in carrying out controlled studies," or assume that the leper's antibodies against the bacillus are somehow ineffective, to explain the gaps.[10]

The paradoxes mount. The Hansen bacillus, like all bacteria, can invade and quickly spread throughout the body within days or weeks, yet leprosy slowly develops over periods ranging from two to twenty-five years, with occasional patients suddenly and inexplicably recovering their normal health. The tuberculoid form of the disease, though causing greater numbers of lesions on the body than the lepromatous form and requiring serious treatment, contains astonishingly few of the Hansen bacteria—too few to do the damage. This particular bacterium, in fact, is only one of many different bacterial species that can be found abundantly in the standard leprous lesions, and may be as irrelevant as the others to causing the disease. And when injected into armadillos, the leading experimental animal for the disease, the Hansen bacteria multiply well without causing leprosy in the animals. In humans, the disease does not even have the typical signs of an infectious disease, including sites of initial attack by the bacterium.

These problems and others have sparked a growing challenge by several scientists around the world, led by Dr. Meny Bergel of the Institute for Leprological Investigation in Argentina, against the Hansen hypothesis. Bergel in particular, having studied patients and conducted lab experiments for over three decades, has concluded that leprosy mainly results from some nutritional deficiency or imbalance. This would explain why people with early stages of the disease often have no active Hansen bacterium infection, though it appears later. It would also make sense of several mystifying clinical observations. Powerful drugs such as rifampicin that efficiently kill the bacteria, and vaccines such as BCG against the related tuberculosis bacillus, have no ability to reverse leprosy symptoms. On the other hand, substances such as cod liver oil or sulfones, which do not kill the bacteria, cause remarkable improvement in lepers.

Normal, healthy rats do not develop leprosy when injected with the Hansen bacillus. But rats fed deficient diets with heavy amounts of oxidized fats do, in fact, develop some symptoms analogous to leprosy, and the bacterium flourishes in skin tissues of the experimentally diseased animals. This line of evidence, combined with the observation that the blood of human leprosy patients is deficient in various vitamins and minerals, argues powerfully for a nutritional cause of the disease.

Leprosy cannot be an infectious disease, and the Hansen bacillus must be basically harmless. If Bergel is at least partly right in blaming the disease on diet, the medical establishment is ignoring a potentially simple method of eradicating the epidemic. Under the influence of the World Health Organization, many nations instead maintain various isolation and quarantine policies for lepers, including forced separation of babies and young children from their leprous mothers.

Another mistaken medical holdover from the days of the first microbe hunters lies in the syphilis story. This is a genuinely infectious venereal disease, first causing genital sores and often spreading from there throughout the body in secondary or tertiary stages, thereby causing a limited variety of symptoms in different patients. From this ability the disease acquired the slightly over-hyped name, "the Great Masquerader." A bacterium was isolated from syphilis in 1905 that fully meets Koch's postulates for causing the disease.

Along with these reasonably well-defined symptoms scientists have classified another stage, known as "neurosyphilis," in which the bacterium supposedly invades the central nervous system, including the brain. This later manifestation of the disease results in dementia and insanity. However, this dementia stage develops only after long incubation periods, and syphilis bacteria cannot be isolated in large numbers from the central nervous system even once these symptoms appear. And infected monkeys have never shown neurosyphilis. The bacterium therefore does not seem to meet Koch's postulates for this particular disease stage.

A better explanation of neurosyphilis may lie, ironically, in the treatment itself. Throughout the nineteenth century, the therapy of choice was mercury, the poisonous heavy metal known to cause nerve and brain damage, especially over long time periods. After the discovery of the syphilis bacterium, doctors began switching their treatment to arsenic-derived compounds developed by Paul Ehrlich and dubbed "magic bullets." With mercury treatment in decline, neurosyphilis began disappearing, but doctors mistakenly credited the stronger effects of the arsenic against syphilis itself.

Neurosyphilis is at best extremely rare today, and probably never verified. But this long-standing belief in the ability of the syphilis bacterium to cause dementia continues to fascinate scientists. Some researchers who raise questions about the true cause of AIDS, for example, have offered the notion that AIDS might be a disguised form of syphilis, or at least that this might explain AIDS dementia. But AIDS may not be infectious at all.

Undoubtedly the most spectacular modern bacterial "epidemic" in America has been Legionnaire's disease, which received an inordinate share of media and official medical attention despite serious questions about the disease itself. The original incident occurred about two weeks after the nation's 1976 Bicentennial celebration, at the Pennsylvania convention of the American Legion. The convention was headquartered in the Bellevue Stratford Hotel in Philadelphia. Within days after the over 4000 conventioneers had disbanded and returned home, many of them began showing up in hospitals throughout the state with severe, sometimes lethal, pneumonias. The entire epidemic ended within a few more days, leaving 182 casualties, including twenty-nine deaths.

A special team of investigators from the federal Center for Disease Control (CDC) spent the next five months trying to isolate the germ responsible. None of over fifty known viruses, bacteria, fungi, or protozoa could be found in all the victims, but that December one CDC lab researcher discovered a previously unknown bacterium in tissue samples from some of the patients. The CDC immediately declared the microbe guilty of causing the Legionnaire's disease, taxonomically designating it *Legionella pneumophila*. According to their hypothesis, the bacteria had infected the legionnaires through the air conditioning system in the Bellevue Stratford Hotel, where it had quietly been growing. Since that date, CDC officials have retroactively blamed previous mysterious epidemics all around the country on *Legionella*, and continue to pin many periodic but small epidemics of flu-like pneumonias on the germ.

But simply finding another germ in such victims cannot tell a scientist whether that microbe actually causes the disease, or whether it may simply be one of the many harmless micro-organisms found in humans and animals. As one microbiologist has stated the point, such germs can always be "secondary invaders," opportunists that take advantage of a sick person's decreased resistance rather than causing the illness in the first place.[11] As discussed throughout this chapter, the only logical standards of proof are Koch's postulates.

Legionella fails the test. The first postulate states the germ must be found in all cases of the disease, and must be multiplying actively enough in the appropriate tissues to explain the symptoms. But even among the legionnaires struck in the 1976 outbreak, ten percent of the victims were never infected by the bacterium. In other pneumonia epidemics, the percentage of sick people positive for the germ has ranged from one percent to this example of ninety percent. Even these figures may be high, since other bacteria can mimic *Legionella* in the laboratory tests. Since CDC scientists often do not think to exclude other bacteria, "limited testing for other bacteria may have inflated the frequency of *Legionella* infections."[12]

So many of these mini-epidemics have lacked *Legionella pneumophila* that the CDC has since isolated dozens of new but related species and strains of bacteria, using most of them as scapegoat germs on which to blame many of the outbreaks they cannot link to *Legionella*. And in those victims who have been infected by the original germ, the microbe appears to be so inactive in the body that it cannot be found in the saliva or mucus. It is, indeed, hard to culture at all, even from the lung tissue it infects.

Koch's third postulate requires the germ to duplicate the sickness in a newly infected host, usually an animal. *Legionella* will cause some symptoms, or even death if injected in large amounts, but only in guinea pigs. While the germ also successfully infects and grows in hamsters and rats, it does not cause serious disease in them. The microbe even seems to have a hard time making the guinea pigs ill, since many cultures of the bacterium fail this experiment. In laboratory cell culture, the microbe grows well in human white blood cells without killing them.

Even CDC experts admit the symptoms of Legionnaire's disease are easily confused with other types of pneumonia, suggesting that perhaps other germs are actually causing the symptoms. This possibility now stands confirmed, since many antibiotics that kill *Legionella* in the lab culture dish do not cure the disease in humans, while many that work in humans cannot kill the bacteria in culture. These latter antibiotics must be killing other microbes in the body.

The evidence indicates *Legionella* is actually quite harmless. Since 1976, CDC and public health investigators have found the bacterium all over the country, in water cooling towers, condensers, shower heads, faucets, humidifiers, whirlpools, swimming pools, and even hot-water tanks, assorted plumbing, mud, and lakes. The bacterium is so universal that between twenty and thirty percent of the American population has already been infected, yet virtually no one ever develops Legionnaire's disease symptoms. Even laboratories testing for this bacterium find problems, because *Legionella* frequently contaminates the experiments from the surrounding air.

Thus the CDC should have dropped *Legionella* and searched for other causes long ago. Pneumonias are often caused by microbes already living in the body, rather than new ones infecting from the environment. The body contains many potentially harmful germs that rarely, if ever, cause illness, until one becomes sick for some other reason. Legionnaire's disease was probably one example of pneumonia caused by standard germs that take advantage of people whose resistance had been lowered.

So what made the legionnaires susceptible? The CDC has presumed *Legionella* did all the work, but the first question to ask should be whether the original cause was even contagious. One month before the CDC isolated the bacterium, a U.S. House of Representatives investigative committee held hearings excoriating the CDC for not having looked for toxic chemicals as a possible cause of the 1976 epidemic. Chairman John Murphy of New York sharply attacked the investigation because "The CDC, for example, did not have a toxicologist present in their initial team of investigators sent to deal with the . . . epidemic. No apparent precautions were taken to deal with the possibility, however remote at the time, that something else might have been the cause."[13]

The outbreak certainly did not fit the pattern of infectious epidemics. The CDC itself has openly admitted that none of the afflicted legionnaires transmitted the disease to anyone else, nor can human-to-human transmission be documented in any other supposed *Legionella* epidemic. In other words, those who have become sick "caught" the disease directly from contaminated water or air only, and never pass it along. The hotel staff in 1976 experienced none of the disease, nor have any doctors or nurses caring for such patients ever contracted the illness. Conversely, some of the legionnaires with the disease stayed only in nearby hotels and never spent any time in the Bellevue

Stratford. Thus the disease was not distributed randomly among people exposed to *Legionella*, as contagion should.

The victims, as it turned out, were textbook examples of people at risk for pneumonia. Not just the average legionnaire, the affected people were heavier smokers, had prior heart and lung conditions, were older, and included many who had received kidney transplants and the accompanying immune-suppressive drugs to prevent organ rejection. Because the convention had taken place during the nation's Bicentennial, these highly susceptible people also engaged in unusually heavy drinking. The "epidemic," such as it was, resulted from the classical risks for pneumonia. Certainly it presented no public health threat.

Representative John Murphy delivered the important lesson: "The early investigators of legionnaires' disease focused so intensely on a biological cause—upon a virus, fungus, or bacteria—that chemicals and poisons were apparently largely overlooked."[14] Yet the CDC and the sensational media coverage of the small and short-lived outbreak terrified the American public at large, and continue to do so in various small epidemics every year. Despite what Congressman Murphy called a "fiasco," the CDC has recovered politically and continues to hold the official view of *Legionella* as a public health threat. The first international conference of scientists studying *Legionella* was held at CDC headquarters in 1978, and a growing number of researchers have earned their salaries producing thousands of papers since that time, creating an entire field of science for studying this modest germ. This deluge of misdirected information has drowned out any public criticism of their flawed and dangerous hypothesis of infection.

The bacteria hunters of the turn of the century failed to grasp the point that vast numbers of harmless microbes exist in the world, and that a scientist who assumes an epidemic to be infectious can always find a microbe that, whether through indirect connection or by sheer coincidence, will correlate with the disease. Microbes have lived on this planet long before humans. We co-exist with a sea of microbes and benefit from many, including those that naturally reside in the human body. Simply finding a microbe is not enough to convict it of causing disease; Koch's postulates must be met. Otherwise such reckless science can obstruct genuine discoveries, creating hysteria in a population fearful of catching the disease. Ironically, public anxiety actually propels microbe hunting, for desperate people will gratefully provide extraordinary money and power to such researchers and public health officials. Scientists with alternative views are pushed aside, for too many non-infectious diseases would put microbe hunters out of business.

Bacteria hunting did actually fade for a time, mostly following the disappearance of serious contagious epidemics from the industrial world. But today microbe hunting has returned in force, searching for viruses as well as bacteria—even though infectious plagues have not returned. This time, however, microbe hunting has become an unmoveable establishment. The reason lies in the explosive growth in funding for biological research, which has built a powerful array of government and private institutions with a vested interest in microbiology. The scientific bureacracy has become immensely larger, and the techniques for finding microbes incredibly sensitive, allowing even the most minute quantities of inactive germs to be isolated from any diseased patient. Now follows the story of modern virus hunting and the political infrastructure built around it.

Chapter 2 Footnotes

[1] Brock, *Robert Koch: A Life in Medicine and Bacteriology*. Science Tech Publishers, Madison, WI, 1988, p. 75.

[2] Ibid., p. 121.

[3] Carpenter, *The History of Scurvy and Vitamin C*. Cambridge University Press, Cambridge, England, 1986, p. 11.

[4] Ibid., p. 127.

[5] Stewart and Guthrie (eds.). *Lind's Treatise on Scurvy*. Edinburgh University Press, Edinburgh, 1953, pp. 408-9

[6] Williams, *Toward the Conquest of Beriberi*. Harvard University Press, Cambridge, MA, 1961, p. 18.

[7] Etheridge, *The Butterfly Caste: A Social History of Pellagra in the South*. Greenwood Publishing Co., Westport, Connecticut, 1972, p. 11.

[8] Ibid., pp. 30-2.

[9] Ibid., p. 99.

[10] Freeman, *Textbook of Microbiology*. W.B. Saunders Co., Philadelphia, 1979, pp. 708-710.

[11] Winn, Legionnaires Disease: Historical Perspective. *Clinical Microbiology Reviews* 1:60-81, 1988, p. 61.

[12] Ibid., p. 71.

[13] House Subcommittee on Consumer Protection and Finance, *Legionnaires' Disease*, Nov. 23-4, 1976, p. 5.

[14] Ibid., p. 6.

Chapter 3

Virus Hunting Takes Over

The scientific process has disintegrated in recent decades. For three thousand years, curious individuals sought the underlying explanations—the causes—of natural phenomena. This pursuit encountered many false starts or became temporarily sidetracked, but progress continued over the long term. After World War II, however, all this unraveled as the lone scientist, often an amateur, gave way to a growing bureaucracy of technicians. The prevailing conception of science and its methods has likewise turned upside down, most people now confusing experimental data with real science.

Starting with the ancient Greek philosophers and continuing until the middle of the twentieth century, the scientist was the creative individual who searched for the simpler explanations. Copernicus and Galileo, for instance, reinterpreted the motions of planets in the sky, inferring that the earth and other planets revolve around the sun, not the sun around the earth. Newton puzzled out why apples should fall down and not in other directions, and discovered the law of gravity. Koch found a method of proving when a germ causes a disease. Einstein seized on seemingly-paradoxical behavior of light, and proposed his theory of relativity as an explanation—without having performed any experiments on the subject. Watson and Crick, who never experimented with DNA, took a second look at the existing physical and chemical data and deduced the structure of the genetic molecule.

Virtually all of the pivotal contributions to science throughout history have consisted less of new observations than of new explanations for old data. Classical scientists did not view their occupation in terms of gathering data, but rather in terms of discovering the logical mistakes and simplifying the complexities of the prevailing explanations. Such work tended to wound egos and invited the anger of colleagues whose pet hypotheses had been sunk, but the scientific enterprise in any case achieved its well-deserved reputation for brilliant innovation.

Because experimentation played such a limited role compared to thinking in classical science, the process was relatively inexpensive. Scientists labored nearly in obscurity, driven not by high-stakes politics or finance but by their own curiosity. Nuclear physicist Ralph E. Lapp, a prominent scientist who served as a researcher and advisor on the Manhattan Project, the Atomic Energy Committee, the Office of Naval Research, and other institutions, experienced science before and after the post-war transition. His early training had predated this change, allowing him to describe the classical situation:

One has to have experienced these lean years in science to remember how frugally money was hoarded for research in physics. In those days no scientist ventured to ask the federal government for funds. He gathered together what money he needed from private sources or earned extra pay as a consultant to pay for his own research. But mostly he acted as a Jack-of-all-trades and built his own equipment. Graduate students were required to take machine-shop practice and learn glass blowing. If he needed Geiger counters he made them himself, and he wired his own electronic circuits. The physicist was the original "do-it-yourself" man on campus...

... When scientists found, as they did after the great crash on Wall Street, that new ideas demanded financial support for their exploitation, they did not think of asking the government to help. Funds to build cyclotrons and other expensive machinery of science were secured from private sources, generally from foundations, and the cost of operations was assumed by colleges, universities, and a few institutes.[1]

All other scientific fields, and indeed academic pursuit in general, faced the same conditions. The little federal money available went mostly into applied biology through the Department of Agriculture.

But then came the Second World War, its immediate aftermath, and the Cold War. The detonation of two nuclear bombs over Japan, products of a program known as the Manhattan Project, violently brought science into public awareness. A team of scientists, equipped with two billion dollars, had invented the new weapon in a round-the-clock engineering effort. This success was soon coupled with the onset of the Cold War, symbolized in the launch of *Sputnik*, the first artificial satellite. This Soviet propaganda coup terrified Americans, creating strong public support for crash science and engineering research efforts for catching up with the Soviets.

The federal government moved to take advantage of this opportunity. The Atomic Energy Commission, formed in 1947, picked up the remains of the Manhattan Project and continued nuclear research. The National Science Foundation was established in 1950, and began disbursing grants for basic scientific research. In the years that followed, a bewildering array of federal science departments and agencies materialized to fund and monitor research of all kinds, both in government facilities and in universities and independent research labs.

This new science establishment was modelled after the Manhattan Project's team-based investigation. Priorities therefore focused on the practical results of science, an appropriate goal for the engineering- and technology-oriented research that first dominated the new federal spending programs. But recognizing that technology is the applied form of fundamental science, the government soon began throwing money at basic research as well, and thus transformed it into an unrecognizable monster. Creative geniuses were swept aside to make way for powerful institutions composed of large teams of specialized technicians, whose only goal was gathering ever-larger quantities of raw data. Where non-conformist individuals once competed with only a handful of peers, they now faced opposition from tens of thousands of irritated colleagues, a crowd that could more easily drown out minority viewpoints. Experiments replaced contemplative thought and analysis, while research became dazzlingly high-tech—and incredibly expensive.

Just before World War Two, the total research and development funding in the United States, public and private together, amounted to approximately 250 million dollars per year. By the mid-1950s, the federal share alone had grown to over two billion dollars, reaching $63 billion in 1989, and in 1993 becoming half of all R & D spending in the United States at $76 billion.[2] Even adjusting for inflation, this federal spending figure has greatly outpaced the growth in our national economy, becoming 1.25% of the entire Gross National Product by 1989. Federal research money has turned into the major funding source for universities and other institutions, expanding and reshaping departments in its wake.

President Eisenhower summarized the problem well in his 1961 farewell address:

> Today, the solitary inventor, tinkering in his shop, has been overshadowed by task forces of scientists in laboratories and testing fields. In the same fashion, the free university, historically the fountainhead of free ideas and scientific discovery, has experienced a revolution in the conduct of research. Partly because of the huge costs involved, a government contract becomes virtually a substitute for intellectual curiosity. For every old blackboard there are now hundreds of electronics [*sic*] computers... The prospect of domination of the nation's scholars by federal employment, project allocations, and the power of money is ever present—and is gravely to be regarded.[3]

Yet, ironically, the same Eisenhower had previously declared in 1957 that "shortages of trained manpower exist in virtually every field," and had pushed for rapid production of more scientists.[4] This supposed "Ph.D. shortage" defined the basis of an important part of the explosive federal spending, a portion of which was devoted exclusively to the subsidy of graduate students and post-doctoral fellows to work in scientific fields. Universities, especially their science departments, became little more than factories turning out new doctorates as quickly as possible.

The results have been predictable. When the American Association for the Advancement of Science was established in 1848, it had 461 scientists as members. It then reached 36,000 members during World War Two, and already passed 100,000 during the 1960s.[5] Today it boasts some 135,000 members, and is only one of many growing science associations. The National Academy of Sciences, in which membership is even today a unique honor reserved for a few scientists, started in 1863 with fifty members. Those ranks swelled to over 600 by the mid-1960s and now stand at 1650.[6] The total number of science doctorates awarded each year has increased from under 6000 in 1960 to nearly 17,000 in 1979.[7] By the mid-1980s, the ranks of Ph.D.s and M.D.s working in science or engineering had swelled to 400,000, a figure that for decades has grown much faster than national employment.[8]

As a result, "Of every eight scientists who ever lived [in the history of the world], seven are alive today [in 1969]"; similar statistics would hold today.[9] Nor has the pressure for further expansion abated, as evidence in a 1990 policy statement of the Association of American Universities referring to an "impending Ph.D. shortage."[10]

Increasing numbers of scientists means many more papers being published in scientific journals, with the publish-or-perish stakes rising constantly. According to one summary, "The first scientific journal... began publication in 1665. By 1800 there were 100 journals; by 1900, 10,000 journals; today [1969], over 100,000."[11] By 1986, an unreadable total of nearly 140,000 papers were being published each year just by U.S. scientists, about one-third of the world total.[12]

Such unrestrained growth in scientific ranks causes serious problems. For example, the increased number of researchers creates more demand for grants to keep them employed, placing pressure on Congress to continue the upward funding spiral. Thus science becomes a powerful lobby in its own right, dominated by the best-funded institutions with full-time public relations staffs. And as these armies of new scientists flood the peer review system, they even act to suppress any remaining dissension by the few remaining thoughtful researchers. Peer review, after all, can never check the accuracy of experimental data, only censor unacceptable interpretations. A scientist's grants, publications, positions, awards, and even invitations to conferences are entirely controlled by his competitors; as in any other profession, no scientist welcomes being out-competed or having his pet idea disproven by a colleague. Former *Science* editor Dr. Philip Abelson presciently described the pressures against dissenters who raise questions publicly:

> The witness in questioning the wisdom of the establishment pays a price and incurs hazards. He is diverted from his professional activities. He stirs the enmity of powerful foes. He fears that reprisals may extend beyond him to his institution. Perhaps he fears shadows, but in a day when almost all research institutions are highly dependent on federal funds, prudence seems to dictate silence.[13]

Few scientists are any longer willing to question, even privately, the consensus views in any field whatsoever. The successful researcher—the one who receives the biggest grants, the best career positions, the most prestigious prizes, the greatest number of published papers—is the one who generates the most data and the least controversy. The transition from small to big to megascience has created an establishment of skilled technicians, but mediocre scientists, who have abandoned real scientific interpretation, and even equate their experiments with science itself. They pride themselves in molding data to fit popular scientific belief, or perhaps in adding non-threatening discoveries. But when someone strays outside accepted boundaries to ask questions of a more fundamental nature, the majority of researchers close ranks to protect their consensus beliefs.

The inversion of science has hit biology particularly hard. The obvious first priorities of the post-war science buildup focused on engineering. Funded primarily by the Defense Department and NASA, this research has produced satellites, the moon landings, the space shuttle, and various weapons systems, as well as cyclotrons and super-colliders for basic physics. But basic research, the more fundamental pursuit that can later be applied to technology and medicine, has grown consistently as a proportion of total research and development in the United States. Most basic science is now concentrated in universities, the rest in a variety of institutes, companies, and federal laboratories. Biology now comprises about a third of the total basic science in this country and about half of all academic research, far larger than physics, engineering, mathematics, social science, or any other field.

Biology's dominance of research has resulted, naturally, from a massive infusion of federal funds, mostly through the National Institutes of Health (NIH). Formerly a backwater agency buried inside the Public Health Service bureaucracy, the NIH has since the 1950s developed a voracious appetite for money. Its 1955 budget hovered somewhere around 100 million dollars; today it spends closer to ten billion dollars. NIH research grants not only fund some in-house labs, but now provide the basic source of funding for universities and other institutes, including research conducted in other nations. Half the total federal research spending on universities and colleges—for all subjects combined—is now provided by the NIH. So while academic institutions formerly provided their own limited monies for research, NIH grants have now become a major source of *income* for the larger and increasingly dependent universities. According to a 1990 article in the *Journal of NIH Research*, "When NIH sneezes, it is the academic community that catches cold."[14]

As science degenerates into technology-driven data-gathering, one would expect disastrous mistakes to be made and amplified. In the case of biology, the new money was grafted onto an establishment long dominated by microbe hunters. Despite the disappearance of infectious plagues, therefore, both science and popular culture have entered a new, revived era of microbiology, now in the form of virus hunting. Because biology is also the foundation underlying medicine, the emphasis on quantity over quality in research must inevitably lead to human tragedy. When nuclear physicist and National Academy of Sciences member Alvin Weinberg called for biologists "to expand even at the cost of individual effectiveness as long as their total output increases," he unknowingly spelled out a dangerous formula.[15]

The trail of politically driven virus-hunting begins in the war on polio, expands in the misdirected war on cancer, and climaxes in the failed war on AIDS.

From Early Virology to Polio

Unlike bacteria, protozoa, or fungi, viruses are not living micro-organisms. Whereas bacteria are single-celled creatures, viruses are much smaller and cannot grow on their own. Composed typically of protein and either DNA or RNA (the genetic molecules), virus particles must infect living cells, tricking their new hosts into producing large numbers of identical viruses.

Only by this means do viruses "survive" and go on to infect new hosts. While countless different viruses exist in the world, each can only infect a limited range of living hosts, and then only specific cell types within the host's body. Every category of living organism, whether animal, plant, or bacterium, is susceptible to infection by some of nature's viruses.

The early microbe hunters began accidentally finding viruses while searching for bacteria. During the eighteenth century, Edward Jenner gained fame for his discovery that humans could be immunized against smallpox by injecting material from cowpox. Jenner could not know that he had used a virus, much less what a virus was, and he lived decades before anyone even proposed bacteria to be disease-causing. When Louis Pasteur turned to rabies research in the early 1880s, he correctly discovered that the disease could be transmitted from one animal to another through its saliva, but was astonished that he could never find any guilty bacterium. Pasteur guessed the cause to be a bacterium too tiny to see even in the microscope; in fact, this was also a virus. Pasteur then became the second person to invent an immunization, this time for rabies.

Not until 1892 did anyone perform the first actual isolation of a virus. Russian bacteria hunter Dmitri Iwanowski gathered fluid from tobacco plants suffering the mosaic disease. He passed this liquid through a filter so fine that the pores allowed no bacteria through, yet to Iwanowski's surprise the bacteria-free filtered liquid easily made new plants sick with the disease. This observation was repeated independently by the Dutch botanist Martinus Willem Beijerinck in 1898, who quickly recognized that the invisible cause was indeed some altogether different kind of infectious agent. He coined the term which led to the microbe's name—"tobacco mosaic virus."

The bacteria-hunting age was still in full swing, but a number of microbiologists became excited enough to begin searching for viruses. In the same year as Beijerinck's report, two German scientists purified a liquid containing "filterable viruses" that caused foot-and-mouth disease in cattle. Walter Reed followed in 1901 with a filtrate responsible for yellow fever, and soon dozens of other disease-causing viruses were being found. Meanwhile, bacteria hunters busy finding germs while ignoring Koch's postulates were isolating and falsely blaming new bacteria for what were in fact viral diseases. Yellow fever, for instance, was independently blamed on two different bacteria, both before and after the virus had been isolated. Influenza, another viral disease, was blamed on at least one bacterium.

The next logical step was to determine what viruses really were. American chemist Wendell M. Stanley accomplished exactly this in 1935, when he created pure crystals of tobacco mosaic virus from an infectious liquid solution. Having these crystals allowed him to study their structure, and he discovered that these crystallized germs could still infect plants with no trouble. In other words, the virus was not a living organism, since it could outlast such deadly treatment and remain infectious. Soon he and other scientists began routinely crystallizing many different viruses. In 1946, Stanley received the first Nobel Prize ever awarded to a virologist, and two years afterward established the Virus Lab at the Berkeley campus of the University of

California, where he later supervised the training of Peter Duesberg (one of the authors of this book) and other scientists in virus hunting.

While viruses were joining the ranks of sought-after microbes, the political institutions that would revive microbe hunting after the Second World War were quietly developing. Congress had in 1798 formed the Marine Hospital Service for the medical treatment of sailors, an agency that was renamed and expanded in 1912, right in the middle of the microbe-hunting era. This new Public Health Service received a mandate to investigate and cure human disease, inevitably focusing on contagious disease. This bias had been reflected in the name of a small subdivision created in 1887, the Hygienic Laboratory, which itself was expanded in 1930 and renamed the National Institute of Health (NIH). True to form, the medical experts trained and hired into these structures could think of no other way to fight disease, and avidly pursued their one skill right on through both World Wars. Even Joseph Goldberger, who realized a vitamin deficiency caused pellagra, spent his fourteen previous years with the Public Health Service waging war on microbes.

The study of infectious diseases was not completely wasted, for in those days they were still leading killers. But not only did microbe hunting often interfere with genuine science, it also faced growing obsolescence as infectious plagues gradually disappeared. Indeed, the last of the serious contagious epidemics in the industrial world was polio. In what will be recorded as one of history's great ironies, the war on polio was nonetheless the very program that launched modern virus hunting.

Polio had always been, and is still throughout much of the Third World today, a nagging problem. Though often fatal, the disease was best known for causing paralysis, and it tended to strike children most commonly. President Franklin Roosevelt, perhaps the most celebrated polio case of all time, in 1938 set up the private National Foundation for Infantile Paralysis (NFIP) for conquering the dread disease. The impetus provided by the Foundation led many key scientists to research poliovirus, as did the sudden, frightening polio epidemic that exploded in the Western nations, brought back home by troops returning from the Pacific theater in 1945.

The virus was first isolated as a filtered liquid in 1908, but as with all viruses, no one could make these non-living entities grow outside the body. Dr. John Enders and two co-workers stumbled on a means of doing so in 1948, by growing the virus in cells cultured from human placentas cast away at birth. A Nobel Prize was awarded to all three researchers a few years later. Wendell Stanley got in on the act, and in 1955 first crystallized the polio virus in his Berkeley lab.

The major medical lesson of viruses had long been that antibiotics, which kill bacteria, are completely useless against viruses. But immunization had been tested since the time of Edward Jenner, and proved to be the only effective technique against viruses. Vaccination works by introducing a weakened or inactivated form of a virus into the body, causing the body's immune system to produce a reserve supply of antibodies against the virus. In theory, if the real virus later infects the body, antibody proteins stand ready to attack the germ.

Now that poliovirus could be grown in cell culture, a vaccine became more feasible. Two groups of researchers had already tried making vaccines from virus grown in monkeys, but both went down in flames when their vaccines accidentally caused polio in several children during their 1935 trials. The first to try a vaccine from virus grown in cell culture was Dr. Jonas Salk, who worked for the NFIP. Salk used chemically inactivated virus in a nationwide field test during 1954, with 400,000 children receiving vaccinations. After the results came in, the secretary of Health, Education, and Welfare (HEW) officially licensed the vaccine the following March.

With this stamp of expert approval, all public apprehensions dissolved and the NFIP moved immediately to begin universal distribution. The NFIP even lobbied for federal money to provide free vaccine to the poor, but fortunately did not succeed. For within weeks, reports came pouring in of children who were becoming paralyzed from the vaccine itself, which contained rare virus particles having survived the inactivating treatment. In other words, fully active polio virus had been injected directly into the bloodstreams of many children. Over 200 people were hit with vaccine-induced polio the summer of 1955, including eleven who died. Federal support would have magnified the tragedy.

Public celebration turned to horror. The disaster forced vaccine production to stop, and within three months a complete political shakeup hit HEW. The secretary resigned, as did the director of the NIH and various other officials. The vaccine was only restarted once screening procedures were tightened, and later another type of vaccine replaced the Salk version altogether.

Into the leadership void at NIH stepped its former assistant director, James Shannon, promoted to director on August 1 of 1955. A disciplined and intensely ambitious man with a Ph.D. in physiology, Shannon was more politician than scientist. Known to his associates for his aggressive, even ruthless leadership style, he had developed grand notions of how science should be restructured through a central authority. The Salk vaccine fiasco handed Shannon a golden opportunity, which he seized without hesitation. This was his chance to refashion what he condescendingly viewed as a small-time agency.

He envisioned nothing less than the building of the largest biomedical research establishment in human history. As he retrospectively described his view, "... the main deficiency preventing progress was the inadequate funding of research... The difficulty seemed to be in the scaling of the system. There were manpower and resources, but they were too modest in size because of the inadequacy of support funds." He revealed more bluntly his "profound conviction that an expansion of the science base for medicine was needed, doable, and should be undertaken with a sense of urgency."[16]

Shannon's aims were well-planned and quite specific: "... success was only possible by breaking out of the confines of the then federal budget for the support of the biomedical sciences... A realistic program would have to provide a continuing expansion of the base for scientists' production and an expansion of physical resources to house the expanding programs. The targets seemed clear."[17] He set about immediately to consolidate his support in both houses of Congress. John Fogarty, chairman of the House appropriations committee, and his counterpart Senator Lister Hill, became Shannon's close allies in his bid to create explosive funding increases for NIH. With their help and the backing of the Eisenhower administration, Shannon successfully doubled the 1956 NIH budget to 200 million dollars for fiscal year 1957, by far the most radical increase in the agency's long history. He continued expanding the NIH until retiring in 1968, by which time the annual budget exceeded one billion dollars. The agency's growth has continued without letup to this very day, its annual spending of about ten billion dollars now making it the powerhouse of the biomedical and academic research establishments.

Shannon had developed a clever strategy for building the size and power of the NIH. He badly wanted the agency to create a huge infrastructure for basic research, but knew that Congress and the public worried more about practical questions of human disease. Using the Manhattan Project and the space program as models of heavily funded enterprises built on World War II and the Cold War, he found ways to paint basic research as having practical applications—by waging "wars" on disease. Shannon had always disliked the NFIP and the Salk vaccine program for having been funded mostly privately, rather than under tight federal control, so he began spending the new NIH budgets funding and taking over polio research in the United States. His war on polio provided grants that trained a growing field of scientists in studying viruses.

This growing virology program meshed well with the microbe hunters who had long dominated the NIH, and helped revive their dwindling fortunes. When Shannon turned to creating a war on cancer over the following several years, the virologists became his frontline soldiers. And when the NIH got involved in the war on AIDS in the 1980s, virus hunters again took charge. Many of the leading scientists in the war on AIDS, such as David Baltimore and Jonas Salk, launched their careers in the wake of the NIH war on polio.

Since the polio epidemic disappeared in the early 1960s, no other catastrophic infectious plague has struck the industrial nations. Cancer and heart disease have become the prominent examples of the non-infectious diseases, mostly of older age, to which medical science has had to turn for employment. But with Shannon's legacy of a reshaped NIH trapped in a virus program of its own making, microbe hunting was rescued from scientific obsolescence and now has a political stranglehold on research that is more powerful than the most obsessive bacteria hunting of times past.

Enter the Slow Viruses

Even the worst falsehood begins with grains of truth. Gradually distorted, exaggerated, and pulled ever further from its original context, the developing myth feeds on an accumulation of smaller mistakes and lies. In an age of the growing scientific machine, individual researchers become helpless to stop the tide of self-reinforcing popular beliefs, guaranteeing the collective triumph of such tragic mistakes. So it has been with the transformation of virology into virus-hunting careerism.

From the discovery of tobacco mosaic virus through the polio epidemic, scientists have found and legitimately blamed many viruses for a variety of diseases, each having passed the acid test of Koch's postulates. But for every truly dangerous virus, many more that are perfectly harmless can be found in humans and animals. NIH-sponsored polio research during the late 1950s proved the point exquisitely; researchers trying to isolate new strains of poliovirus accidentally found numerous closely-related passenger viruses that also infected the digestive system. Scientists classified some of these microbes as "orphans"—viruses without corresponding diseases. The virus hunters could not bring themselves to believe microbes could exist without being harmful, and expected even these "orphan" viruses would someday find appropriate sicknesses.

When trying to blame such a passenger virus for a noninfectious disease, however, one nagging problem haunts the virus hunter: the laws of probability dictate that the illness will rarely strike the victim at the same time as the harmless infection, since the two are not really connected. When microbes infect a new host, they cause sickness within the time they need to grow and take over the body—days or weeks at most—else the host's immune defenses neutralize the invader and prevent disease altogether. Therefore if scientists wish to convict an innocent virus, they must invent some magical new property for it. For example, they can suppose a "latent period" of months or years between the time the virus invades the body and the appearance of symptoms.

Behind this myth of latent periods lies a grain of truth, albeit a very tiny one. Even with infections by normal viruses, a few exceptional victims suffer pre-existing health problems that prevent their immune systems from reacting decisively against the virus, allowing it to continue growing and damaging the host for a long period of time. In principle, this can happen with virtually any type of virus, but is extremely rare. When such a chronic infection does occur, as with a small percentage of hepatitis cases, the virus keeps growing abundantly in the body and can easily be found by experimental tests. Or in some cases, like herpes viruses, the germ can hide out in some recess of the body, breaking out periodically to infect again. In both examples, only the weakened immune system of the host allows the infection to smolder or occasionally reappear. The notion of a "latent period," in contrast, is a miraculous property credited to some viruses as a natural characteristic that can *override* the host's health, even after the virus has completely disappeared from the body. Such a concept allows scientists to blame a long-neutralized virus for a disease that appears years later.

The latent period concept, now used to connect HIV with AIDS, can be traced back to the days of the war on polio. The researcher who popularized this modern myth is today a leading figure in the war on AIDS, one whose career epitomizes the evolution of the virus hunters over the last three decades.

D. Carleton Gajdusek is a man full of apparent contradictions. His seventy years and hint of a stomach bespeak comfortable authority, yet he has been described as emotionally immature, on occasion embarrassing col-

leagues during his scientific lectures with descriptions of exotic sexual practices in tribal cultures. Seemingly a family man who has adopted thirty-four
children, almost all boys, from obscure villages of New Guinea and nearby,
he nevertheless remains unmarried and "has no interest in women," according
to Nobel laureate Sir Frank Macfarlane Burnet.[18] He resides in a luxurious
Maryland estate of over one hundred acres with a huge swimming pool, yet
prefers spending much of his time traveling the world and living in areas of
absolute destitution. By training he is a pediatrician with early appointments
at leading universities, but has for decades now worked as a virologist for the
NIH.

Having spent a great deal of time studying contagious childhood diseases
around the world, Gajdusek was sponsored by the National Foundation for
Infantile Paralysis and sent back to New Guinea in 1957. There a doctor with
the local health department introduced him to a disease called kuru, a mysterious ailment that attacked the brain, rendering the victim increasingly spas-
modic or paralyzed until death within months. The syndrome existed only
among the 35,000 tribal villagers in one set of valleys, mostly the Fore tribe.
Before Gajdusek's arrival, no outsider had ever described kuru, although the
Fore tribesmen told him the condition had begun appearing a few decades
previous.

Gajdusek's initial study assumed the disease to be infectious. He
reported that the natives routinely cannibalized their dead relatives for
nutritional purposes, a practice that they told him had begun around the same
time as the arrival of kuru. Gajdusek decided that kuru was transmitted by the
eating of deceased victims' brains. Yet when he searched for a virus, he ran
into a baffling absence of evidence. None of the typical signs of infection
could be found in the patients. Their bodies showed no inflammation and no
fever, no changes were registered in their supposedly infected spinal fluid,
their immune systems failed to react as if any microbe had invaded the body,
and those people with suppressed immune defenses had no greater risk of
catching the disease. Another scientific group soon arrived from Australia,
and concluded that kuru might be genetically inherited. Having been
convinced the disease was not infectious after all, Gajdusek did not even
bother trying to discourage the cannibalism. As he explained to one
interviewer, "We told [the tribespeople] we had no objection to their
mortuary cannibalism, which expressed love for their dead relatives, although
the government and missionaries did. It provided a good source of protein for
a meat-starved community."[19]

Upon arriving back in the United States, Gajdusek was hired by the NIH
to work at its institute for studying neurological disease. While continuing to
monitor kuru incidence, he devoted his time to laboratory study of the condition. Word of his discovery of kuru meanwhile made its way to England,
where another virus hunter was investigating a sheep disease known as
scrapie, which had also involved brain degeneration symptoms. The English
researcher suggested to Gajdusek that kuru might be caused by a "slow
virus," one with a long latent period.

Gajdusek was immediately hooked by the revolutionary idea, despite his own "misgivings" that genes, toxins, or nutritional deficiencies might be the cause .[20] Again determined to find the elusive virus, he tried to transmit kuru from victims to chimpanzees. But none of the animals became sick when injected with blood, urine, or other bodily fluids from kuru patients, nor from the cerebrospinal fluid that surrounds the brain, which should have been full of the alleged brain-destroying virus. Indeed, the monkeys contracted no disease even from eating kuru-affected brains.

Only one bizarre experiment did work, in which the brains of kuru patients were ground into a fine mush and injected directly into the brains of live monkeys through holes drilled in their skulls. Within months to years, some of the experimental monkeys suffered coordination and movement problems. Surprisingly, though, even this extreme method could not transfer kuru to dozens of other animal species. And no virus could be seen in the brain tissue, even using the best electron microscopes.

At this point, one might expect Gajdusek would have suspected something was seriously wrong with his virus hypothesis. If signs of the invisible virus could not be found anywhere but in unpurified brain tissue, did not elicit any defensive reactions by the body, and could not be transmitted in pure form to animals, then probably no virus existed at all. Homogenized brain tissue of dead kuru patients, full of every imaginable protein and other compounds, should in itself be plenty toxic when inoculated into monkeys' brains.

Nevertheless, the sick monkeys convinced him and his colleagues he had found a virus. Since he could not isolate it apart from the brain tissue, he decided to study the virus and its structure with a standard experiment; he would define which chemical and physical treatments would destroy the microbe, thereby gathering clues about its nature. But to his astonishment, almost nothing seemed to harm the mystery germ. Powerful chemicals, boiling temperatures, ultraviolet and ionizing radiation, ultrasound—no matter how he treated the brain tissue, it still caused "kuru" in his lab monkeys. Further tests also proved that no foreign genetic material, which all viruses require for their existence, could be found anywhere in kuru-affected brains.

Employing the strongest virus-destroying treatments, Gajdusek had failed to render the kuru brain tissue harmless in his experiments. His results lent themselves to one obvious interpretation: no virus existed in the first place, so it could not possibly be destroyed. Having spent over five years on this project, however, Gajdusek clung tightly to his virus hypothesis. Unfazed by his disappointing experiments, he turned the results upside down and argued that the "kuru virus" was actually a new type of super-microbe, or as he put it, an "unconventional virus." This new virus also needed to act as a slow virus, since long time periods elapsed between an act of cannibalism and the onset of kuru; he liberally suggested latent periods extending into years or even decades.

At an earlier time, and in another context, Gajdusek would probably have been ignored by serious scientists. But he dropped this hypothesis into the midst of a biomedical research complex rapidly ascending to political power, one dominated by virus hunters. The year was 1965, polio had largely disappeared, and the burgeoning ranks of NIH-funded virologists desperately sought any new research direction on which to use their skills. Thus they embraced Gajdusek's slow virus hypothesis enthusiastically. They listened uncritically when he claimed a similar unconventional virus caused Creutzfeldt-Jakob disease, a rare brain disorder that seems to strike mostly Westerners having undergone previous brain surgery (perhaps such medical operations could be the real cause). They paid attention when he proposed slow or even unconventional viruses as the causes of a huge laundry list of nerve and brain disorders, ranging from scrapie in sheep to multiple sclerosis and Alzheimer's disease in humans. They did not even flinch when he threw an array of leukemias and other cancers into the pot. They remained entranced, and awarded him the 1976 Nobel Prize for medicine, for the kuru and Creutzfeldt-Jakob viruses he has still never found. And the NIH promoted him to head its Laboratory of Central Nervous System Studies.

In the meantime another crucial, if embarrassing, bit of information has emerged as a challenge to Gajdusek's virus-kuru hypothesis. The published transcript of his Nobel acceptance speech, in a 1977 issue of *Science* magazine, included a photo ostensibly showing New Guinea natives eating their cannibalistic meal. The photo is not very clear. When colleagues asked Gajdusek if the photo truly showed cannibalism, he admitted the meal was merely roast pork. According to *Science*, "He never publishes actual pictures of cannibalism, he says, because they are 'too offensive'."[21] Unconvinced, anthropologist Lyle Steadman of Arizona State University has investigated and directly challenged Gajdusek's claim:

> Yet, says Lyle Steadman "there is no evidence of cannibalism in New Guinea." Steadman, who spent 2 years doing fieldwork in New Guinea, notes that he often heard tales of cannibalism but when he probed, the evidence evaporated.[22]

Gajdusek, angered by the hint of malfeasance, has insisted "he has actual photographs of cannibalism, but he would never publish them because they 'so offend the relatives of the people who used to do it'."[23] This statement contradicts his earlier claims that the tribesmen proudly ate their dead relatives out of respect, quitting the practice only in deference to outside pressure from government authorities. Steadman, having seen Gajdusek's unpublished photos, has publicly stated they depict the aftermath of a tribal murder, but show no consumption of the dead body. For evidence of cannibalism, Gajdusek also cited Australian arrests of tribesmen for the alleged crime—which were based on hearsay accusations. So perhaps New Guinea natives stand falsely accused of ritual cannibalism.

In addition, few people outside of Gajdusek's original research team have ever personally witnessed kuru victims. This means we also depend on his own descriptions and statistics for our knowledge of the disease itself, particularly since he claims that cannibalism and kuru both ceased to exist within a few years after his 1957 trip. Phantom viruses, transmitted through phantom cannibalism, cause a phantom disease.

Yet Gajdusek has reshaped the thinking of an entire generation of biologists, his seductive message of slow viruses having landed on eager ears. He and the virus hunters inspired by him have aggressively built their careers chasing viruses and attributing to them latent periods, in order to connect them to non-infectious diseases.

SMON, the nerve-destroying disease that struck Japan during the 1960s, became one unfortunate example. Japanese virologists, greatly impressed with Gajdusek's accomplishments, spent years searching for slow viruses they presumed would cause the disease, and thereby delayed finding the true cause—a prescribed medication.

Another example of a pointless virus hunt was diabetes. Beginning in the early 1960s, some scientists tried to blame this non-contagious syndrome on the virus that also causes mumps. The evidence has been pathetically sparse, forcing virologists to point to occasional children who coincidentally become diabetic after they have also suffered mumps, or if they really stretch their case, to argue that both mumps and diabetes become most common during the same annual season in one county of New York state.

Having become soldiers without a war, veteran polio virologists managed to invade the diabetes field as well, proposing since the early 1970s that coxsackie viruses may cause the disease. Antibodies against several strains of these harmless viruses, first discovered as by-products of polio research, have been found in a few diabetic children. But between twenty and seventy percent of young diabetics have never been infected, and the remainder have already neutralized the virus with their immune systems long before the onset of diabetes. Apparently an equal percentage of *non*-diabetic children have also been infected with these coxsackie viruses. Needless to say, none of the above viruses meets Koch's postulates for causing diabetes.

Hilary Koprowski, like his inspiration Gajdusek, typifies the modern virus hunter. Although Koprowski's virology career began earlier, Gajdusek's work redirected and helped rescue Koprowski from the obsolescence that threatened all polio researchers after the war on polio. Koprowski is today a comfortable multimillionaire who takes time to enjoy life. "Whenever the occasion permits, he is ready to delight his friends with piano performances," says one colleague of this man who almost chose a music career.[24] Instead Koprowski joined the virus hunters, and has like so many of his colleagues found his newest calling in the war on AIDS. Perhaps the major obstacle to his success has lain in his personality, for he has been described as "mild-mannered" and prefers the sidelines in any controversy.[25] He certainly cannot be described as obscure, but despite his plodding persistence and modest success in following every virus hunting trend, he has long seemed to play second fiddle to some of his peers.

His work on viruses started at the Rockefeller Institute in New York. By the late 1940s he moved across town to the Lederle pharmaceutical company, where he worked feverishly to develop a polio vaccine. By 1954 he had invented one, but Jonas Salk was announcing the field trials for another vaccine, and Koprowski's already-tested product was shunted aside by Salk's public acclaim. Koprowski left Lederle in 1957 to take a position as director of the privately endowed Wistar Institute of Pennsylvania, where he began tests on humans and stepped up the campaign to approve his vaccine. By now Albert Sabin had tested his own polio immunization on millions of people in foreign countries, completely overshadowing Koprowski's equally successful but less promoted vaccine. Nevertheless, Koprowski's day did arrive. His vaccine became the standard used by the World Health Organization in Africa during the late 1950s and 1960s.

In the meantime he spent several years studying rabies virus and creating another vaccine against that disease, which attacks the brain and nervous system. But because rabies is relatively rare, Koprowski's vaccine never achieved the stardom of other immunizations. More importantly, however, his rabies research placed him squarely in the field of neurological diseases just in time to meet up with Gajdusek's kuru work. The study of legitimately disease-causing viruses had only driven Koprowski into dead ends, whereas the news of "slow" viruses enticed him with visions of groundbreaking science. He quickly realized that the notion of slow viruses could become a useful tool, allowing him to blame slow, non-infectious diseases on viruses— which had previously been recognized as fast-acting agents. He participated as a "program advisor" in Gajdusek's first major conference on slow and unconventional viruses, held in 1964 at NIH headquarters in Bethesda, Maryland. From that point forward, Hilary Koprowski joined the new virus-hunting trend from which he would never turn back.

His first big opportunity to take a crack at slow viruses came at the end of the 1960s. Subacute sclerosing panencephalitis (SSPE), a mouthful of a name for such a rare condition, attacks a small number of school children and teenagers each year, causing dementia, learning disabilities, and finally death. Doctors first recognized SSPE in the 1930s, and by the 1960s the virus hunters were searching for an SSPE germ. At that time, the most fashionable viruses for research belonged to the myxovirus family, including the viruses that caused influenza, measles, and mumps; microbe hunters therefore started by probing for signs of myxoviruses. Excitement mounted after trace quantities of measles virus were detected in the brains of SSPE patients, and in 1967 most of the victims were found to have antibodies against measles. The fact that SSPE only affected one of every million measles-infected people, and that this rare condition appeared from one to ten years after infection by measles, posed no problem: the researchers simply hypothesized a one- to ten-year latent period. It was little wonder they also could so easily rationalize that one virus could cause two totally different diseases.

Koprowski's foray into SSPE research began in the early 1970s. He began isolating the measles virus from dying SSPE victims, a nearly impossible task because their immune systems had long before completely neutralized the virus (some SSPE cases, moreover, had never had measles, merely the measles vaccine). His characteristic patience nonetheless paid off, yielding a tiny handful of virus particles that could be coaxed out of some people to begin growing again, if only in laboratory cell culture. Koprowski quickly saw the significance of this difficult procedure, for he soon discovered that the only viruses remaining so many years after the original measles infection were a few damaged leftovers that could barely grow. Rather than concluding measles virus had nothing to do with SSPE, he employed the new logic of virus hunting, inverting this data to argue that *defective* measles virus caused SSPE!

Koprowski continued this line of SSPE research for several more years. But in 1985 Gajdusek himself entered the SSPE fray, publishing a paper with leading AIDS researcher Robert Gallo in which they proposed that HIV, the supposed AIDS virus, caused SSPE while remaining latent. With hardly a blink, several leading virologists jettisoned the old measles-SSPE hypothesis in favor of a newly popular, but equally innocent, virus. Not all virus hunters have yet made the switch, but only time will tell.

Multiple sclerosis (MS), the notorious disease that also attacks the nervous system and ultimately kills, has provided yet another opportunity for the virus hunters. First they blamed measles virus starting in the 1960s, since many MS patients had antibodies against the virus. Ten years later others suggested mumps virus, which is similar to measles. The early 1980s brought the coronavirus hypothesis of MS, this category of virus being better known for causing some colds. In 1985, with Gajdusek stealing his thunder for SSPE, Koprowski found his chance to board a new ship. He, too, published a scientific paper that year with Robert Gallo, in this case arguing that some virus similar to HIV now caused MS. Unfortunately for Koprowski, even this hyothesis was doomed to abandonment in the name of fashion within just a few years.

Phantom Viruses and Big Bucks

Most virus hunters prefer chasing real, if harmless, viruses as their deadly enemies. But Gajdusek's "unconventional" viruses—the ones neither he nor anyone else have ever found—have been making a comeback in recent years. Given the abundance of research dollars being poured into biomedical science by the NIH and other agencies, opportunistic virus hunters have been finding creative ways to cash in. One increasingly successful method utilizes modern biotechnology to isolate viruses that may not even exist.

Not surprisingly, the first scientist to invoke this phantom virus methodology picked up the abandoned pieces of Gajdusek's work on kuru and scrapie. A professor at the University of California at San Francisco, Stanley Prusiner believed unreservedly in the notion of "unconventional viruses," and wanted to be the person to find out just what they were. Most scientists, faced with brain tissues that contain no foreign molecules, would hardly know where to begin, and would simply move on to other questions. But not Prusiner. Obsessive to a fault, he began arguing in the early 1980s that the very definition of a virus should be changed. The basic concept of an infectious microbe incorporates the assumption that it is genetically alien to the host it invades. Prusiner speculated instead that the scrapie agent could be a host protein, one of the normal molecules found in healthy brains. Trying to explain why only some individuals become sick, he added that the "prion," as he dubbed these hypothetical infectious proteins, would have to be a mutant or chemically altered form of the normal protein that could somehow reproduce even without its own genetic information.

This upside-down proposal proved too much to swallow even for the most dedicated virus hunters, and Prusiner labored under a cloud of controversy for years. Then in 1990 he applied the latest high-tech tools to the problem. Having isolated an alleged prion protein, he genetically engineered a mutant form of the corresponding human gene into a strain of mice, hoping they would now develop scrapie. Some of them certainly did, but only months after they were born. But considering that the change had been made in their genetic structure, they should have had brain disease the moment they were born; indeed, their brains should never have formed properly at all. Worse yet for the Prusiner hypothesis, new prions cannot be found in the brains of these genetically altered mice. He has never mentioned the possibility that any random genetic change in mice might as easily induce sickness. Nor has he advertised the embarrassing discovery of mutant "prion" proteins in normal, healthy humans.

Yet Prusiner has touted his experiments' dismal results as breakthrough successes. The virus-chasing establishment, having grown large enough to hunger for more research avenues, has extended a warm welcome for the prion hypothesis—even though the prions are not, technically speaking, viruses. Prusiner was awarded with a prestigious membership in the exclusive National Academy of Sciences in 1991, and major papers in top scientific journals now herald his phantom achievements.

Hepatitis, or liver disease, has also yielded profitable virus hunting opportunities in recent years. Hepatitis can be a truly painful affliction, starting like a flu but progressing to more severe symptoms, including high fevers and yellow skin. At least three varieties seem to exist. Hepatitis A is easily infectious, spread through unsanitary conditions, and is caused by a well-characterized virus. Hepatitis B also results from a virus (discovered in the 1960s) and is transmitted mostly between heroin addicts sharing needles, among sexually active people, or in the Third World from mothers to their children around birth.

A third type of hepatitis was found in the 1970s, a type restricted to heroin addicts, alcoholics, and patients who have received blood transfusions. Most scientists assumed these cases were either hepatitis A or B, until widespread testing revealed neither virus in the victims. Roughly 35,000 Americans die each year of any type of liver disease, a fraction of those from this "non-A, non-B hepatitis," as it was known for years. This form of hepatitis does not behave as an infectious disease, for it rigidly confines itself to people in well-defined risk groups rather than spreading to larger populations. This fact has certainly not prevented virologists from eyeing the disease, hoping one day to find a virus causing it.

That day arrived in 1987. The laboratory for the job was no less than the research facility of the Chiron Corporation, a biotechnology company located directly across the bay from San Francisco. Equipped with the most advanced techniques, a research team started its search in 1982 by injecting blood from patients into chimpanzees. None of the monkeys contracted hepatitis, although subtle signs vaguely resembling infection or poisoning did appear. For the next step, the scientists probed liver tissue for a virus. None could be found. Growing desperate, the team fished even for the smallest footprint of a virus, finally coming across and greatly amplifying a small piece of genetic information, encoded in a molecule known as ribonucleic acid (RNA), that did not seem to belong in the host's genetic code. This fragment of presumably foreign RNA, the researchers assumed, must be the genetic information of some undetected virus. Whatever it was, liver tissue contained it only in barely detectable amounts.

The Chiron team used newly available technology to reconstruct pieces of the mystery virus. Now they could test patients for antibodies against this hypothetical virus, and soon discovered that only a slight majority of non-A, non-B hepatitis patients had any evidence of these molecules in their bodies. Koch's first postulate, of course, demands that a truly harmful virus be found in huge quantities in every single patient. For that matter, his second postulate requires that the virus particles be isolated and grown, although this supposed virus has never been found intact. And the third postulate insists that newly infected animals, such as chimpanzees, should get the disease when injected with the virus. Thus this hypothetical microbe fails all three tests. But Koch's standards were the furthest thing from the minds of the Chiron scientists, who announced in 1987 they had finally found the "hepatitis C" virus.

Now more paradoxes are confronting the virus hypothesis. Huge numbers of people testing positive for hepatitis C virus never develop any symptoms of the disease, even though the "virus" is no less active in their bodies than in hepatitis patients. And according to a recent large-scale study of people watched for eighteen years, those with signs of "infection" live just as long as those without. Baffled by these embarrassing facts, scientists defend their still-elusive virus by giving it an undefined latent period extending into decades. In other words, a virus that may not even exist will now take longer than your lifetime to kill you.

Such nonsense does not faze the virus-hunting research establishment, though. Indeed, rewards are generally showered upon any new virus hypothesis, no matter how bizarre. Chiron did not spend five years pursuing its own virus for nothing; they immediately began cashing in on the expensive research program. Having patented the test for the virus, the company put it into production and began a publicity campaign to win powerful allies. The NIH-supported virology establishment soon lent the full weight of its credibility to the hepatitis C virus camp, but Chiron needed a special attention-getting stunt to help sell the test. As Chiron's CEO, Edward Penhoet, boasted, "We have a blockbuster product."[26] They wanted more than just approval from the Food and Drug Administration (FDA); a regulatory order to test the blood supply would reap enormous sales for Chiron.

Their big chance presented itself in late 1988 as a special request from Japanese Emperor Hirohito's doctors. The monarch was dying and constantly needed blood transfusions; could Chiron provide a test to make sure he received no blood tainted with hepatitis C? The biotech company jumped at the opportunity, making for itself such a name in Japan that the Tokyo government gave the product its approval within one year. The Emperor died in the meantime, but excitement over Chiron's test was fueled when the Japanese government even placed hepatitis C high on its medical priority list. Chiron's test kit now earns some 60 million dollars annually in that country alone.[27] By the middle of 1990, the United States followed suit. The Food and Drug Administration not only eagerly approved the test, but even recommended the universal testing of donated blood. The American Association of Blood Banks yielded to the pressure, mandating the five-dollar test for all 12 million blood donations made each year in this country—raking in another 60 million dollars for Chiron while raising the nation's medical costs that much more. And all this testing is being done for a virus that has still never been isolated. Whether or not phantom viruses cause disease, they certainly open gold mines.

Government-backed profits for the test kit have generated another all-too-common part of virus hunting. Edward Penhoet, CEO for Chiron, also holds a position as professor on the Berkeley campus of the University of California. In his same department is professor Donald Glaser, who founded his own biotech company, Cetus. With Chiron's new income from the hepatitis C test, Penhoet's company recently bought out Glaser's company, creating an extra layer of hidden politics among university faculty.

Unfortunately for Peter Duesberg, who belongs to the same department, his supervisor is yet another professor who moonlights as a consultant for Chiron Corporation—and displays intense hostility to Duesberg for challenging modern virus hunting. Such conflicts of interest have become standard fixtures in university biology departments, quietly violating the official image of academic neutrality between colleagues.

The modern biomedical research establishment differs radically from any previous scientific program in history. Driven by vast infusions of federal money, it has grown into an enormous and powerful bureaucracy that amplifies obvious mistakes while stifling dissent. Individual researchers have been forced to specialize in the face of a torrent of useless and misinterpreted data, hemmed in by heightened peer pressure and commercial conflicts of interest. Those who play along see their careers advance; those who raise questions become objects of derision. The public has no choice but to take the momentary "consensus" of expert opinion at face value.

Such a process no longer can be called science, which by definition depends on self-correction by internal challenge and debate. With team cooperation and technical skills having replaced independent thinking, the virus hunting disasters described in this chapter must inevitably dominate.

Having invented the conceptual tools for blaming innocent viruses as causes of disease, virologists were finally ready to enter the public spotlight in a big way. Robert Koch's principles had vanished from their minds, conquered by the latent period and statistical correlations. The next chapter tells the story of the misdirected war on cancer, whose virus-chasing veterans would go on to become the generals and soldiers in the war on AIDS.

Chapter 3 Footnotes

1 Lapp, *The New Priesthood: The Scientific Elite and the Uses of Power.* Harper & Row, New York, 1965, pp. 39-40.
2 Greenwood, *Solving the Scientist Shortage.* Public Affairs Press, Washington, D.C., 1958, p. 23; *Science & Engineering Indicators—1989.* National Science Board, Dec. 1, 1989; The Month in AIDS, *Rethinking AIDS* 1(7):1, July, 1993.
3 Lapp, Op cit., p. 14.
4 Greenwood, Op cit., p. 2.
5 Lapp, Op cit., p. 41.
6 Ibid., p. 42.
7 *Postdoctoral Appointments and Disappointments.* National Research Council, 1981, p. 79.
8 *Doctoral Scientists and Engineers: A Decade of Change.* National Science Foundation, March, 1988.
9 Reagan, *Science and the Federal Patron.* Oxford University Press, New York, 1969, p. 11.
10 *The Ph.D. Shortage: The Federal Role.* Association of American Universities, Jan. 11, 1990, p. iv.
11 Reagan, Op cit., p. 12.
12 *Science & Engineering Indicators—1989,* Op cit., pp. 106, 121.
13 Lapp, Op cit., p. 30.
14 Shodel, NIH Overview. *Journal of NIH Research* 2:19-24, 1990, p. 22.
15 Klaw, *The New Brahmins: Scientific Life in America.* William Morrow & Co., New York, 1968, p. 148.
16 Shannon, The National Institutes of Health: Some Critical Years, 1955-1957. *Science* 237:865-868, 1987, p. 866.
17 Ibid., p. 866.
18 Moseley, Interview: D. Carleton Gajdusek. *Omni,* March, 1986, pp. 62-68, 104-106; confirmed by Gajdusek, "Man in Isolation," Hitchcock Lecture, Wheeler Auditorium, University of California, Berkeley, Jan. 11, 13, and 18, 1982; also confirmed by Gunther Stent (former Chair, Dept. of Molecular & Cell Biology, U.C. Berkeley), personal communication with Peter Duesberg, March 7, 1994.
19 Moseley, Op cit., p. 68.
20 Gajdusek, Gibbs, and Alpers (eds.), *Slow, Latent, and Temperate Virus Infections.* Government Printing Office, Washington, D.C., 1965, p. 5.
21 Kolata, Anthropologists Suggest Cannibalism Is a Myth. *Science* 232:1497-1500, 1986.
22 Ibid.
23 Ibid.
24 Kaplan, Three decades of collaboration with Hilary Koprowski. *Journal of Cellular Physiology* 2(Suppl.):1-6, 1982, p. 5.
25 Williams, *Virus Hunters.* Alfred A. Knopf, New York, 1959, p. 346.
26 Barnum, U.S. biotech is thriving in Japan. *San Francisco Chronicle,* May 12, 1992, pp. C1, C4.
27 Ibid.

Chapter 4

A War on Cancer

Polio was the last major contagious epidemic to strike the industrial world. Its ravages had virtually ceased by the early 1960s, leaving microbe hunters with few medically important diseases to study. Without such practical questions to answer, human virology was threatened with becoming a purely academic field facing gradual extinction. In populations whose life expectancies were no longer cut short by infectious plagues, the new medical frontiers lay in the diseases of older age—heart disease and cancer.

The microbe hunters, however, had no desire to become obsolete, and gradually recognized the importance of attaching themselves to cancer research. This transition began at the turn of the century, and became complete after the end of the polio epidemic. Cancer was certainly a wide open field, for the varied diseases collectively known as "cancer" exuded plenty of mystery. Indeed, the subject proved so confusing that any scientist naive enough to probe its secrets was scorned by other biologists. Only the microbe hunters, having correctly identified the causes of many infectious diseases, had the audacity to believe they could now solve the cancer problem. So they began proposing cancers to be contagious, caused by various germs.

During the early decades, the microbe hunters themselves discovered the pitfalls of cancer research. Their observations on microbes in cancer were at best inconsistent, sporadic, and obscure, more so than for any other approach to studying the disease. Thus the other cancer biologists, who were investigating everything from carcinogenic chemicals to cell metabolism, soundly rejected the microbe hypothesis of cancer. This should have permanently ended the hunt for infectious cancer agents. Amazingly, over the next several decades the microbe hunters not only rescued themselves from this initial quandary and the threat of obsolescence, but even managed to seize control of the entire cancer field. Finally reaching the pinnacle of political success, they were well-positioned to dominate AIDS research from the start. This is the story of their rise to power—despite having no scientific evidence for their germ-cancer hypotheses.

During the early part of the century, while infectious diseases were rapidly declining, a few microbe hunters began to sense the changing tide. Cancer was on the rise, if only because people now lived long enough to develop it, and its puzzling nature invited innumerable conflicting explanations. The early microbiologists began applying their tools toward chasing hypothetical cancer-causing germs. The bacteria-hunting followers of Koch and Pasteur took first crack at the problem:

During the heyday of bacteriology, many attempts were made to find a microbial cause of cancer. Bacteria, fungi, and other micro-organisms, often named after their discoverer, were isolated and proposed as candidates. But none of the claims withstood the rigorous criteria of bacterial causation enunciated by Koch.[1]

Bacteria hunting died with the last of the bacterial epidemics. But virus hunting was gradually arriving, as the more sophisticated technologies for working with viruses became available. The virologists, moreover, wished to try their hand at explaining cancer.

However, they faced a bothersome paradox in trying to blame viruses for cancer. As they were discovering, the typical virus reproduces by entering a living cell, comandeering the cell's resources in order to make new virus particles, a process that ends with the disintegration of the dead cell. Cancer, on the other hand, is a disease of cells that continue to live. Something goes wrong with perfectly normal cells, and they begin changing their behavior and appearance, refusing to cooperate with the rest of the body. Such abnormal cells eventually begin growing relentlessly, invading nearby tissues and ultimately spreading throughout the host. The patient dies once these increasingly voracious parasites have caused enough disruption. So, if viruses kill cells, how could they possibly cause some cells to grow *too well*?

As luck would have it, virologists discovered a few special types of virus that do not kill cells. And in rare circumstances, an occasional virus has been known to cause a tumor in some extraordinarily susceptible animal; these are freak accidents of nature.[2] Because they were searching relentlessly, virus hunters did indeed come across a few of these exceptional cases and learned to repeat them in artificial laboratory conditions. As with any example of science gone awry, cancer virology began with perfectly legitimate observations; only decades later did the virus hunters exaggerate the importance of these early results, seizing upon them as precedents for convicting innocent viruses in ever more radical departures from reality.

The first known tumor virus surfaced in 1908, when a pair of Danish veterinarians studied leukemia in chickens. Vilhelm Ellermann and Oluf Bang experimented and discovered that something tiny enough to pass through a bacteria-screening filter—a virus—would meet Koch's postulates in causing the same leukemia in newly infected chickens. The following year, a virologist named Peyton Rous, who worked at New York's Rockefeller Institute, made an even more dramatic finding. When a farmer brought him a chicken with a large, well-developed solid tumor, Rous discovered that some filterable virus from the bird produced amazingly rapid tumors in other chickens within weeks or even days of infection.

But neither of these experiments shook the scientific world. Virologists generally kept themselves busy with more clear-cut viruses that caused common diseases, especially in humans, scrupulously avoiding the confusing pitfalls of cancer research. Conversely, the cancer biologists had observed patients and also experimented on animals, recognizing that cancer was not contagious. At that time cancer researchers did not even consider leukemia a cancer at all. Further, they dismissed Rous's virus as some oddity of chickens. Tumor biologists also knew they could not find viruses in the human cancers they studied, and therefore refused to take seriously the observations of the early cancer-virus hunters.

Several more animal tumor viruses were found during the 1930s. A possible leukemia virus was noticed in certain strains of mice, as was another virus that caused breast cancer in some mice and seemed to pass from mother to child through the milk. Both cancers, however, proved almost impossible to duplicate in the lab, and would only affect special strains of mice weakened through generations of incestuous inbreeding, a process long known to cause medical problems in humans and animals. The same viruses, when injected into more typical mouse strains, produced no effect.

A researcher at the Rockefeller Institute meanwhile isolated the cause of warts in rabbits, a virus that performed more consistently. A handful of virus hunters became excited when Peyton Rous injected the wart virus into new rabbits, which occasionally caused true cancers rather than mere warts. But this virus, found in wild rabbits, would induce the dramatic tumors only when infecting domestic rabbits.

In a sense, both sides of the virus-cancer controversy were right. These viruses could genuinely cause some rare cancers, though only in specially susceptible animals under precise conditions. Yet such exceptions bore no relevance for human and animal tumors in general. Such scattered observations by virus hunters did not sway the cancer investigators. When Franklin Roosevelt signed the 1937 legislation creating the National Cancer Institute (NCI), a report issued by an advisory group of cancer biologists declared without hesitation that "The very exhaustive study of mammalian cancer has disclosed a complete lack of evidence of its infectious origin," and dismissed viruses as "agents that may be disregarded"[3] The report echoed the view common among cancer researchers. With no real evidence on which to stand, the field of cancer virology faced certain death.

As a new federal institute charged with managing the fight against cancer, the NCI turned its main attention to developing radiation and chemotherapy treatments against tumors. Of the twenty-four grants disbursed by NCI during its first five years, only two funded virus research, both relatively small. Ironically, however, over the next two decades the NCI would become the very instrument that kept cancer virology alive. Despite their second-class status, a few virus hunters managed to secure positions in the new agency, enabling them to keep their profession alive. During the 1940s they isolated the milk-borne virus indirectly promoting breast tumors in some susceptible mice, and found the human wart virus. They even managed to revive some research on Peyton Rous' chicken tumor virus, by then known as the Rous Sarcoma Virus (RSV). The steady trickle of virus experiments did little to advance a general understanding of cancer, but it did begin attracting a few virus hunters to the field. Their one trump card lay in the Rous virus, which stood out for causing its tumor within days of infection, in contrast to chemicals, radiation, and other factors that required months to produce a few tumors in animals.

One of these new cancer virologists, Ludwik Gross, began his tumor virus work at the Veterans Administration Hospital in the Bronx, New York. Having returned from the Second World War only to be rejected from an NCI job, Gross accepted a position at the hospital because they allowed him lab space in the basement for part-time research. He picked up the work first done in the 1930s on a virus suspected of causing mouse leukemias, one that only seemed to induce cancer in the more sickly inbred strains but not in healthier mice. After years of persistent study, he finally isolated the virus in the early 1950s. As a leukemia virus that could only cause disease after months of chronic infection in newborns of certain mouse strains, his finding stirred little interest. But during one of his virus isolation procedures, Gross also accidentally found a virus that caused a much more pronounced tumor of salivary glands in the mice.

Although Gross's latter virus showed more tumor-causing potency than most other known viruses, its importance would also have been dismissed as irrelevant to medicine, since human cancers contained no viruses and were not contagious. Yet these two mouse viruses soon became the foundation upon which a revival of tumor virology was built. Only a couple of years after Gross announced his findings in 1953, James Shannon took over as director of the National Institutes of Health. By this time the NCI had become a branch of the NIH. The sudden cash flow that followed, and the spending priority on polio, uncorked the virus hunting bottle. Many scientists decided to redirect their careers toward cancer viruses, and emerged from every corner to claim a piece of the new pie.

At the NCI, Sarah Stewart, a former NIH researcher trained in virus research, had already begun duplicating the work of Ludwik Gross in isolating his two viruses. She discovered that the second virus not only caused tumors in the salivary glands, but also induced many other cancers throughout the bodies of her newborn mice, and therefore dubbed it "polyoma" (meaning "many faces"). A number of the cancer biologists continued to criticize the virus discovery, but virologists enthusiastically followed her lead. The challenge became obvious: to find a virus that causes cancer in *humans*.

The war on polio provided an unexpected opportunity for finding cancer viruses. In 1959, the Salk polio vaccine was in wide distribution, and the Sabin vaccine was undergoing large-scale trials in foreign countries. Almost simultaneously, two scientists independently found a new virus in the monkey kidneys in which polio virus was being mass-produced for the vaccine—in other words, a contaminant. The virus was native to monkeys, and caused some cell death in the kidney tissues. Inspired by the polyoma discovery, both researchers injected this virus into newborn hamsters in an attempt to cause cancer, even though neither yet knew of the other's work. To the investigators' excitement, the hamsters did indeed get tumors from the virus. As the fortieth virus isolated from monkey cells, it was named Simian Virus 40, or SV40.

The new virus was first publicly announced in 1960. Millions of children in the United States and abroad had already been immunized with vaccine contaminated with this potentially cancer-causing virus. Another million soldiers had received vaccines for a different disease that had been similarly contaminated. Huge studies tracking vaccinated people soon confirmed no unusual cancer cases among them, but the virus hunters had achieved their victory. In the wake of the near-panic over SV40, growing amounts of research dollars were earmarked for cancer-virus study; in 1959, for example, NCI specifically reserved the extraordinary sum of one million dollars for the field. And the notion that viruses might cause cancer in humans had been firmly embedded in the thinking of the scientific community. As suggested earlier by NIH investigator Robert J. Huebner, one of many scientists to join the growing polyoma research program, "Wouldn't it be interesting if more tumor viruses turned out to be similar to and spread like the 'common cold'?"[4]

Meanwhile the mouse leukemia virus first isolated by Gross had created a parallel field in the tumor virus hunt. Dozens of scientists rushed to find leukemia viruses in animals and humans. From 1956 to 1970, at least a dozen different viruses were isolated from mouse leukemias by researchers throughout the United States and other parts of the world, even as the NIH was disbursing new grants all over the globe. None of these viruses proved to be any more potent than the first one. Several reports of viruses infecting human leukemic cells also poured in, though none met Koch's postulates. The researchers chasing such human viruses knew how to get public attention: one lab named a virus after its discoverer, Elizabeth S. Priori, giving it the intriguing name "ESP virus."

While achieving only dubious results, the net effect of this research was to draw large numbers of virus hunters into studying cancer. As the war on polio wound down, its soldiers switched to the only medical field left with high expectations of success, bringing with them many harmless human viruses they had isolated as by-products of their polio research. Ludwik Gross and other virologists openly argued that human cancer viruses would soon be found. Albert Sabin and many of his fellow polio virologists attended conferences and listened to the new clarion call. Talk of vaccines against cancer filled the air.

Himself a poliovirus veteran, Nobel laureate Wendell Stanley quickly entered the national spotlight as one of the leading lobbyists for a full-scale cancer virus program. Taking his cue from the reorganization and expansion of the NIH, he began using many a speaking opportunity from 1956 forward to push the virus-cancer hypothesis. At the Third National Cancer Conference, held in Detroit in 1956 and partly sponsored by the NCI, Stanley declared

> I believe the time has come when we should assume that viruses are responsible for most, if not all, kinds of cancer, including cancer in man, and design and execute our experiments accordingly...
> ... Literally dozens of hitherto unknown human viruses have been discovered during the past year or so [mostly as by-products of polio research]... The discovery of this great array of hitherto unknown viruses coursing through human beings made necessary a special conference devoted to these agents. This conference was held in May, 1956, at the New

York Academy of Sciences under the thought-provoking title of "Viruses in Search of Disease." Thus we have today many more human viruses than we know what to do with; hence there is now certainly no reason to shy away from giving consideration to viruses as causative agents in cancer for lack of the viruses. Actually these recent developments lead one to suspect that there are many more undiscovered viruses present in presumably normal human beings.[5]

Scientists now had plenty of raw material—many human cancers to explain and a growing list of (evidently harmless) viruses to blame them on. The new NIH money rolled in as Stanley and others beat the propaganda drums for a new virus hunt. As had happened so often in the history of microbe hunting, such battle cries ultimately generated terrible medical disasters. Only this time the obsession was better financed and organized than ever before.

Slow Viruses to the Rescue
No amount of enthusiasm, by itself, could bridge the giant chasm between viruses and cancer. The handful of cancer-causing viruses found in some animals were considered odd precisely because most viruses kill the cells they infect, rather than making them grow better. And as clinical cancer specialists knew all too well, human tumors rarely contained any active virus particles that could be detected. Nor did they expect to find any, since cancer typically behaves as a non-infectious disease: most tumors develop gradually over years or even decades, rather than striking quickly and affecting large populations, as seen in flu epidemics and other contagious diseases. Against such common sense the virus hunters somehow had to justify their anticipated cancer viruses.

Carleton Gajdusek's sudden popularity in the early 1960s derived largely from the cancer virus crowd. His hypothetical "slow viruses" presented part of the answer they were looking for—viruses that could supposedly act as slowly as the cancer. The cancer virologists lent their full support to promoting Gajdusek, and he responded in kind. Already at the 1964 scientific conference on "unconventional" viruses hosted at the NIH, he proposed in his introductory presentation some nine human tumors as possibly being caused by slow viruses, including two types of leukemia.

But even this invention would not suffice. Virologists needed some way to rationalize the absence of detectable viruses in tumors, and the inability of such hypothetical microbes to kill the infected cells. A full decade before Gajdusek arrived on the scene, a French biologist named André Lwoff had already supplied this missing ingredient. As with so many virus-hunting myths, the notion of dormant cancer viruses began with a minor but genuine observation that was later twisted.

Lwoff began his microbiology career in the 1920s with the Pasteur Institute in Paris. Over the next twenty-five years he developed better methods for culturing microbes and learning about their nutritional requirements. During the mid-1930s, while his nutrition work continued, he heard about a strange phenomenon being studied at the Institute. According to a couple of his peers, certain strains of bacteria could be infected by a virus that would often become dormant. The virus literally went to sleep inside the cell, rather than killing its host and infecting new cells. Then at some later time, seemingly normal bacteria could suddenly burst open, releasing the newly reactivated virus.

Since many prominent scientists refused to believe the observations were true, Lwoff himself payed little attention to the studies. But one year after the end of World War Two, his interest in the subject was revived at a conference in the United States. Returning to Paris with a grant from the U.S. National Cancer Institute, he set up his own research program to study this virus latency. After a series of careful experiments, he proved that the virus could indeed become latent in the infected cell for varying periods of time, and would reawaken when exposed to ultraviolet radiation. Soon even the most hardened skeptics were convinced.

The phenomenon was certainly interesting, but it only applied to a few viruses. Most lack the ability to become dormant, and must either kill the infected cell immediately or fail altogether. Nevertheless, Lwoff's timing could not have been more perfect for the cancer virologists, and he soon made the connection. From 1953 onward he argued forcefully that cancer resulted from the reactivation of dormant viruses, which would begin to recruit cells to form tumors. His hypothesis struck the right chord. Ludwik Gross, while in the process of experimentally describing his mouse leukemia virus, echoed the emerging view:

> When inoculated into a susceptible host [mouse], the agent remains dormant, or harmless for its host, until the host reaches middle age. At that time, for obscure reasons, the hitherto latent agent becomes activated, causing rapid multiplication of cells harboring it. This results in the development of leukemia and the death of the host.[6]

Gross had also made a legitimate observation; his mouse virus happened to be another rare example of one that would become latent for a time, and one that could only cause leukemia in specially susceptible, newborn mice. Both he and Lwoff, however, encouraged the increasingly popular belief that all tumors might be caused by such viruses.

At this point the virus-cancer view ran head-first into another fundamental problem. In the frenzied drive to isolate tumor agents from humans after the mid-1950s, scientists could find no virus that had been consistently reactivated in all tumors of a given type. By Koch's first postulate, this would eliminate all such microbes as tumor-causing candidates. But the virus hunt was in full swing, and no researcher intended to give up the focus of his career. So rather than abandon cancer viruses in favor of Koch's postulates, the scientific herd chose to stretch the notion of virus latency.

The mouse leukemia virus discovered by Gross did have a latent period, but it seemed to cause the cancer only after awakening to multiply aggressively in the body. The polyoma and SV40 viruses, on the other hand, although unable to reappear after being cleared out by the immune system, could sometimes insert their genes into infected cells. Either situation—a reactivated virus or active viral genes left behind—could potentially have worked as an explanation for cancer, though only in immune-deficient animals. But unable to find such tumor viruses in humans, biologists stepped off the cliff's edge by endorsing what they perceived as a minor change. According to the revised view, viruses could cause tumors long after infection *even while remaining latent.*

Under the spell of this new paradigm, Koch's postulates and most other formal rules of science disintegrated. Now a virus could perform miracles. It could infect a new host one day, remain latent for any arbitrary amount of time, and then cause a deadly cancer without even being present. Moreover, scientists could now pretend that any cancer was infectious simply by blaming it on any virus they found in the patient's body, without fear of being disproven. One would not even need to find the virus to prove its guilt.

This self-delusion joined hands with the hunt for human leukemia viruses, and, in the 1960s, claimed its first success. The story began with Dennis Burkitt, a British surgeon working at a medical school in Uganda in the late 1950s. He noticed large numbers of children with a malignant lymphoma, a cancer of white blood cells. Determined to investigate further, he spent three years conducting huge surveys of doctors all over Africa, asking them detailed questions about their lymphoma patients. Drawing the points on a map, he found the cancer struck people throughout central Africa, especially along the eastern side. Upon seeing that the risk of getting the disease depended on which climate people lived in, Burkitt proposed that the cancer was contagious, possibly transmitted by insect bites. His idea suited the leukemia virus program splendidly.

News of an obscure disease in Africa, reported by a virtually unknown English medical doctor, tended at first to be ignored. Although this fate greeted his 1958 paper, one doctor back home in London, seeing his opportunity, paid attention. M. Anthony Epstein, working at London's Middlesex Hospital, contacted Burkitt in 1961 and arranged to have sample tissues flown back to England. There Epstein began searching for a virus.

By the end of 1961, word of Burkitt's strange lymphoma and its transmission by insects brought magazine and television reporters to his doorstep. The media, like most people, had not yet caught up with the new belief in infectious cancer among scientists, and broadcast this curiosity all over the world. Another source of this news was a young C. Everett Koop, later to become U.S. Surgeon General, who encouraged virologists to study the newly discovered lymphoma after his trip to Africa. As pressure mounted, Epstein struggled to make the tumor cells grow in lab conditions. Succeeding by 1963, he and his new lab associate Yvonne Barr spent more months looking for the virus under the electron microscope. The following year one showed up, a previously unknown herpes-class virus. Once they could find the virus in almost every single culture of cells from Burkitt's lymphoma patients, Epstein and his co-workers officially proposed their virus to be the cause.

This Epstein-Barr virus has since been shown instead to cause mononucleosis, the so-called "kissing disease," for which it may meet Koch's postulates. But where the virus causes mononucleosis before the body's immune system has suppressed it, Burkitt's lymphoma strikes an average of ten years *after* the immune defenses have neutralized the virus. During mononucleosis, the virus multiplies actively and infects many cells; during Burkitt's lymphoma, it sleeps soundly in its continuing dormant state (Epstein could only find the virus growing in cells cultured outside the body for quite some time, having given the virus a chance to reactivate after arriving in the laboratory, with no immune system to interfere). Not that these absurdities worry the virus hunters, for Epstein and others simply insist that the virus has a ten-year latent period for causing cancer.

Because the virus itself can rarely be found in a lymphoma patient, researchers must test whether the blood contains antibodies against Epstein-Barr virus, indicating the patient was infected sometime in the distant past. Investigators first became excited when they discovered that all Burkitt's lymphoma victims had the antibodies. Upon wider testing, however, they quickly realized that all central Africans, with or without the cancer, also had the antibodies. In the United States, where a small number of people have also developed this lymphoma, roughly half the population has been infected by Epstein-Barr virus. Apparently most children catch the virus from their mothers during the first few months of life. Now two more paradoxes raised their ugly heads. Why did the vast majority of infected people never get the cancer, and why is it less common than having symptoms of mononucleosis? And why is an infected African one hundred times more likely to contract the lymphoma than an infected American?

To answer these questions, Epstein and his colleagues resorted to yet another virus hunting invention: the "cofactor." If Africans face a higher risk of cancer, scientists explain away the problem by hypothesizing that since Africans are also more likely than Americans to be infected with malaria, perhaps malaria helps bring on the cancer. Just like that. Now the virus researchers would like everyone to believe that a disease requires two separate infections, not just one. To explain away other discrepancies, more cofactors can be thought up.

The American and European lymphoma cases have provided an even bigger blow to the Epstein-Barr virus hypothesis. Twenty percent of the patients have no antibodies at all against the virus, meaning they have never been infected. Further, over two-thirds of the cases have no traces left of the virus in their tumor tissues, not even tiny fragments. What could be causing Burkitt's lymphoma in these people? Something else, according to virologists, that remains unknown. Koch's first postulate no longer enters the equation.

Finally, evidence gathered at the level of the DNA shows that each patient's cancer originated from a single white blood cell. If virus infection caused cells to become cancerous, one should find every tumor having originated from the millions of infected cells, but each cancer comes from only a single cell. Virus hunters simply cannot explain why all the other infected cells remain normal.

Many scientists have found the above paradoxes too much to swallow. Within just a few years of the announcement of Epstein-Barr virus, many researchers were already expressing serious doubts about the virus hypothesis of Burkitt's lymphoma. "Today epidemiologists disagree amongst themselves about whether or not Burkitt's lymphoma is an infectious disease," declared a well-respected 1973 textbook.[7] Other prominent scientists have admitted having reservations, and Epstein has felt obliged to defend his hypothesis in leading journals.

Possibly worried about the future status of the Epstein-Barr virus, several scientists in the 1960s began proposing that it also caused a second cancer. Nasopharyngeal carcinoma, a tumor occurring at the back of the nasal passages, mostly shows up in adults in China and India, parts of Africa, and among Eskimos in Alaska. The virus was blamed for this cancer using the excuse that many of these patients have antibodies against the virus. But, as with Burkitt's lymphoma, many of these victims also have never been infected by the virus, while it is dormant in the rest.

So now Epstein-Barr has become a virus that causes at least three diseases, two of them cancers that only appear long after the virus has settled into permanent latency. Despite all doubts, most virologists today thoroughly believe in this virus-cancer hypothesis. It is taught as unquestioned doctrine in college courses and textbooks, and employs large numbers of virus hunters in performing endless experiments on the virus. Epstein has even worked on a vaccine against the virus in order to protect the world from cancer—though the cancer patients hardly need immunization, given that their antibodies have long ago suppressed the virus. After years of work and spending nearly ten million dollars on research, British scientists have announced they will be testing a new vacccine in late 1993 or early 1994. Once they expand the trials, they will need decades to see if they can prevent cancer. Of course, they will fail.

Most importantly, however, the Epstein-Barr virus helped accelerate the hunt for cancer viruses. The search specifically for leukemia viruses had grown so dominant that the NCI had set up a special Acute Leukemia Task Force in 1962. Under James Shannon's leadership, the NCI had learned to set up programs that would attract more funding from Congress, making it easily the largest and most powerful of institutes under the NIH umbrella. The first of these, established during the 1950s, involved a huge effort to develop chemotherapy treatments for cancer; the second, begun in 1962, was a testing program to find potentially cancer-causing chemicals in the environment. The third was built around the leukemia virus group in 1964, and became known as the Virus-Cancer Program, which by 1968 took under its wing all other cancer virus research. Illustrating the complete reversal of fortunes on the part of the virus hunters, this third program became the only major NCI effort to determine the fundamental cause of cancer.

These special programs did the trick. The NCI budget, at some ninety million dollars in 1960, rocketed to more than twice that figure by 1970. Fueled largely by the Epstein-Barr virus discovery, the Virus-Cancer Program quickly seized the lion's share of this new funding. Its 1971 spending level had reached $31 million, almost equal to the other two cancer programs combined. Thus cancer virology came to dominate the NIH itself, holding the most powerful position within the entire biomedical research establishment. Some grumbling at this inequality periodically surfaced from other types of scientists, but the growing budgets and accumulating prizes spoke more authoritatively in the politics of science. Even the sheer volume of research papers published by the virus hunters, growing rapidly during the 1960s, tended to drown out all criticism.

Yet the rise of virology had only begun. The next leap forward came with President Nixon's War on Cancer.

Full Declaration of War

James Shannon's retirement from directing the NIH left a decided vacuum at the top of the biomedical research pyramid. In the absence of his firm control, the growth of NIH temporarily slowed. Although its budget had reached one billion dollars the previous year, the spending increases during the subsequent two years ended up being smaller than before.

"After 15 years of soaring affluence, the leaders of American biomedical science were poorly conditioned for austerity," recalled Daniel S. Greenberg, editor and publisher of *Science & Government Report*. The NIH certainly faced no financial troubles whatsoever, for spending was still moving upwards. Nevertheless, "The [research] community rang with alarms and doomsday prophecies." The bloated but hungry science establishment and its lobby wanted some way to relive the glory days of James Shannon. "Their decision: maneuver the government into declaring war on cancer."[8]

After three years of aggressive lobbying by wealthy political strategist Mary Lasker, plus a Senate-created National Panel of Consultants on the Conquest of Cancer, public drum-beating by columnist Ann Landers, self-serving testimony by medical scientists, and even a procession of cancer victims led before Congress, the National Cancer Act was passed in 1971 and signed at a large press conference by Richard Nixon two days before Christmas. Some lobbyists had openly boasted this would bring about a cure for cancer by 1976. Others drew the analogy with the moon landing, persuading legislators that the shower of money would work similar miracles for medicine.

In the final analysis, neither benefit materialized. But some $800 million extra poured into the NCI over the next five years, bringing with it equally generous sums for the rest of NIH. The largesse of the War on Cancer has continued up to the present day. Once again the growth of biomedical research skyrocketed, much of the money being used to train yet greater numbers of new scientists who would themselves become grant dependents. Of all research areas so funded, virus hunting grew the fastest and emerged by the 1980s as unquestionably the dominant force in the science establishment. Its research now fills over one thousand pages of scientific journal space every month.

The Virus-Cancer Program of the NCI had positioned the cancer virologists to be first in line for the War on Cancer. Prominent spokesmen such as

Wendell Stanley, Ludwik Gross, and André Lwoff had kept up the crusade for the growth of this field right up to the early 1970s. Along the way they were joined by many others, including Robert J. Huebner, a veteran of the war on polio who, until 1968, had run a lab at the National Institute of Allergy and Infectious Diseases, another branch of the NIH. He then transferred to the NCI, where he was given one of a handful of well-funded labs. Having first studied coxsackie viruses and other spinoffs of polio research, he switched into the cancer field by adding to the growing literature on the polyoma virus. In 1969 he published a key paper amplifying André Lwoff's hypothesis, proposing that all human cancer was caused by latent viruses that awoke to cause tumors when radiation or other insults struck the body.

That same year, Nobel laureate James Watson decided to get a piece of the action. Watson had parlayed his Nobel Prize (for discovering the molecular structure of DNA) into a powerful position as head of the Cold Spring Harbor research facility on Long Island in New York state. Seeing the rise of cancer virology, he brought SV40 research to the laboratory in 1969. From that point forward, he added his prestigious voice to the ranks of virus hunters. By 1974 he hosted the Cold Spring Harbor Symposium on tumor viruses, the first international cancer meeting held exclusively for virologists. It proved so popular that annual meetings have been held there ever since, becoming the most highly respected tumor virus conference worldwide.

Not all virologists held as much enthusiasm. In his 1966 Nobel acceptance speech, Peyton Rous, the discoverer of the Rous Sarcoma Virus of chickens in 1909, admitted having left the study of viruses altogether for several years after his finding. He had failed to isolate any other tumor viruses, and had felt the field held little promise. Despite having re-entered cancer virology, Rous could only comment by 1966 that "The number of viruses realized to cause disease has become great during the last half century, but relatively few have any connection with the production of neoplasms [cancers]."[9]

Regardless of Rous' skepticism, the very fact he had won a Nobel Prize for his chicken sarcoma virus helped boost the prestige of the Virus-Cancer Program. Between such awards, the public advocacy by highly visible scientists, and some landmark discoveries in 1970 (see below), the cancer-virus field benefited more than any other program under the War on Cancer. Even the man appointed as NCI director to manage this war, Frank Rauscher, was a virologist. This favored position caused some resentment by other scientists. A 1974 report issued by an outside committee outlined the problem:

> First, the committee said, the VCP [Virus-Cancer Program] is too expensive. (It costs about $50 million to $60 million a year and consumes slightly more than 10 percent of the total NCI budget.) Second, the program must be opened up to the scientific community. At present, it is run by a handful of persons who have undue control over large amounts of money, which goes to only a limited number of laboratories. Furthermore, the individuals who award contracts are in a position to award them to each other, which somehow does not seem quite right.[10]

The virus hunters certainly comprised a powerful and entrenched clique that increasingly dominated biomedical research. Minor bureaucratic reforms altered the operational details, but as the money continued to flow their influence only grew. Given this built-in bias, cancer biology could not help but search for more viruses.

Cervical cancer emerged during the 1960s and 1970s to become possibly the single most important virus-cancer project of all time. Not only did the virus hunters blame the tumor on two totally different viruses, but they have managed to cultivate public interest through a widespread campaign of fear. Readers of the *Los Angeles Times Magazine* opened their March 11, 1990 issue to find disturbing news. A large color photograph of a young, frightened-looking married couple drew one's eye to the ominous title, "Dangerous Liaisons." Several paragraphs down, the story explained further:

> Patty and Victor Vurpillat are infected with a strain of human papilloma virus—HPV—the virus that lurks behind one of the country's fastest-spreading sexually transmitted diseases and is rapidly becoming a prime suspect in the search for the causes of cervical cancer.
> As much as 15% of the population may already be carrying the virus—a fact that many health officials view with alarm...
> As a result, millions of Americans find themselves condemned to a sentence of life beneath the cloud of HPV, carrying in their tissues an incurable and highly infectious virus that may eventually unleash a devastating cancer...
> ... There are no drugs that can rid the body of the virus, just as there is no vaccine.[11]

Making no attempt to calm public fears, the article and its medical sources instead fanned the flames:

> What's more, some people are spreading the virus unknowingly: It is transmitted by contact with warts, and warts often go unnoticed. Some physicians suspect that HPV may even occasionally be spread indirectly—perhaps on a tanning bed, toilet or washcloth.[12]

But biomedical authorities certainly want far-reaching powers to respond to this supposed crisis:

> HPV infection is rampant among her clients, says Catherine Wylie, who oversees the family-planning program at the H. Claude Hudson Comprehensive Health Center... The spread will continue, she says, until the law requires that partners of people who have HPV be tracked down and treated.
> "Our women have sex early because they marry at 16 to 18," Wylie said recently. "As long as this disease is not reportable, and there's no partner follow-up and treatment, I think we're going to have an epidemic of cervical cancer."[13]

For the victims, the diagnosis can be as devastating as the threat of cancer itself. For Patty Vurpillat,

> "It was just awful—not knowing what's going on with your body and if you're going to be OK or not," she said recently. "There's a certain percent chance you're going to be all right. But then, maybe you're not."[14]

In the case of Annie, diagnosed by Dr. Louise Connolly of the Manhattan Beach Women's Health Center,

> "It was horrible, just horrible," Annie remembers, referring to her fear of what Connolly might find. "There you are, spread-eagle, for [nearly half] an hour. None of it really hurts... But every time she'd stop and look at something, I'd think, 'Oh God, oh God, oh God.'"[15]

And for "Nan Singer," whose husband developed genital-type warts,

> Even after she confronted him, her husband was reluctant to see a doctor... Nan felt betrayed and disgusted; their sexual relationship deteriorated. Existing problems in their marriage grew worse.
> ... [Nan] believes her husband's response to the disease contributed significantly to their subsequent divorce.[16]

The disease in question—cancer of the cervix—is a relatively common tumor that develops slowly, and can eventually destroy a woman's reproductive ability or even cause death. As with most cancer, the risk of contracting it increases with age, especially after mid-life.

Microbe hunters first began reinterpreting the study of cervical cancer with their microbiological tools in the nineteenth century, when an Italian doctor conducted surveys and found the tumor more often among married women than among nuns. To the eager bacteria hunters, this could only mean that sexual activity was the risk factor for the cancer, which was translated to mean some sort of venereal infection was at fault. A variety of microbes were indeed blamed for causing the disease, including the bacteria that cause syphilis and gonorrhea, as well as mycoplasma and chlamydia bacteria and the trichomonas protozoa.

Modern virus hunters seized control of the cervical cancer field in the mid-1960s, shortly after the Epstein-Barr virus had been isolated and blamed for causing Burkitt's lymphoma. Because Epstein-Barr was a strain of herpes virus, all other herpes viruses immediately became popular among tumor-virus chasers. By 1966 virologists had revived the observation that women with cervical cancer tended to have had more sexual contacts than those without. That same year one lab reported that a higher proportion of the cancer patients had previously been infected by herpes virus than had people without the tumor.

This proved too tantalizing a thread to pass up. Within two years, researchers were able to distinguish two different herpes simplex viruses: type 1 was the most common, causing sores around the mouth, while type 2 caused its sores in the gential areas—including the cervix. The latter became the target for the virus hunters, who proposed it to be the cause of the cancer.

Declaration of the War on Cancer provided massive new levels of funding, and this research accelerated during the 1970s. Trying to explain why a tumor would appear only years after the original herpes infection, scientists were forced to construct a new hypothesis: according to this idea, the virus would first infect and kill millions of cells, occasionally making a mistake and mixing with the DNA of the cell, and become impotent in the process. In other words, the virus would mutate the genetic code of a few cells, leaving only a piece of the original virus stranded therein. Such cells would survive the infection and eventually grow into a tumor, and years later this leftover piece of the virus could still be detected in the tumor cells.

But as more data accumulated, several embarrassing facts came to light. About 85% of all American adults have been infected by this same herpes virus (many without symptoms), including women without any hint of cervical cancer. And scientists consistently found many women with the tumor but who had never been infected by the herpes virus. Even among those women with both the cancer and past herpes infection, the leftover pieces of the virus in the tumor cells were always different and inactive, meaning that no particular part of the herpes virus was needed to cause the cancer.

In 1976, desperate but not willing to abandon the herpes virus hypothesis, researchers seriously proposed in the prestigious journal *Nature* the "hit-and-run" hypothesis—that the herpes virus briefly infects cervix cells in the unsuspecting woman and makes some mysterious, undetectable change. Then it abruptly vanishes, leaving behind no evidence of the infection, so that the tumor can somehow develop many years down the road.[17] This idea threatened to make virus hunters a laughingstock. How could anyone perform experiments to test for a hypothetical event that left behind no evidence? The "hit-and-run" hypothesis nevertheless survived into the early 1980s, by which time scientists quietly retreated out of the herpes virus hypothesis altogether.

Meanwhile, in 1977 a virologist named Harald zur Hausen, working at the German *Krebsforschungszentrum* (Cancer Research Center) in Heidelberg, proposed another virus as the agent causing cervical cancer. Human papilloma virus (HPV), the mild virus that causes warts, seemed to him a reasonable possibility, based on the assumption that cervical warts could occasionally turn into full-fledged cancers.

By the early 1980s, as virus hunters were fleeing the increasingly silly herpes virus hypothesis, some researchers found broken, leftover pieces of the papilloma virus in the tumor cells of some patients. Soon everyone had joined the new parade, never hesitating to ask if they might be making the same mistake as with herpes virus.

Indeed, the evidence for the papilloma hypothesis has since fallen apart. When zur Hausen and his colleagues discovered that at least half the American adult population, and therefore half the adult women, had been infected by the virus, yet only one percent of women develop the cancer in their lifetimes, they began to see a discrepancy. Not that anyone has been thinking about it, but Koch's first postulate has also tested the credulity of the cancer virologists, since at least one third of all women with cervical cancer have never been infected by the virus. The rest of the cervical cancer patients are not all infected with the same strain of papilloma virus; over a dozen different varieties of the virus can be found in these women.

An incredibly long time elapses between infection by the virus (in those who do get infected) and the onset of the tumor. Papilloma virus tends to be contracted by women who are younger and more sexually active—estimated at an average twenty years of age. Cervical cancer, a disease of older age, strikes women in their forties through their seventies. By subtraction, zur Hausen calculates a whopping "latent period" ranging between twenty and fifty years! Nor does the virus reactivate when the cancer appears; in keeping with the revised Lwoff hypothesis of viral latency and cancer, scientists simply assume the virus caused some sort of important mutation twenty to fifty years earlier, and can therefore remain soundly asleep in the tumor tissue. But this explanation cannot account for several key facts. For one thing, the leftover pieces of the virus cause entirely different, and therefore irrelevant, mutations in the genetic code of each tumor. More strangely yet, each cervical cancer grows up from one single cell, leading to the obvious question of why all the other millions of infected cervical cells never develop into tumors. The final blow to this virus hypothesis lies in the fact that an equal number of men have genital warts, yet rarely do they contract any penile cancers. A truly deadly cancer virus that can infect both sexes should cause tumors in both sexes equally well, a conundrum that leaves virologists utterly perplexed.

As with virtually all cancers, the dynamics of cervical cancer development simply do not match the behavior of viruses. Papilloma virus causes papillomas, or warts. These small overgrowths of slightly abnormal cells can appear (or disappear) almost overnight, and are not true cancers. But most cancers, including cervical cancer, are diseases of old age, developing slowly over many years or decades. The phenomenon of cervical cancer progression begins with "hyperplasias," meaning excessive growths of nearly normal cervical tissue. Most or all of these hyperplasias regress and disappear, while a few may instead grow further into "dysplasias," meaning larger growths of abnormal cells. Even such dysplasias are potentially reversible. But the occasional dysplastic growth can give rise to "neoplasia"—meaning "new growth," or cancer. And a percentage of such cancers can even become malignant, invading surrounding tissues and spreading throughout the body. The major feature of cancer progression is that it is irregular, unpredictable, and gradual—quite unlike the rapid and consistent development of warts. While virus hunters have speculated that warts might somehow further develop into cervical cancer, the reverse may be true; the active cell growth in dysplasias may simply encourage papilloma viruses to become active.

Perhaps better explanations exist in some of the other risk factors for cervical cancer: other than aging, two of the most important factors coinciding with the tumor are long-term smoking and oral contraceptive use. The latter contains powerful sex steroid hormones that directly regulate the function of cervical tissues, and might explain the superficial correlation between cervical cancer risk and the number of sexual contacts a woman has had. In any case, cancer of the cervix is no infectious disease.

Nevertheless, the virus hunters continue to push for the virus-cervical cancer hypothesis, which today remains one of the most popular and widely accepted among scientists. To help rationalize away some of the paradoxes, they have even revived herpes simplex virus-2 as a "cofactor" for the papilloma virus—two zeroes that hardly add up. Yet the biotechnology company Digene Diagnostics, based in Maryland, has won government endorsement for its papilloma virus test. Already widely in use, the test is now recommended by medical research authorities for some seven million American women each year, although only 13,000 cervical cancers appear each year in this country. The reason for promoting the test may have something to do with its price—ranging from $30 to $150 per person. And given that a woman who tests negative today may become infected tomorrow, there is no upper limit to testing. Many research laboratories are also kept in business with NIH grants to study endlessly every detail of the papilloma virus, and thus scientists would be the last to re-evaluate this virus hypothesis. Unfortunately for tens of thousands of women each year, the ongoing media publicity and the tests can have devastating psychological consequences, not to mention the damage from preventive treatments for women who have little more than harmless warts.

Another product of the War on Cancer emerged during the 1970s, when the virus hunters took up research on liver cancer. This time their sights focused on the hepatitis B virus.

Most people infected by this virus either experience no symptoms at all or experience a temporary liver inflammation, after which their immune systems clear the virus from the body, leaving behind only antibodies against the virus. In a few cases, however—one out of every 1000 infected people in the industrial world, five percent of those infected in Asia—hepatitis B can become a chronic infection that neither escalates to kill the patient nor disappears. Instead it gradually wears away at the victim, constantly damaging the liver while causing on-again, off-again symptoms. People develop chronic hepatitis for understandable reasons, when their immune responses have deteriorated from alcoholism, heroin addiction, or the malnutrition so common in the Third World.

Scientists first noticed an overlap between hepatitis B virus and liver cancer in the 1970s. Nations with high rates of infection also had many cancer patients. Upon closer inspection, some studies revealed that people with chronic virus infections had an enormously higher risk of eventually developing the tumor. In 1978 a paper was published arguing that chronic hepatitis infection directly damaged the liver enough to cause cancer, and another virus-cancer hypothesis was born. No one bothered to point out, however, the complete absence of any evidence for liver cancer being contagious.

As researchers began jumping onto the new bandwagon, they uncovered data that unraveled the virus hypothesis. For one thing, only a tiny fraction of chronic hepatitis cases ever progressed to the cancer, that fraction being much higher among Asians than among Americans. And unlike in the industrial world, where the cultures of drug abuse and prostitution largely transmit the virus, Asians mostly become infected by their mothers around the time of birth. Since liver cancer in the Third World shows up in people between the ages of thirty and sixty years, virologists simply calculated the latent period between infection and cancer as ranging from thirty to sixty years—longer than the life expectancies of many people. No researcher stopped to ask whether other health risks might also strike the victim during those many decades, obviating the need to blame a virus.

The case for the virus hypothesis degenerated further when most liver cancers were found in patients who had been infected only once, not chronically, by hepatitis B virus. Rather than continuing as a chronic infection, the virus had been cleared from the body. Hoping to rescue the virus hypothesis, scientists resorted to an old favorite among cancer explanations: perhaps the tumor could result from cells in which the virus accidentally combines with the genetic material to produce mutations. But follow-up investigations showed that the pieces of viral DNA did not affect any consistent part of the cell's genetic structure, implying that such mutations were random, inconsequential accidents. And as with cervical cancer, each liver tumor arose from a single cell at the start, while millions of other cells had been infected with the virus, producing untold numbers of mutant cells. Why did all these other cells remain normal? No answer has been offered. More importantly, many liver cancer patients have never been infected by hepatitis B at all; in the United States, at least one quarter of all these tumor patients have never encountered the virus.

Finally, the virus hypothesis has failed miserably when put to the test of Koch's third postulate. Upon injection into chimpanzees, the human hepatitis B virus does infect and inflame liver tissues, but no liver cancer ever appears. The virus, in fact, cannot cause cancer in any animal.

Hepatitis B infections that do not become chronic cannot possibly cause liver cancer. On the other hand, chronic infections might damage the liver enough to promote the tumor. But the more likely explanation for this non-infectious cancer may lie in the health risks, including drug abuse and malnutrition, that allow chronic infections in the first place. Perhaps these risks in themselves cause cancer. Only a small amount of scientific research has examined diet in connection with this cancer, far too little to be sure.

Despite all evidence to the contrary, most scientists still believe wholeheartedly in the hepatitis B-liver cancer hypothesis. It has even become the primary justification for mass immunization programs against the virus in Asian countries, where people inherit the virus at birth and usually suffer no harm. As two biotechnology experts recently put their argument, "While hepatitis B infection may be asymptomatic, chronic carriers have a high risk of developing hepatic [liver] cancer."[18] After three to six decades, no less. Huge government-sponsored vaccination programs are already underway in several Asian nations. Until recently the cost for immunization was $100 per person, now having declined to $38. Given cooperation by the World Health

Organization and various governments, such figures can spell enormous income, even as they place strains on the economies of nations like Taiwan and Thailand. Over two million people have been vaccinated, and large field trials are being conducted. Since most of these people have been "vaccinated" by natural infection anyway, soldiers in the War on Cancer cannot explain how adding an artificial vaccine could possibly help. Yet they keep marching on.

King Retrovirus

Even among the modern virus hunters, a hierarchy of sorts has developed over the years. Those studying the most popular viruses receive the bulk of the awards and grant money, looking down their noses at the other virologists. The "lesser" virologists understand their place in the structure and display proper reverence for their superiors, while still retaining the confidence of aristocracy relative to the rest of the science establishment.

Since 1970, the most elite circle within virology has belonged to the retrovirus researchers. The rise to power of this special club, numbering roughly a couple of hundred until recently, started as the conquest of a bare handful of scientists whose story begins in the 1950s.

Harry Rubin had spent years as a veterinarian, tending mostly after farm animals throughout the United States and Mexico. Having tired of this work, he turned to academic research science and learned the methods of culturing cells and growing viruses at the California Institute of Technology in Pasadena. Wendell Stanley took notice of this aspiring virologist, and in 1958 brought Rubin to his Virus Lab at the University of California, Berkeley. This move took place just as the cancer-virus hunt was ascending among scientists.

Before moving to Berkeley, Rubin had become fascinated by the chicken tumor virus discovered half a century earlier by Peyton Rous—the Rous Sarcoma Virus (RSV). Most researchers had since moved on to other viruses, largely because they could only grow RSV in live chickens, which was expensive and time-consuming as well as being too clumsy for good experiments. Determined to find a better technique, Rubin turned to the culture dish. He soon found a way to grow chicken cells in dishes, and then learned how to infect them with RSV. Every cell infected by the virus immediately became a cancer cell, a change that could be seen easily in the dish.

Having achieved this laboratory breakthrough, Rubin began lobbying colleagues to study the Rous virus, which he sensed might contain clues to the role of viruses in cancer. Until 1958 he supervised Howard Temin (recently deceased), a young doctoral student equally interested in cancer viruses. Rubin trained Temin in the new methods of culturing RSV, and together they observed some strange behaviors of the virus that convinced them both it was fundamentally unlike most other viruses. Rather than killing cells shortly after infection and then departing, RSV seemed to become part of the cell, incorporating itself into the genetic material permanently.

Now thoroughly possessed with this idea, Temin moved on to establish his own lab at the University of Wisconsin in 1960. There he performed more experiments, deciding that RSV did indeed copy its own tiny amount of genetic information into DNA, before inserting this short piece of DNA into the infected cell's DNA and becoming a permanent resident. But having failed to prove this notion, he faced mild disbelief (though cautious interest) from most scientists when formally proposing his hypothesis in 1964. He and several colleagues nevertheless labored away for the next several years, confident they would prove their point.

Temin finally succeeded in 1970, isolating an enzyme (a protein catalyzing chemical reactions) that did the work of making a DNA copy of the Rous virus RNA. He announced his finding to an excited crowd of virologists at the International Cancer Conference in Houston, Texas. Because the Rous virus copies its genetic information from RNA to DNA, the reverse of the cell's own process, it was later designated a "retrovirus."

Where Temin saw vindication, others saw golden opportunity. The quickest of these was David Baltimore, a young associate professor at the Massachusetts Institute of Technology. Baltimore had spent the past several years studying the poliovirus in detail, a remnant of virus research from the 1950s. Like so many of his fellow veterans of the war on polio, he found his research slipping into medical irrelevance as the 1960s wore on, and realized he would soon have to enter the cancer field. He had a keen sense of politics, and had gradually been building his position within the research establishment by cultivating relationships with influential scientists. But he wanted something bigger, and Temin's announcement opened the door.

The inside joke making the rounds among the top virologists immediately after the meeting went something like this: "Can you guess who took the fastest plane out of Houston? Answer: David Baltimore." This story reflected an important truth. Upon hearing the news of Temin's finding, Baltimore instantly transformed himself into a retrovirus researcher:

> Baltimore confesses that he "jumped the fence" for two days to do the experiment. The virus used was obtained by a phone call to his old friend and NCI project monitor George Todaro.[19]

Baltimore's rush to duplicate Temin's observations paid off. His paper was published alongside Temin's in the prestigious journal *Nature*, and they shared the Nobel Prize in 1975 for the discovery of the retrovirus enzyme, dubbed "reverse transcriptase." Having jumped into the field in the nick of time, Baltimore rescued himself from a dead end and began his personal rise to the very top of the virus-hunting establishment, his career built largely on such political savvy.

Several other scientists also rushed to confirm the enzyme's existence. One of the first was a chemist-turned-virologist, Peter Duesberg, another young researcher noticed by Wendell Stanley. In 1964 Stanley hired Duesberg right out of Germany's Max Planck Institute and into the Virus Lab in Berkeley, where Duesberg promptly went to work studying viruses.

Duesberg had decided to stay on with the Virus Lab, and by 1970 had become an assistant professor at the university. Having also formed a friendship with Harry Rubin, he had previously decided to take up the retrovirus field. His research question seemed straightforward: How did the Rous virus cause cancer? The problem, however, had baffled scientists, especially since the virus seemed identical in every respect to many other chicken retroviruses that were entirely harmless. Collaborating with virologist Peter Vogt, Duesberg solved the puzzle in 1970, demonstrating that the Rous virus contained an extra gene that caused cancer. Rous' virus turned out to have been a freak accident of nature, having picked up and mutated a gene that made it a cancer virus; remove the gene, and the virus becomes perfectly harmless.

The Temin and Duesberg discoveries, respectively, suddenly launched a new field to the forefront of virus hunting. Soon researchers found that many of the tumor viruses long studied had also been retroviruses, including the breast cancer virus of mice and the leukemia viruses in many animal species. But unlike the Rous virus, few of these others contained special cancer genes. So whereas the Rous virus caused massive tumors within days in almost any chicken, these other retroviruses had to maintain active infections of the body for many months before causing a leukemia, and then only in specially susceptible strains of animals. In short, no retroviruses ever killed cells, and only rare ones caused tumors in animals. They simply proved to be benign passenger viruses.

But the wave of excitement following the 1970 discoveries helped pass Nixon's National Cancer Act the next year, and retrovirus scientists quickly rode to power. A 1970 *Nature* editorial accurately predicted that the new retrovirus findings "are likely to generate one of the largest bandwagons molecular biology has seen for many a year... it is especially the case today when cancer is one of the few remaining passwords to the dwindling [*sic*] coffers of the granting agencies in the United States."[20] *Nature* itself jumped on the bandwagon, launching a parallel journal under the title *Nature: New Biology*, its purpose being specifically the publication of retrovirus papers.

As a group, the retrovirologists have had more to say about science policies than anyone else, including what directions biomedical research should take and which researchers should get the funding and awards. They have redefined the scientific enterprise and with it our popular culture. Their voices carry enormous weight, and when they choose to blame another retrovirus for cancer, AIDS, or any other disease, the governments of the world and the news media obediently cooperate.

The next logical step for the retrovirologists was to isolate their first human retrovirus, preferably one that causes cancer. A major effort materialized, but every investigator who tried ended up facing enormous frustration. Hints and echoes of retroviruses would briefly appear, only to vanish upon closer inspection. Many of the experiments suffered from flawed design, while others detected genuine retroviruses that turned out merely to be contaminating animal retroviruses. Scientists should not have been so surprised at the failure, for chronic retrovirus infections are much more common in specially vulnerable animal strains derived from long-term incestuous inbreeding; retroviruses can be much harder to find in wild animals and humans. But this point was lost on the virus hunters.

Inspired by the breast cancer virus found decades earlier in certain inbred mice, researchers focused much of their energy on the search for a similar human retrovirus. The work began almost immediately after 1970 and continued into the 1980s. In mice, the virus generally passed from mother to offspring through the milk; scientists used this as their starting point. Several studies examined human mothers with breast cancer, failing to see any higher occurrence of the tumor among their breast-fed daughters. Such results hardly discouraged the virus hunters, who promptly turned their high-powered electron microscopes to human milk and samples of breast tumor tissues. A number of reports were published throughout the 1970s by some of the most prestigious investigators claiming to see "viruslike particles"[21]. Many such particles were also seen in milk from tumorless mothers, while contradictory reports found no such particles in milk or tumors.

Retrovirologists began applying a battery of increasingly sophisticated biotechnology to hunt down the elusive virus. Some thought they found reverse transcriptase (the unique retrovirus enzyme) in milk and tumor samples, others probed breast cancer tissues for genetic information resembling that of the mouse retrovirus and got some positive signals, and still others checked for virus pieces that might be recognized by mouse antibodies against the mouse virus. Fewer than half of the human breast tumor tissues studied reacted with the antibodies, but this was enough to excite the virus hunters.

Indeed, these findings led to a sensational press conference in October, 1971, at the National Academy of Sciences. There, in the middle of an otherwise routine meeting with reporters, several virologists dropped hints they were finding cancer viruses in human breast milk. Reporters began rapid-fire interrogation. Sol Spiegelman, one of the first retrovirologists to have jumped on the Temin bandwagon the year before, lived up to his flamboyant reputation by openly suggesting some women should not breast-feed their babies. Peppered with more questions, Spiegelman repeated himself: "Look, if a woman has a familial history of breast cancer in her family and if she shows virus particles and if she was [*sic*] my sister, I would tell her not to nurse the child."[22]

Soon one of his colleagues standing beside him piped up, "Why inoculate a child with virus particles? I mean, it's clear." By this time the meeting was taking on a life of its own as the scientists began making contradictory statements. An air of deadly secrets and cover-ups filled the room, and Spiegelman gleefully feigned caution: "I mean, you cannot start a scare like this when we don't really know for sure that this virus particle is the causative agent." The next day, headlines in the major newspapers and on television screamed dire warnings over breast-feeding. The number of mothers influenced by the brief news flurry may never be known.[23]

To this day, however, no human retrovirus has ever been isolated from breast cancer, relegating these many expensive research projects to the trashbin of falsely positive results so common in experimental science.

Retroviruses ultimately saw their major impact in reviving the old virus-leukemia program. All leukemia viruses studied in mice and other animals before 1970 offered no insights for understanding human cancer, for they caused leukemia only in a few young, sickly animals under special laboratory conditions. Such viruses did nothing to normal, healthy wild animals. Similarly, such retroviruses could not be expected to affect healthy humans.

But a cat retrovirus isolated in the 1960s, though really no different than other retroviruses, served as the tool for virologists to bridge the gap. Named Feline Leukemia Virus (FeLV) for its laboratory effects on cats, the virus became the primary object of study by Myron ("Max") Essex, a rising professor at Harvard University's School of Public Health. He picked up this research once others had shown that young lab cats could become leukemic after months of continuously active infection. Outside the lab, however, as many as two-thirds of all cats eventually catch FeLV, quickly and permanently neutralizing the infection with their immune systems. Leukemia among such animals appears only rarely, each year in four of every 10,000 cats. Indeed, because leukemia is a cancer of blood cells and therefore causes immune deficiency, retrovirus infections in leukemic patients may simply reflect harmless opportunistim. But Essex wanted to prove the cat leukemia an infectious disease, and had to argue that FeLV could cause the tumor even while remaining latent. In so doing, he was certainly not the first.

Nevertheless, veterinarians and the news media alike have accepted cat leukemia as infectious. The specter of leukemia epidemics among household pets, aggrandized with suggestions of transmission to their human owners (since disproved), has popularized Essex's own nostrum for the perpetual crisis. Having founded his own biotechnology company, Cambridge Bioscience Corporation, Essex has recently developed a vaccine against the FeLV virus that should boost his income handsomely. One year after approval in 1989, the vaccine had already sold to half the estimated French market of cat owners. Unfortunately for the owners, they have no idea that in most cases their cats already have natural immunity against the virus from past infection, nor that a vaccine can do nothing against a virus that becomes latent anyway. Nor, for that matter, that the virus fails Koch's first postulate: one-third of all leukemic cats have never been infected by FeLV at all, the same proportion as among healthy cats.

The more important consequence of Essex's research, however, lay in its inspiration of a *human* leukemia virus search. When Robert C. Gallo arrived in 1965 at the National Cancer Institute fresh out of medical school, his NIH bosses put him to work treating leukemia patients and researching potential new therapies. After several years of labor he considered tiresome, Gallo found his chance to move up in the ranks following Temin's 1970 retrovirus announcement.

The glamor of new retrovirus discoveries, and of the free-flowing cancer money, attracted Gallo to the retrovirus field. Its science-by-press-release style better suits Gallo than boring laboratory benchwork, for he is even now a man who prefers to climb the scientific ladder through public relations and personal connections. The tempting appeal of popularity regularly draws him away from the lab, and he spends much of his time alternately befriending and intimidating his acquaintances according to their obeisance. Journalists and political figures are as typically found in his company as are prominent scientists.

Gallo got his first taste of glory in 1970 when he joined several better-established virologists, including Sol Spiegelman, in chasing retroviruses in human leukemia. They quickly found evidence of the reverse transcriptase enzyme in tissue samples from leukemic patients. During the first week that November, the Pasteur Institute sponsored a tumor-virus conference in Paris. Spiegelman seized the opportunity for publicity. The lectures were being given on a stage at the nearby Hilton Hotel, the podium standing in front of a huge curtain that parted in the middle. When the time came for Spiegelman's presentation, he began by solemnly announcing the evidence of retroviruses in leukemia patients.

In the middle of his speech, the curtain suddenly parted and an impeccably dressed bellboy walked up to him, holding a telegram on a silver platter. Spiegelman picked up the envelope, opened it with dramatic flair, and read to the audience the late-breaking news from his laboratory back in the United States. Several more patients had just been tested—with positive results for the virus. The hushed audience of some four hundred, including such colleagues as Temin, Lwoff, and Duesberg, did not realize until later the entire ploy had been carefully planned in advance. Spiegelman rounded up the act with a final touch of melodrama: "In an impassioned plea for cooperation rather than competition Spiegelman said 'the prize here is to help sick kids get over leukaemia' and not, to paraphrase his words, a weekend in Stockholm."[24] Stockholm, of course, is the city in which the Nobel Prize is awarded.

Gallo learned much from this experience. For his own positive results in a few leukemia patients, he was rewarded by being named head of NCI's brand new Laboratory of Tumor Cell Biology. The year was 1972, and the new department was a product of the lavish War on Cancer funding.

The retrovirus work of Essex had also brought Gallo fully into the virus arena. Gallo's team accelerated the intensive hunt for the first human retrovirus. But his earlier results in competition with Speigelman turned out to be nothing more than false positives, mistaken observations that were simply lost in the rapidly growing scientific literature. Still, the virus search was stepped up. By 1975 his lab had finally isolated a retrovirus from human leukemia cells. To Gallo's dismay, however, he faced humiliation when he presented the finding at the Virus-Cancer Program's yearly conference. Other scientists had tested his virus and discovered it to be a mixture of contaminating retroviruses from woolly monkeys, gibbon apes, and baboons. Gallo tried to save his reputation, speculating wildly that perhaps one of the *monkey* viruses caused the human leukemia. This excuse did not fly, and he later described the event as a "disaster" and "painful," admitting that it placed "human retrovirology, and me with it, at a very low point."[25]

But virus hunting was the fashion, and Gallo doggedly pursued retroviruses for the next few years. In 1980 he finally reported having found the first known human retrovirus. The virus was isolated from human leukemia cells grown for a long time in the lab, with no immune system to interfere or suppress the virus. Gallo's team even had to shock the cells repeatedly with potent chemicals to coax the soundly sleeping virus out of latency. No such virus could be found in a second batch of leukemic cells, but Gallo remained unfazed, giving the new virus a name with strong propaganda value—Human T-cell Leukemia Virus, or HTLV.

Gallo's next step was to find a disease for his virus. Having made up his mind it should cause some leukemia, he began scouring the world for a connection to such a cancer. With the help of other scientific teams, Gallo soon found HTLV concentrated among residents of the Japanese island of Kyushu, as well as in certain parts of Africa and among Caribbean people. Among these peoples also happened to exist one type of leukemia, a disease since dubbed Adult T-Cell Leukemia (ATL). Having found an overlap between his virus and a cancer, Gallo swung the weight of scientific consensus behind his hypothesis, which now ranks among the most popular virus-cancer programs. Even standard biology textbooks now discuss Gallo's hypothesis as unquestioned fact.

But no one should worry about catching this leukemia. By testing the blood supply, the Red Cross counted some 65,000 Americans as having been infected by HTLV, of whom about 90, or one out of every thousand, have contracted the cancer. Kyushu natives fare little worse, with only one percent of infected people developing the leukemia ever in their lives. For that matter, not a single American infected by HTLV through a blood transfusion has ever developed the disease. Conversely, quite a number of people worldwide have this cancer without HTLV infection. Gallo and his colleagues, however, have calculated a means of circumventing this latter problem—by redefining the disease. Doctors may not diagnose patients as having "ATL" unless the victim also has antibodies against the virus; uninfected patients with identical leukemias are categorized under a different clinical name. This little trick handily abolishes one of the gaps between the disease and the virus.

HTLV researchers can change other rules, too. Having first assumed the virus is spread between adults, scientists calculated a "latent period" between infection and leukemia of five years. Soon they adjusted that to ten years, then thirty, as they found increasing numbers of healthy carriers of HTLV. Once they decided the virus is transmitted sexually, while the leukemia strikes roughly at age sixty, they subtracted twenty from sixty to generate a forty-year latent period. Then, upon realizing that the virus is actually transmitted from mother to child around birth, the latent period grew to an official fifty-five years.

Even when the leukemia does strike a patient, the virus continues to sleep soundly, forcing doctors to test for antibodies instead of the virus itself. Again, as with cervical and liver cancer, the virologists assume the virus must cause a mutation in each cell upon infection, and before entering latency. In this case, however, a virus-mutation hypothesis is at least plausible, for the very nature of retroviruses dictates that they combine with the cell's genetic material as soon as they infect it. However, of the millions of cells infected by HTLV, only one ultimately gives rise to the leukemia, the other cells functioning normally as ever.

Now researchers have granted the virus yet another disease: HTLV-Associated Myelopathy (HAM), a brain disease modeled after kuru and other "slow virus" syndromes. To maintain even a tenuous connection between the virus and HAM, Gallo and his colleagues have decreed that the disease must be renamed HAM when the patient is infected with HTLV. All identical cases without the virus must be diagnosed under their old disease names.

Given the political power of the retrovirologists within the research establishment, such patent nonsense not only survives but can even be made profitable. Since 1989, the American Association of Blood Banks has required testing the blood supply for HTLV, tacking an extra five to eleven dollars onto each of the twelve million blood donations every year. For scientists holding interests in the biotechnology companies producing HTLV tests, the income is enormous.

Flushed with victory, Gallo did not stop with his first human retrovirus. He isolated a second one in 1982, from a patient with a different type of leukemia. The old virus became "HTLV-I," the new one "HTLV-II." But since that time HTLV-II has only been retrieved from one other patient with a similar leukemia, while plenty of cases have been found without the virus. So although Gallo continues referring to it as a leukemia virus, most other scientists prefer caution so long as the virus has only been found in two patients. Gallo's second virus, much to his chagrin, remains a virus in search of a disease.

Perhaps the strangest disease reshaped by the Virus-Cancer Program is one that has no particular cause, no definable symptoms, not even a consistent name, and has only appeared in the last ten years. This bizarre syndrome confuses virtually every scientist who examines it, yet it is beginning to generate one of the virus hunters' greatest potential boondoggles to date.

Its most recent and formal name is Chronic Fatigue Syndrome (CFS). It has also been tagged with such labels as Chronic Epstein-Barr Virus Syndrome, Chronic Mononucleosis Syndrome, Chronic Fatigue and Immune Deficiency Syndrome, and several others. Its symptoms cover wide-ranging ground, from persistent flu-like conditions, weakness, and malaise to skin problems, immune deficiencies, dementia, and even possibly cancers. Indeed, one cannot even be sure the people rediagnosed under this heading have anything in common.

The most consistent description sounds very much like a bad flu, or in some cases a mononucleosis, that hangs around for months or years. Some "outbreaks" have occurred—around Lake Tahoe in 1984-5, part of a symphony orchestra in 1984, a smattering of cases around the country. But whatever it is, CFS does not behave as a contagious disease. Infectious diseases, especially those transmitted casually, share certain behaviors: they prefer to strike the weak, the very young and the very old, and do not discriminate between the sexes. Chronic Fatigue, in contrast, generally attacks white people between the ages of twenty and fifty, the healthiest age group. It also seems to prefer women over men, by a huge margin.[26] Further, the syndrome appears in people with striking health risks. The great majority of CFS patients describe themselves as having depression and being high-strung or under prolonged psychological stress.[27] They tend to be people with allergies,[28] and the bulk of its victims are successful, affluent "yuppies," the reason CFS has been nicknamed the "yuppie flu."[29] At least a few of these people also admit to long histories of drug abuse and alcoholism, although studies rarely inquire about this.[30] A number of patients with CFS-related conditions have cancers of the immune system, such as lymphomas, which do cause immune deficiencies, malaise, and other symptoms identical to CFS.[31] Chronic Fatigue could be the consequence of any of these factors, or may just be a patchwork of unrelated mild conditions.

But the virus hunters could not resist even this confusing mess. The first hypothesis of its cause centered around the Epstein-Barr virus, known to cause mononucleosis and blamed by the virus hunters for causing Burkitt's lymphoma. This virus has been downplayed as a CFS germ in recent years, mostly because too many CFS patients have never been infected by it, and because most of the healthy adult population also have been infected.

In 1988 Robert Gallo's research team jumped into the fray, publishing papers arguing that Human Herpes Virus-type 6 (HHV-6), a virus found two years earlier in Gallo's lab, caused CFS. However, other researchers have since discovered that almost all adults under age forty have been infected by this virus. When checking CFS patients to see whether the virus had reactivated from latency in their bodies, scientists found the virus remaining dormant in thirty to sixty percent of the victims, depending on the study.

Hilary Koprowski's Wistar Institute also briefly got involved, announcing evidence in 1990 that Chronic Fatigue patients had antibodies against HTLV-II, Gallo's second retrovirus. But one-quarter of the CFS cases had never been infected, whereas a number of healthy people had. This brief attempt to resurrrect HTLV-II and find a disease for it has since attracted little notice.

The Centers for Disease Control (CDC) and the NIH have nonetheless begun pouring research dollars into Chronic Fatigue, virtually guaranteeing that researchers will find and blame more harmless or irrelevant viruses. These two agencies spent a combined total of $4.5 million in 1991, with promises of more to come.[32] The CDC even formulated an official clinical definition for the syndrome in 1988. Such funding creates political pressures to assume Chronic Fatigue is a new, infectious disease. In late 1988, when NIH researcher Stephen Straus published evidence that emotional depression may cause most CFS, he stepped into trouble.[33] "Dr. Straus's research findings (and his own attitude) on [CFS] are out of the mainstream of current biomedical research," sniffed one CFS activist. "Dr. Straus seems to be at odds with his own government agency."[34]

Ironically, only one observation about Chronic Fatigue seems clear: no virus could possibly cause such a baffling, non-specific, and non-infectious syndrome.

The No-win Cancer War

At a press conference on February 4, 1992, an informal group of scientists released a signed statement evaluating the War on Cancer. In this sharply-worded presentation, the sixty-eight prominent researchers made several poignant observations:

> We express grave concerns over the failure of the "war against cancer" since its inauguration by President Nixon and Congress on December 23, 1971. This failure is evidenced by the escalating incidence of cancer to epidemic proportions over recent decades. Paralleling and further compounding this failure is the absence of any significant improvements in the treatment and cure of the majority of all cancers...
>
> We express further concerns that the generously funded cancer establishment, the National Cancer Institute (NCI), the American Cancer Society (ACS), and some twenty comprehensive cancer centers, have misled and confused the public and Congress by repeated claims that we are winning the war against cancer...
>
> Furthermore, the cancer establishment and major pharmaceutical companies have repeatedly made extravagant and unfounded claims for dramatic advances in the treatment and "cure" of cancer.[35]

Two months later, the *Journal of the American Medical Association* reflected this widespread view in an article on the same topic:

> By some estimates, the federal government has spent as much as $22 billion on this effort in the past 20 years...
>
> However, some critics contend that this war is being lost. They argue that too little change is being seen in death rates from many major cancers...
>
> Whatever the case, the fact remains (the American Cancer Society said last week...) that about 83 million persons now alive in this country eventually will contract cancer—"about one in three, according to present rates."[36]

This disaffection with the War on Cancer had begun appearing by the early 1980s, voiced by some of the most prestigious scientists in the business. By that time the public had also lost interest in the program, which had not delivered on its ambitious promises.

Respected science watcher Daniel Greenberg has commented on the early signs of this failure:

> The gusher of new money financed rapid expansion of a previously low-keyed quest for a cancer virus, which in turn might lead to the magic bullet of a cancer vaccine. University scientists were appalled to find that most of the virus money was being dished out to industrial firms, without peer review. An outside inquiry concluded that the virus program, which would soon cost $100 million a year, was intellectually shoddy and unproductive.
>
> It was reorganized to emphasize research by NCI scientists and peer-reviewed university researchers, and became one of the prime movers of the

molecular biology revolution... But the early stumblings of the virus program were duly noted...

In 1975, shorty after stepping down as the senior health official in the Department of Health, Education, and Welfare (HEW), Charles Edwards, a doctor and research administrator, wrote that the cancer program was based "on the politically attractive but scientifically dubious premise that a dread and enigmatic disease can, like the surface of the moon, be conquered if we will simply spend enough money."[37]

Cancer treatment arguably accomplishes little today. This problem is rooted mostly in our lack of understanding the cause of cancer. The War on Cancer budget was squandered by politically powerful virus hunters in their obsessive search for tumor viruses.

If anything, the cancer fight greatly strengthened and consolidated virus hunting, and placed the retrovirologists in charge. At the same time, they needed some new war to revive their popularity after the cancer debacle. Thus when AIDS appeared in 1981—a textbook example of a non-contagious syndrome—the virus hunters were poised and eagerly waiting to take advantage of another opportunity. The next chapter tells the story of how they seized control of the war on AIDS, mobilizing the entire world behind their latest virus hunt while boosting their own prominence beyond their wildest dreams.

Chapter 4 Footnotes

[1] Stetten and Carrigan (eds), *NIH: An Account of Research in Its Laboratories and Clinics.* Academic Press (Harcourt Brace Jovanovich), New York, 1984, p. 350.

[2] All such viruses could only work in immune-deficient animals that could not suppress the virus, including newborn mice or chickens. Some of these viruses contained special "cancer genes," which created tumors withing days of inoculation, but most tumor viruses could only barely promote cancer in already-susceptible animals. The leukemia viruses, for example, only caused cancer in selected strains of laboratory animals that had become progressively more sickly through many generations of careful inbreeding. Unlike healthier animals in the wild, such lab animals more easily developed cancer or other disease in response to mild insults. Often a successful experiment required putting a lab animal through extraordinary conditions, such as forcing female mice through many extra rounds of pregnancy. The very fact that such "tumor viruses" could only affect these weak animals under odd conditions indicated that they would never cause cancer in humans.

[3] Stetten, Op cit., p. 353; Studer and Chubin, *The Cancer Mission: Social Contexts of Biomedical Research.* Sage Publications, Beverly Hills, 1980, p. 21.

[4] Williams, *Virus Hunters.* Alfred A. Knopf, New York, 1959, p. 438.

[5] Stanley, The virus etiology of cancer. *Proceedings of the Third National Cancer Conference*, pp. 42-51, 1957.

[6] Lwoff, Introduction. In: *RNA Viruses and Host Genome in Oncogenesis*, pp. 1-11, Emmelot and Bentvelzen (eds). American Elsevier Publishing, New York, 1972.

[7] Tooze (ed). *The Molecular Biology of Tumour Viruses.* Cold Spring Harbor Laboratory, Cold Spring Harbor, NY, 1973, p. 56.

[8] Greenberg, What Ever Happened to the War on Cancer? *Discover*, March, 1986, pp. 47-64 (p. 55).

[9] Rous, The Challenge to Man of the Neoplastic Cell. *Science* 157:24-28, 1967 (p. 26).

[10] Culliton, as quoted in Studer and Chubin, Op cit., p. 84.

[11] Scott, Dangerous Liaisons. *Los Angeles Times Magazine*, March 11, 1990, pp. 10-19, 37 (pp. 12, 16).

[12] Ibid., p. 12.

[13] Ibid., pp. 12-13.

[14] Ibid., p. 12.

[15] Ibid., p. 14.

[16] Ibid., p. 16.

[17] Galloway and McDougall, *Nature* 302:21, 1983, cited as reference #195 in Duesberg and Schwartz, Latent viruses and mutated oncogenes: No evidence for pathogenicity. *Progress in Nucleic Acid Research and Molecular Biology* 43:135-204, 1992.

[18] Yuan and Hsu, Vaccines in Asia. *Genetic Engineering News*, Oct. 1, 1992, p. 14.

[19] Studer and Chubin, Op cit., p. 67.

[20] Central Dogma Reversed. *Nature* 226:1198-9, 1970.

[21] Weiss, Teich, Varmus, and Coffin (eds). *RNA Tumor Viruses.* Cold Spring Harbor Laboratory, Cold Spring Harbor, NY, 1982, p. 1226.

[22] Wade, Scientists and the press: Cancer scare story that wasn't. *Science* 174:679-80, 1971.

[23] Ibid.

[24] The Paris Fashions. *Nature* 228:609-10, 1970.

[25] Gallo, *Virus Hunting — AIDS, Cancer, & the Human Retrovirus: a Story of Human Discovery.* Basic Books, New York, 1991, pp. 81, 85.

[26] Ostrom, *What Really Killed Gilda Radner?* That New Magazine, New York, 1991, p. 13, 353.

[27] Cherfas, Chronic Fatigue as chameleon. *Science* 249:1240; Ostrom, Op cit., *passim.*

[28] Ostrom, Op cit., pp. 145-146.

[29] Ibid., p. 13.

[30] Ibid., pp. 32, 153.

[31] Ibid., pp. 27-28, 121-122.

[32] Ostrom, *50 Things You Should Know about the Chronic Fatigue Syndrome Epidemic.* TNM, New York, 1992, p. 62.

[33] Ostrom, *What Really Killed Gilda Radner?*, Op cit., pp. 56-61.

[34] Ibid., p. 73.

[35] Epstein, Bingham, Rall, and Bross. Losing the "war against cancer": a need for public policy reforms. *International Journal of Health Services* 22:455-69, 1992.

[36] Gunby, Battles against many malignancies lie ahead as federal 'war on cancer' enters third decade. *Journal of the American Medical Association* 267:1891, 1992.

[37] Greenberg, Op cit., p. 62.

Chapter 5

AIDS: The Virus Hunters Converge

Robert Gallo has not been the only public figure to declare how lucky we are that AIDS surfaced at the right time. Had this epidemic struck years earlier, so goes the common belief, medical science would have been unprepared to deal with the crisis. But in what would seem to be an amazing coincidence, the crucial technology for confronting this plague emerged just as the first AIDS cases were being documented in the early 1980s. The ability to grow and measure T cells, a central component of the body's immune system, arrived in the nick of time to see AIDS patients losing their T cells. The techniques for detecting and isolating retroviruses had just evolved to the point that the Human Immunodeficiency Virus (HIV) could be found. And a huge, well-financed establishment of scientific research teams had been set up, ready to gather vast quantities of data on any new disease.

But the construction of AIDS as a "contagious disease" caused by a virus had little to do with science and even less to do with luck. "Was the NIH's apparent preparedness for the epidemic an accident?" asked Edward Shorter in his 1987 book, *The Health Century*.[1] No, he concluded, it resulted from the enormous funding of science in preceding years. Shorter hardly knew how right he was. Virus hunters, sitting at the apex of power in the immense biomedical research establishment, found themselves in the right place at the right time. They needed a success because their lease on public support, extended for a few years by the War on Cancer, was wearing thin amidst their failures. Using their new technology, the virus hunters could now find whatever they wanted, conveniently ignoring time-proven and logical principles of microbiology. When AIDS appeared, they were poised to take full advantage of the situation.

The NIH, however, did not lead the charge against this new syndrome in the early 1980s; many scientists at first refused to believe it even existed. Virus hunters had more experience searching for viruses in older, better-recognized diseases such as hepatitis or cancer. The overfunded science bureaucracy was simply too cumbersome to exploit such a new phenomenon before most people had even heard of it. The NIH and other large structures proved more effective in mobilizing the scientific community behind a virus hunt, and crushing all opposition, only after AIDS had been widely sold as a pandemic threat.

This new syndrome also had little chance of exciting the lay public. Since it was found mostly in male homosexuals and heroin addicts, it was too obscure to concern the average heterosexual person preoccupied with career

93

and family. Even among homosexuals, AIDS was at first actively ignored as an obstacle to their sexual freedom.

Yet, against all the odds, AIDS launched a bandwagon almost overnight. Less than two years after the first five cases were identified, the syndrome officially became the federal government's top health priority. By then the virus hunters had already elbowed past each other to find a viral culprit, and HIV was just being discovered. How could this epidemic have mushroomed into a virus-hunting bonanza so rapidly? The answer lies in a parallel branch of biomedicine: public health. In order to understand this movement's role in blaming AIDS on a virus, one must first understand its history.

Public health seeks to prevent disease rather than treat it, and is based on the notion that a healthy lifestyle is not a matter of personal responsibility, but of government management. Unlike the academic style of research scientists, public health professionals take a more activist approach to disease—quarantining individuals or populations, seizing control of food and water supplies, conducting mass immunizations, pushing slogans in health campaigns, running aggressive family planning programs, regulating or restricting access to items ranging from cigarettes to dietary supplements, or otherwise targeting anything they believe is a risk factor for disease. Public health experts are inclined to view almost any disease as an emergency, although they favor infectious epidemics as objects of their wars.

The federal government officially adopted such a system in 1912 with the reorganization of the Public Health Service (PHS), headed by the Surgeon General. Based largely on the German model, PHS members formed a corps of commissioned officers, complete with uniforms, that dispatched teams to impose quarantines and other crisis-control measures on cities with contagious epidemics.

The National Institutes of Health, one branch of the PHS, became its center for biomedical research. Though originally responding to requests from state governments for epidemic control, the NIH always felt more at home with laboratory research. When James Shannon restructured NIH in the 1950s to centralize its role in basic science, the agency finally left public health activism altogether.

Its heir had already been born during World War Two. In early 1942, anticipating outbreaks of malaria like those in the first World War, the Public Health Service established a special unit called Malaria Control in War Areas (MCWA). Its primary mission was to prevent spread of the disease among the hundreds of military bases throughout the southern United States, which MCWA accomplished mostly using pesticides to kill malaria-carrying mosquitoes. The program's success cannot really be measured, since malaria had already been vanishing in the industrial world during the years preceding the War.

The creators of the MCWA clearly anticipated their own obsolescence following the end of the second World War. Within weeks of U.S. entry into the War and before the Surgeon General had officially established MCWA, its soon-to-be leaders were already discussing their long-term prospects. Justin Andrews and Louis Williams, two of the agency's founders, were smitten with grandiose visions of public health management on a national scale, which they greatly preferred over ultimately disbanding MCWA. So by the time the War was ending in 1945, these MCWA officials convinced Congress to extend their authority to include civilian malaria control. While not terribly glamorous, the new work kept the program alive. The Public Health Service then reorganized the MCWA in 1946, creating the permanent Communicable Disease Center (CDC), based in Atlanta, Georgia (the name has been changed several times since 1967, though the initials have remained nearly constant).

This new agency absorbed all remaining public health activities of the NIH. The CDC enthusiastically responded to all calls for help from states experiencing disease epidemics of various kinds. While malaria remained the focus of CDC energies, its resources were stretched to branch into new diseases such as rabies, typhus, and even tapeworms. Still, the CDC leadership felt almost claustrophobic, trapped with too little discretionary power or opportunity for expansion. They wanted the agency to assume full control over the nation's public health system, rather than being relegated to serving state and local health departments on request. At the same time their disease-control mission was increasingly being regarded as obsolete, prompting serious discussions about abolishing the Center altogether.

The situation changed in 1949 when the CDC brought on board Alexander Langmuir, an associate professor at the Johns Hopkins University School of Hygiene and Public Health. Langmuir was the CDC's first V.I.P., bringing with him both his expertise in epidemiology (the statistical study of epidemics) and his high-level connections—including his security clearance as one of the few scientists privy to the Defense Department's biological warfare program. Like the rest of the CDC, he strongly hoped to empower the agency to monitor and exert authority over all epidemics throughout the nation. His dream might have stood little chance of materializing in an age of vanishing infectious disease. But because civil defense ranked high in government priorities at that time, officials of the Public Health Service listened when Langmuir proposed that the CDC develop a comprehensive disease surveillance system to detect the earliest signs of a biological warfare attack. Such an infrastructure could also serve to control hypothetical epidemics, using such techniques as quarantine measures and mass immunizations.

By the start of the Korean War, Langmuir had talked public health officials and Congress into giving the CDC contingent powers to deal with potential emergencies. He shut down the malaria project, freeing millions of dollars to create a special new division of the CDC. In July of 1951, he assembled the first class of the Epidemic Intelligence Service (EIS), composed of twenty-three young medical or public health graduates. After six weeks of intensive epidemiological training, these EIS officers were assigned for two years to hospitals or to state and local health departments around the country. Upon completing their field experience, EIS alumni were free to pursue any career they desired, on the assumption that their loyalties would remain with the CDC and that they would permanently act as its eyes and ears. The focus of this elite unit on activism rather than research was expressed in its symbol—a shoe sole worn through with a hole. As one former CDC consultant put it to us, epidemiologists have long referred to the service as the "medical CIA."

Every summer since 1951 a new class of carefully-chosen EIS recruits has been trained, some classes exceeding one hundred people in size. Although a complete list of EIS officers and alumni was available until the spring of 1993, its members rarely advertise their affiliation; now the membership directory has been withdrawn from public circulation and the list has become secret. Over the last four decades, the CDC has quietly placed nearly 2000 EIS trainees in key positions throughout this country and the world. Many work in the CDC itself, others in various agencies of the federal government; one of the original 1951 graduates, William Stewart, went on to become the Surgeon General of the United States during the late 1960s. Some have staffed the World Health Organization, including Jonathan Mann and Michael Merson, the two directors of its Global Program on AIDS, while their fellow agents can be found in the health departments of foreign nations. Several dozen have entered university public health programs as teachers and researchers. Roughly 150 have taken jobs in state or local health departments, closely watching every little outbreak of disease. Hundreds have become private practice doctors, dentists, or even veterinarians, while others work in hospitals. Some have joined biotechnology or pharmaceutical companies, or have even risen in the ranks of major insurance corporations. Some reside within tax-exempt foundations, helping direct the spending of trust funds on medical projects.

A few have even seized prominent positions in the media. Lawrence Altman became a medical journalist for the *New York Times* in 1969, since rising to become its head medical writer. Bruce Dan joined ABC News as its Chicago medical editor for six years beginning in 1984, the same year he became a senior editor of the prestigious *Journal of the American Medical Association*, a position he held for nine years; *JAMA* regularly publishes a section written by the CDC. Marvin Turck has held the title of editor at the University of Washington's *Journal of Infectious Diseases* since 1988. These three men were recruited into the EIS in 1963, 1979, and 1960, respectively—each one years before he entered the media.

Regardless of which career paths EIS alumni take, the vast majority of them retain their contacts with the CDC. Not only do they constitute an informal surveillance network, but they can even act as unrecognized advocates for the CDC viewpoint, whether as media journalists or as prominent physicians. And they serve as a reservoir of trained personnel for any CDC-defined "emergency." As Langmuir himself described it in 1952, "One of the primary purposes of the Epidemic Intelligence Services of CDC is to recruit and train such a corps of epidemiologists… As a result of their experience, many of these officers may well remain in full-time epidemiology or other public health pursuits at federal, state, or local levels. Some, no doubt, will return to civilian, academic, or clinical practice, but in the event of war they could be returned to active duty with the Public Health Service and assigned to strategic areas to fulfil the functions for which they were trained."[2]

The EIS network has functioned very much as Langmuir first envisioned, except that it has grown up in the post-contagion industrial world, where infectious diseases have become subject matter for historians. The awaited biological attack never arrived, and in its absence the CDC would have faced extinction had it not turned to mobilizing the nation behind increasingly futile wars against impotent diseases. The CDC has exploited public trust by transforming flus and other minor epidemics into monstrous crises, and by manufacturing contagious plagues out of non-infectious medical conditions. Whereas the virus hunters in the National Institutes of Health and academia have made themselves appear useful by blaming harmless or even nonexistent viruses as culprits in well-established diseases, the CDC and its EIS infrastructure have possessed the resources needed to exaggerate or even fabricate the epidemics themselves. They have pushed the science establishment into action before anyone could raise questions, magnifying biomedical disasters beyond the wildest excesses of decades past. Thus CDC officers have become the shock troops of the microbe hunters.

Searching For Epidemics

During the decades after its founding, the CDC became increasingly desperate for public health emergencies. Tuberculosis was no longer the scourge of industrial nations, measles had largely stopped taking lives, and other potentially fatal diseases ranging from diphtheria to pneumonia ceased striking fear in the hearts of the public. Only polio was left, and by the 1960s it, too, basically vanished. In identifying "epidemics," then, the CDC was forced to pounce on continually smaller outbreaks of disease. Before long, experts began defining contagious epidemics on the basis of disease "clusters." Almost any coincidence of two or more closely-spaced persons contracting the same disease could qualify as an incipient epidemic, even if they occur weeks or months apart.

Clustered outbreaks, however, provide no evidence of an infectious disease. When the bacteria hunters sought to blame scurvy, pellagra, and other vitamin deficiency diseases on microbes, they mistakenly cited clusters of sick people to argue the diseases were spreading. Likewise the virus hunters pointed to clusters to support their indictment of viruses for SMON and other non-contagious diseases. Clustering actually reveals very little information; it can reflect several people sharing the same diet, behavior, or environmental hazard of almost any kind, not just common exposure to a germ. Even in cases of truly infectious disease, clusters may only indicate a group of people are susceptible to a sickness for similar reasons, while other people infected by the same microbe will remain healthy—in other words, that no epidemic will ensue. If anything, epidemiologists have classically studied clusters of sick people as clues to subtle environmental hazards, not infectious agents.

But when public health officials issue ominous warnings about mysterious disease outbreaks, they terrify the public with visions of deadly pandemics. The CDC has developed this technique into a fine art. Most people have no idea of the over 1000 outbreaks of disease each year, including colds, flus, hepatitis, and numerous non-infectious syndromes, all running their course and disappearing often despite remaining unexplained by scientists. These many outbreaks provide the CDC with its inexhaustible source of epidemics.

The first genuine success of the CDC emerged from the polio epidemic. Ironically, it was the vaccine against polio, not the disease itself, that provided the opportunity. The Salk vaccine was entering its large-scale testing phase in 1954, and Alexander Langmuir wanted a piece of the action for his fledgling EIS. Insisting on CDC participation in the field trials, Langmuir was able to assign EIS officers around the country to monitor newly immunized children. The EIS aggressively followed up the first cases of vaccine-induced polio appearing in the spring of 1955, ultimately uncovering the hundreds of victims that received national attention over the next several months. The findings of the EIS investigation led to the suspension of Salk vaccine, and to the political shake-up at the National Institutes of Health that brought James Shannon to power. Although this incident involved neither a natural epidemic nor biological warfare, it built the CDC's reputation as an efficient surveillance agency, an image it has since exploited to full advantage.

The next major CDC initiative ended less spectacularly, yet the agency emerged untarnished. The spring of 1957 brought news of a flu sweeping nations of the Far East. Influenza is generally a rather benign disease, but CDC officials decided to conjure up memories of the deadly 1918 flu epidemic that returned with U.S. soldiers from Europe and killed nearly half a million people. The decision to predict a deadly flu epidemic was completely arbitrary, considering that 39 flu seasons had since gone by without disaster. Ignoring the fact that circumstances in 1918 differed radically from 1957, the CDC rang the alarm over an imminent Asian flu epidemic. A frightened nation quickly jumped into line. Congress gave Eisenhower a half million dollars, a large sum at the time, into which Langmuir dipped to expand the ranks of the EIS. The flu did arrive by summer and continued spreading until the following winter. As soon as the epidemic began slowing, public health officers rushed to issue warnings of a second round.

In the end, the CDC and other agencies accomplished little or nothing to slow the epidemic. Large numbers of vaccine doses were crash-produced, but mostly after the flu season had finished. The flu itself was probably no worse than in any other year, but the heightened surveillance of the disease, together with the frantic public warnings, helped feed the false impression of a particularly horrible epidemic. Several leading public health experts openly criticized the over-hyped flu scare, some of whom suggested the whole incident merely helped stimulate vaccine sales. But the CDC came out ahead anyway, trumpeted in the press as an heroic group and having gained public acceptance of mass immunization on command. Since the Asian flu, the CDC has regularly produced vaccines of unproven effectiveness for each new flu season, and has maintained a permanent flu surveillance program.

With its political standing secured, the CDC began expanding its reach into virtually any disease over which it could gain authority. Collaborations with other biomedical institutions often worked to promote both parties. One such arrangement directly fueled the Virus-Cancer Program. During the early 1960s, EIS personnel were assigned to investigate every cluster of leukemia cases reported anywhere in the country, searching for a virus on the assumption leukemia was infectious. The efforts amounted to little more than a wild-goose chase, but, in medical circles, the repetitive publicity surrounding these random clusters drummed into every scientist's head the notion that viruses must cause cancer. Most researchers, after all, had readily accepted the belief that clustering somehow proved a disease to be contagious. The National Cancer Institute backed this EIS project enthusiastically, and ultimately bene-fited through the extra funding it received for chasing cancer viruses. Robert Gallo became one of the young scientists powerfully influenced by such epi-demiological hype.

Until the advent of AIDS, however, the CDC's most ambitious pro-gram—and its most embarrassing disaster—played itself out in 1976. By that time the EIS network of officers and alumni had so widely penetrated hospi-tals, health departments, and other institutions that potentially any minor dis-ease outbreak could easily be detected and blown out of proportion. In January, 1976, five soldiers at Fort Dix, in New Jersey, contracted a flu. One of them died after over-exerting himself against doctor's orders. Such a minor episode met the CDC criteria for a cluster, and the agency sprang into action.

Since 1966 the CDC director had been David Sencer, a medical doctor by training with experience in various research, public health, and administrative jobs and who had just received an honorary membership in the EIS in 1975. He apparently had grandiose plans for expanding the former Communicable Disease Center, which had since been renamed the Center for Disease Control. The flu outbreak at Fort Dix handed him an opportunity to replay the Asian flu public relations victory of 1957, only on a larger scale. Using wild leaps of logic, he declared an imminent flu epidemic that would rival the deadly plague of 1918. The disease was nicknamed "swine flu," based on the belief that pigs were the reservoir for this human virus.

Sencer placed the EIS network on full alert to monitor for cases of swine flu. The large Auditorium A, located in CDC headquarters in Atlanta, became the command center—called the "War Room." Set up especially for this oc-casion, it contained "banks of telephones, teleprinters, and computers, the hardware for an unprecedented monitoring system which, to work, also re-quired a typing pool, photocopy machines, and doctors sitting at rows of desks in the center of the room."[3] Experts worked around the clock, week af-ter week, chasing down every rumor of flu clusters.

Sencer officially called for the most aggressive emergency immunization crusade in history, to be conducted before the flu season arrived. Congress initially favored the idea; not understanding the flimsy science and the virus-hunting politics underlying the dire warnings of crisis, the naive legislators could easily be manipulated by the CDC's alarmist rhetoric. President Ford constituted a committee that met within two days of Sencer's vaccination proposal, and decided to back Sencer's plan, which would run up costs in the hundreds of millions of dollars. The air of panic spread rapidly: "Minutes af-ter the meeting ended, President Ford appeared on national television and called for the vaccination against swine flu of every man, woman, and child in the United States."[4] The plan gained momentum, despite the fact that even the massive EIS surveillance program could not find *any* more cases of swine flu.[5]

But when early testing showed that the vaccine produced side effects in twenty to forty percent of inoculated people, and potentially deadly reactions such as high fevers in one to five percent, insurance companies smelled a rat and backed away from supporting the program. With no insurance coverage, Congress became nervous and also began retreating before the plan came up for a vote. Now Sencer faced serious trouble, his whole reputation standing on the line. No longer able to back out quietly, he chose instead to push more agressively. The word went out to the EIS network to pursue actively any flu-like illness whatsoever.[6] Sencer had to convince Congress that the swine flu epidemic was real.

Meanwhile another CDC official took advantage of the swine flu alert for his own purposes:

> By early July 1976 David Fraser, M.D., hoped that a suitable epidemic would soon appear in the United States.
> His definition of "suitable" was quite specific: the outbreak would have no known cause; it could present a serious threat to human life and might even have claimed some victims, thus providing the corpses for all-important tissue samples. With every day that passed, his need for that epidemic grew more urgent. He cast his net wide for news that somewhere between Alaska and the Mexican border a mysterious malady had surfaced. He made sure he was never far from a telephone.[7]

Fraser was the head of the Special Pathogens Branch of the CDC, the section charged with investigating infectious diseases with unknown causes. He had been an EIS member since 1971, and he was awaiting two new EIS trainees who would shortly be assigned to his office. He wanted to give them field experience through managing a real epidemic. With the EIS on full alert, a "suitable epidemic" was likely to be found on short order, easily selected from the thousand or more disease outbreaks occurring each year in this country.

The first disease big enough to meet both Sencer's and Fraser's needs surfaced in Philadelphia, days after American Legion members had returned home from their July convention. On Monday morning, August 2nd, after receiving word of a few pneumonia cases, personnel in the CDC's swine flu War Room established contact with Jim Beecham, a brand new EIS officer barely settling down to his assignment in the Philadelphia health department. The CDC could not directly intervene in the situation without an invitation, and Beecham helped arrange one immediately. Within hours three EIS officers flew down to Philadelphia. They were joined by David Fraser the next morning, followed within days by a team of dozens of CDC experts.

State and local health departments had been willing to accept EIS officers on temporary assignment because of their qualifications and training. But as Philadelphia health officials now discovered, this amounted to a

Faustian pact. When the CDC personnel arrived, pre-positioned EIS members such as Beecham and top health advisor Robert Sharrar stopped obeying local authorities and began following orders from the incoming CDC team. Local officials became helpless to stop the tide of events. The CDC seized the initiative, fomenting wild rumors that this "Legionnaire's disease" was the beginning of the swine flu pandemic. The media proved cooperative; the *New York Times* assigned none other than Lawrence Altman, an EIS alumnus, to cover the story.

With nationwide hysteria rapidly developing, Congress suddenly changed its collective opinion on the swine flu bill, pulling it out of committee and passing the legislation within days. By the time the CDC team officially acknowledged that Legionnaire's disease was not swine flu after all, President Ford had already signed the vaccine bill into law. Having done Sencer a favor, David Fraser continued managing the CDC investigation for a few more weeks, allowing his new EIS people plenty of training. After testing the patients for infection by a variety of germs, the CDC experts found nothing consistent and packed their bags to leave. The epidemic itself weighed so little in their minds that they had neglected even to blame an innocent germ for the disease. The case was declared unresolved and effectively dropped, leaving Philadelphia officials to pick up the pieces.

This cavalier treatment and the one-track focus on infectious microbes so enraged New York Congressman John Murphy that he held hearings on Legionnaire's disease in November. Calling CDC officials to testify on their "fiasco," Murphy humiliated the agency for not having found the epidemic's cause, and for ignoring the possibility of non-contagious or toxic causes.[8] "The CDC, for example, did not have a toxicologist present in their initial team of investigators sent to deal with the swine flu epidemic," he fumed at the meetings. "No apparent precautions were taken to deal with the possibility, however remote at the time, that something else might have been the cause."[9] David Fraser particularly felt the brunt of the attack. Still smarting, he returned to Atlanta and put laboratory experts to work on the tissue samples collected from Philadelphia. Fraser's own area of expertise lay in bacteria, not viruses, and the researchers under his supervision searched hard for bacteria. Within a few weeks they found one, a harmless microbe that inhabits soil as well as plumbing in most buildings (see Chapter Two). Even though the bacterium fails Koch's postulates for causing disease, the CDC, through a clever series of scientific papers and press releases, cleared its reputation and convinced the unsuspecting public it had brilliantly discovered the cause of Legionnaire's disease. In the process the CDC created a whole field of study devoted to this bacterium, which now employs a respectable number of scientists.

The swine flu program, on the other hand, collapsed miserably and could not be salvaged. Millions of people received the vaccine starting in October, although many were not told of the possible side effects. Soon reports of hundreds of cases of paralysis began pouring in, ultimately including at least 600 cases and 74 deaths. This time the CDC preferred not to notice, and used its full resources to cover up or explain away the man-made syndrome, trying to classify the victims as having died of other diseases. Ultimately the vaccine's side effects could no longer be hidden, and the incredibly expensive scandal cost David Sencer his job as CDC chief. In a case of appalling irony, the swine flu epidemic itself never materialized. Only the CDC's immunization program caused sickness and death.

Allegheny County Coroner Cyril H. Wecht personally investigated some of the vaccine's most unfortunate victims, including several fatalities. In a stinging indictment of this CDC program, he wrote in 1978:

> The government should limit itself to facilitating public programs. Employing high-pressure sales tactics like Madison Avenue mass media promoters to push a program is not commensurate with this objective. Certainly, when people's lives are at stake, cheap politics has no place.[10]

Inventing AIDS

The aftermath of the swine flu and Legionnaire's disease fiascos left the CDC reeling for a few years. The agency tried gradually to rebuild its reputation by delving more heavily into other areas of public health, ones not always tied to infectious disease. Or at least its leaders tried to give that appearance. In 1980, for example, the agency was restructured into several units, each focusing on different issues, and as a whole was renamed to the plural—the Centers for Disease Control. None of these reforms brought the kind of stardom hoped for during the swine flu episode, but the agency certainly held its own and continued to grow. Of course, it still openly preferred contagious diseases as subjects of investigation.

The National Institutes of Health was likewise beginning to enter uncertain times, particularly as the War on Cancer was dragging on without any tangible results. The virus hunters had consolidated their position with their so-called cancer viruses, but none had made enough of a public impression to justify their lavish funding. Public patience was beginning to wear thin, and even many scientists were growing critical.

Both the CDC and the NIH, representing the public health and biomedical research establishments, desperately needed a new war to revitalize themselves. Contagious epidemics had long proven the most effective at mobilizing public interest, and the medical and health establishments had spent vast sums of money establishing themselves on microbe hunting foundations. Yet microbe chasers had exhausted their opportunities with virtually every major disease, from hepatitis to cancer and more; now they had no clear direction to march, no significant diseases to conquer. The virus hunters were heavily armed soldiers without a war to fight.

The AIDS epidemic became their salvation. Here was a brand new plague, too dauntingly unfamiliar to allow criticism of virus-hunting wisdom, and growing quickly enough to compel urgent action. It was an epidemic that allowed no time to think, only to act. Once recognized and taken seriously, it could easily be exploited by the virus hunters of the huge NIH-funded research establishment. But to identify the syndrome and label it contagious, the CDC and its Epidemic Intelligence Service would first have to stake their claim.

That opportunity arrived late in 1980. Michael Gottlieb, a young researcher at the medical center of the University of California, Los Angeles, wanted to study the immune system and began scouring the hospital for patients with immune deficiency diseases. By November Gottlieb was introduced to one such case. The patient, who suffered from a yeast infection that had taken hold in his throat, also had a rare pneumonia that refused to go away. The *Pneumocystis carinii* microbe that caused the pneumonia was known to inhabit the lungs of almost every human on the planet; the disease rarely struck anyone but cancer patients, whose chemotherapy treatments would destroy their immune systems and leave them vulnerable to such normally benign germs. But this young man, in his early 30s, was taking no such therapy. Given his age, he should have been a specimen of perfect health. In any case, this was Gottlieb's big chance to try out the brand new technology for counting T cells, one subset of white blood cells that participate in the immune system. The patient turned out to have very few T cells at all, much to Gottlieb's amazement. On the other hand, scientists knew very little about what a "normal" level of T cells should be, or any other white blood cells for that matter.

The next several months of searching gathered three more such cases of immune deficiencies in reponse to Gottlieb's request. All three displayed the same candidiasis, or yeast infection, as well as the *Pneumocystis* pneumonia. And they all had "low" T cell counts, the only parameter Gottlieb was really interested in testing. By April of 1981, he decided he had a hot new syndrome on his hands. He called up the local public health department to ask for data on any similar patients elsewhere in Los Angeles. The staffer he spoke with, Wayne Shandera, was an active EIS officer trained the previous year. Shandera perked up at the news, and found one more such case to add to the list. Now a pattern was emerging: all five men were active homosexuals.

Gottlieb knew precisely what this discovery could mean for his career, and ecstatically raced to take the credit. Randy Shilts recorded in his 1987 book, *And the Band Played On*, that Gottlieb phoned *The New England Journal of Medicine*. "'I've got something here that's bigger than Legionnaire's,' he said. 'What's the shortest time between submission and publication?'"[11] The *Journal* refused to bend traditional rules of publication for the brash UCLA scientist. Frustrated and impatient, Gottlieb turned again to Shandera, who contacted the CDC. He figured this was precisely the sort of outbreak that the CDC would be only too happy to publicize without delay.

Shandera was right. James Curran, an official in the Venereal Disease Division of the CDC, wrote "Hot Stuff. Hot Stuff' on the announcement and hurried it into press with the agency's *Morbidity and Mortality Weekly Report*.[12] Like Gottlieb, beleaguered CDC leaders could easily see the political benefits of managing another epidemic on the scale of Legionnaire's disease. On June 5, the report was published, written so as to imply that these five unexplained cases spelled a major new disease. Despite the fact that the five victims had no contacts with each other, the report wasted no time suggesting this might be a "disease acquired through sexual contact."[13]

By this time new cases were being reported to the CDC, some of whom suffered the rare blood-vessel tumor known as Kaposi's sarcoma. The CDC immediately set up a special task force, called Kaposi's Sarcoma and Opportunistic Infections (KSOI), to find the cause of this syndrome. All of the known patients had been active male homosexuals who reported using "poppers," the volatile nitrite liquid that had become the rage in the homosexual community for its ability to facilitate anal intercourse, as well as to maintain erections and prolong orgasms. This drug presented itself as the obvious explanation, especially given its known biochemical toxicity. But CDC experts had bigger plans for this illness, which could only mobilize public concern if it were believed to be infectious and therefore a threat to the entire population. The microbe-hunting bias of the KSOI Task Force was set in stone through its composition. Of the dozen or so members, its three leaders came from the venereal diseases section of the CDC, including two EIS officers (Harold Jaffe and Mary Guinan) and James Curran, who became the group chair. Other members specialized in studying viruses or infectious parasites.

Curran and his associates further stacked the deck by allowing only two alternative hypotheses on the agenda: either this syndrome was a short-lived tragedy caused by a single bad lot of poppers, or it was contagious.[14] The task force failed even to consider the possibility that the long-term use of poppers might itself cause immune deficiency, a situation analogous to the connection between long-term smoking and lung cancer. The KSOI Task Force strategy was simple. The poppers hypothesis would be thrown out as soon as they could prove the victims had used different batches of the drug; the infection hypothesis would be supported by defining "clusters" of patients. The EIS network would assist the effort with extensive legwork, finding as many patients as possible and tracing their sexual partners. As historian Elizabeth Etheridge has demonstrated, based on later interviews with Harold Jaffe and other Task Force members, the fix was in: "While many of the patients were routine users of amyl nitrites or 'poppers,' no one in the KSOI task force believed the disease was a toxicological problem."[15]

As expected, no bad lot of poppers could be found. The results of the cluster study were equally predictable. The men turning up with such rare and fatal diseases had all spent years in extremely promiscuous homosexual activity, generally involving hundreds or thousands of sexual contacts. Many patients tracked down by the CDC personnel could ultimately be traced through chains of sexual encounters to other immune deficiency patients, especially given their enormous sexual activity over time. The CDC investigators had their hands full in trying to trace each patient's list of partners, considering the long "latent period" preceding AIDS.[16] Once again the "cluster" method of epidemiology proved its worthlessness, for even non-contagious diseases usually appear in such clusters. Nevertheless, the CDC accepted the clusters as proof of the infection hypothesis and anounced their results one year after Gottlieb's first report.[17] Most outsiders began yielding upon seeing the supposedly impressive cluster study.

The KSOI Task Force members then tried to prove the syndrome was spreading to heterosexuals. Using hepatitis B as their model, they hunted down every heroin addict and every blood transfusion recipient, including hemophiliacs, who might have conditions vaguely resembling the immune deficiencies in homosexuals. EIS personnel scoured hospitals and monitored local health departments for patients with serious opportunistic infections.[18] Within months a small handful of heroin users, and one hemophiliac in Colorado, were found with similar problems. The hemophiliac had actually lived much longer than expected, given the severity of his blood clotting disorder; he was dying primarily of internal bleeding, but also happened to contract a *Pneumocystis* pneumonia that caught CDC attention. His pneumonia, and the diseases of the heroin addicts, were immediately rediagnosed to include them in the new immune deficiency epidemic. One KSOI Task Force member, EIS officer Harry Haverkos, even traveled both to Florida and Haiti to include Haitians suffering from malnutrition—who tended to have different diseases altogether.[19] By adding more diseases to the definition of AIDS, all such patients could now be reclassified under the new epidemic.

Having intimidated most skeptics into believing the syndrome to be a single contagious disease, the CDC now had to swing the most powerful biomedical and political institutions behind its new war. Support would be hard to gather unless the disease had an easily remembered name; by July of 1982 the CDC decided to call it the Acquired Immune Deficiency Syndrome (AIDS). This name also swept under the rug any connection between the syndrome and risk groups, a move favored both by the CDC and the homosexual rights movement.[20] "Certainly, the gay groups were putting much pressure on Congress [because of] the emphasis... on AIDS being a gay disease. They wanted the emphasis put some place else," acknowledged one CDC official.[21] In addition, more federal money had to be appropriated, to give this disease more respectability and to attract more experts into this new field. CDC officials soon developed contacts on several Congressional staffs, and before long they had won two powerful Representatives as allies: Phillip Burton of San Francisco, and the powerful Henry Waxman from Los Angeles, who controlled the House committee in charge of health issues. Both Congressmen wasted no time in raising a public furor over the immune deficiency syndrome, holding hearings and demanding crash spending programs. Facing little organized opposition, Burton and Waxman succeeded in diverting millions of additional dollars to the CDC and other agencies.

Meanwhile the CDC twisted arms at medical conferences and in journals. They lobbied doctors at every possible opportunity, spreading word of a new epidemic. More importantly, they used scare tactics to try to get blood suppliers to screen out homosexuals, or at least people previously infected with hepatitis B, from donating blood. The CDC held meetings with the Red Cross and various blood supply associations, demanding immediate screening procedures. CDC representatives remained infuriated even when blood bank officials pointed out that the CDC had produced no serious evidence that AIDS was infectious. EIS member and CDC official Bruce Evatt, who worked with the KSOI Task Force, later admitted this to be true:

> CDC was calling shots on almost no evidence—educated guesses rather than proof. We did not have proof it was blood-borne; we had five hemophiliacs and two or three blood transfusion cases. We did not have proof it was a contagious agent; we had epidemiological evidence suggesting it.[22]

That "epidemiological evidence" was little more than the loaded cluster studies.

To step up the pressure on medical institutions, CDC leaders used their full array of public relations skills to plant stories on AIDS in the news media.[23] By late 1982, dozens of articles were appearing in national print media, exploding to hundreds per month during the first half of 1983.[24] *Time* and *Newsweek* jumped into the act, running cover stories on the mystery disease and hyping up the supposed danger to the general population. *Newsweek*'s cover of April 11, 1983, called AIDS "the Public-Health Threat of the Century."[25] Eight months earlier, Dan Rather had broadcast a special segment on AIDS on the "CBS Nightly News." As the unsuspecting public became fearful, the biomedical establishment began to take notice of the CDC campaign.

Now someone had to start searching for a virus to blame for AIDS. Bacteria were less favored as potential culprits, given that antibiotics did not control AIDS; besides, virus hunting had become the dominant political trend in science. The scientists with the appropriate laboratories, resources, and experience mostly worked at the NIH, but their small AIDS research program had so far focused on poppers, finding that homosexuals who had inhaled the most nitrites for the longest times had the highest risk of developing AIDS. Researchers were now beginning to test the chemical on mice, the logical next step. Such powerful evidence, however, could no longer budge CDC officials, who had thoroughly convinced themselves AIDS had to be contagious. They began exerting pressure on the NIH to hunt viruses, using every scientific meeting and social occasion to collar researchers.

One of the earliest NIH responses came from its National Institute of Allergy and Infectious Diseases (NIAID), a traditional hot spot for virus hunters. Deputy clinical director Anthony Fauci started up an AIDS research program by early 1983 under his own supervision, readily embracing the CDC's view of AIDS as an infectious disease. Researchers at the National Cancer Institute (NCI) responded more slowly, partly because of their ongoing poppers studies. But by April of 1983, the NCI had established its own AIDS task force, and viruses soon replaced poppers as the focus of research.

Now came the big question: which virus to blame? Finding one would be the easy part; since AIDS patients were inherently full of infections, virus hunters would almost have too many choices. In his 1981 report on the first five AIDS cases, Michael Gottlieb had offered the first suggestion—the herpes-class cytomegalovirus. This virus had been isolated in the 1950s and found to cause a disease similar to mononucleosis, but was so mild that few people other than cancer patients undergoing chemotherapy ever suffered from cytomegalovirus disease. The virus spreads easily, and has infected perhaps three-quarters of the adult population, although most people are healthy enough to avoid symptoms. The virus had infected virtually all sexually active homosexuals, including all five of Gottlieb's AIDS patients. Over the next two years, the cytomegalovirus hypothesis picked up steam, attracting researchers in key positions around the country. Part of its popularity derived from the widely accepted belief that two other herpes viruses—Epstein-Barr and herpes simplex 2—could cause cancer. Some scientists even hypothesized that the Epstein-Barr virus itself might cause AIDS; this second hypothesis embraced a strange contradiction, since the Epstein-Barr virus was simultaneously believed to cause Burkitt's lymphoma, a cancer in which it was supposed to make white blood cells grow too well (see Chapter Four). To cause AIDS, it would have to *kill* the very same cells.

While the cytomegalovirus hypothesis slowly gained supporters, retrovirologists also discovered the up-and-coming AIDS research bandwagon. Despite their prestige and Robert Gallo's recent discovery of the first human retrovirus, the glow of the War on Cancer was fading fast. Leukemia hardly afflicted enough Americans to cause widespread concern over any hypothetical HTLV-I epidemic, nor could anyone convincingly argue leukemia had spread as an infectious disease. However, despite the retrovirus hunters desperately needing some new disease to blame on a retrovirus, most of them had spent too many years trying to explain cancer to think of anything else. The door to AIDS would have to be opened by a retrovirus hunter outside the NIH-academic complex, one not committed to studying cancer.

In stepped Donald Francis. A conscientious objector against the Vietnam War, he received a medical degree in the late 1960s, finished his residency training, and was recruited into EIS in 1971. Virtually his entire career since that time has revolved around the CDC, in which he has risen to ever more powerful positions. His job history reads like a tour guide, having worked in public health assignments in parts of Africa and the Far East, as well as having lived in various states on both U.S. coasts. He gained much of his experience imposing strict, even truly coercive, public health measures—which, ironically, may not have made much of a medical difference. "Years of stamping out epidemics in the Third World had also instructed Francis on how to stop a new disease. You find the source of contagion, surround it, and make sure it doesn't spread," wrote author Randy Shilts.[26] Francis partly demonstrated his methods in 1976 when he was sent to Zaire to control Ebola Fever, one of the uncountably many Third World diseases that are constantly appearing and vanishing without explanation:

> When it became obvious that the disease was spreading through autopsies and ritual contact with corpses during the funerary process, Dr. Don Francis, on loan to the World Health Organization from the CDC, had simply banned local rituals and unceremoniously burned the corpses. Infected survivors were removed from the community and quarantined until it was clear that they could no longer spread the fever... The tribespeople were fu-

rious that their millenia-old rituals had been forbidden by these arrogant young doctors from other continents. The wounded anger twisted their faces.[27]

Ebola Fever, as it turned out, had been transmitted primarily through the use of dirty needles in one particular hospital, not through the native burial process. Nor did the CDC and WHO teams accomplish much. According to historian Elizabeth Etheridge, "The epidemic was virtually over before their work began."[28] The guilty hospital had already closed itself, and the epidemic disappeared spontaneously. Nevertheless, for his stern techniques, Francis was credited by his peers for "singular brilliance."[29]

Francis returned to school in the late 1970s for a graduate degree researching the so-called Feline Leukemia Virus in Max Essex's laboratory at Harvard (see Chapter Four). Thus Francis joined the circle of retrovirus hunters. But he has preferred public health activism over research science, and since 1981 has developed the reputation as one of the CDC's most fanatic proponents of aggressive health controls over the population (in the early meetings between CDC and the blood bank associations over possible AIDS transmission through the blood supply, Francis became known for his table-pounding confrontational style and his urgent demands).

By the time Gottlieb's report on the first AIDS cases was published in June of 1981, Francis had reached a high position within the CDC's Hepatitis Laboratories Division, and had worked for years with the homosexual community in organizing a major hepatitis B study. Upon hearing that these mysterious patients had lost their T cells, he saw an opening and leapt for it. A mere eleven days after the Gottlieb report—when only five AIDS cases officially existed and only a handful of other possible ones had been reported—Francis placed a telephone call to Max Essex. Randy Shilts described the start of the conversation: "'This is feline leukemia in people,' Francis began." Retroviruses were generally known to prefer infecting white blood cells, including T cells, he reasoned. Further, in Shilts' words, "… feline leukemia has a long incubation period; this new disease must have long latency too, which is the only way it was killing people in three cities on both coasts before anybody even knew it existed."[30] On that June day, no one could even say for sure that this was even a real epidemic, nor had any retrovirus been found in AIDS patients. Yet Francis had already mapped out the entire future of AIDS research: this new syndrome would be contagious, caused by a retrovirus with a long latent period between infection and disease. According to Shilts, "Francis was already convinced."[31] This decision had no basis in any scientific evidence, but was destined to shape scientific thinking for years to come.

For as soon as Francis had made his decision, he transformed himself into a relentless champion of this retrovirus-AIDS hypothesis. He doggedly pushed this view whenever someone would lend him an ear, and even when no one would. Within a year, KSOI Task Force head James Curran was echoing the Francis hypothesis, as were other key CDC staffers. Max Essex eagerly joined in, helping Francis lobby NIH to find a new retrovirus. The perfect man for the job was Essex's old friend, Robert Gallo, who headed a huge and well-funded retrovirus lab at the National Cancer Institute. By 1982 both Essex and Gallo were searching part-time for an AIDS retrovirus.

But rather than waiting for some new virus to be discovered, Essex decided to use something more readily available. Gallo had already found HTLV-I, the first known human retrovirus, which he believed caused T-cell leukemia after a long latent period. Why couldn't this virus also cause a second disease, AIDS? This would not be the first time virus hunters had blamed a single virus for two or more radically different diseases. And in this case, HTLV-I would infect the same T cells in both diseases.

Therein, however, lay the problem. If HTLV-I caused infected cells to grow into cancers, it could not also kill those same cells. Indeed, retroviruses had seized the high ground of cancer research during the 1970s precisely because they did not kill infected cells, but rather integrated themselves into the cell's genetic material, and therefore could be thought of as potential cancer-causing agents. Still, Essex's hypothesis, implicating HTLV-I, tickled Gallo's fancy—until he finally noticed the contradiction. Gallo then quietly changed the name of the virus; for Human T-cell *Leukemia* Virus he substituted Human T-cell *Lymphotropic* Virus, meaning one that favors infecting T cells. This new name implied neither cancer nor cell-killing, thereby maintaining an ambiguity that could allow the virus to cause both diseases at once.

Late in 1982, while Essex and Gallo were reporting many AIDS or immune-suppressed patients who had been infected by HTLV-I, a French retrovirologist named Luc Montagnier was seizing the opportunity to stake his claim on an AIDS virus. Working at the Pasteur Institute in Paris, he cultured cells from a patient with swollen lymph nodes but no AIDS. Within weeks he isolated a new retrovirus. Not being prone to overstatement, he cautiously named his new find the Lymphadenopathy-Associated Virus (LAV), though certainly hoping it would be accepted as the cause of AIDS. Knowing he faced an uphill battle, he decided to enlist Gallo's help in promoting this discovery. That later proved to be a fatal mistake.

As soon as Gallo caught wind of the new retrovirus, he hit the roof. The CDC was putting heavy pressure on him to find an AIDS virus, and he was having trouble gaining widespread support for his HTLV-I-AIDS hypothesis, especially from cancer virologists who hated to lose a leukemia virus. Now a lesser French virologist had beaten him to finding another human retrovirus. Gallo began quietly telling colleagues that Montagnier had made a mistake. Hedging his bets as always, Gallo also generously offered to write the short summary for the beginning of Montagnier's upcoming scientific paper. The unsuspecting French scientist agreed, and Gallo wrote in it that the new virus was closely related to his HTLV-I and -II retroviruses. So while Gallo was denouncing Montagnier's discovery and stepping up his own campaign to make HTLV-I the "AIDS virus," he was also trying to take credit for the new virus.

Montagnier's paper was published, and Gallo spent the next several months furiously trying to find the same virus. Finally, by April of 1984 he was ready to announce having found a similar retrovirus, which he unsurprisingly named HTLV-III. He had prepared four separate papers reporting his discovery of the virus and its isolation from a number of AIDS patients. Ethical protocol among scientists required that he first publish those papers, allowing his peers to analyze the results before he went to the news media. But not wanting to struggle against any skepticism, Gallo pulled a *coup d'etat* on Montagnier by holding a press conference on April 23, more than a week before the papers were to be printed in the journal *Science*. Margaret Heckler, Secretary of Health and Human Services, sponsored the huge event and introduced Gallo to the press corps. Backed by the full prestige of the federal government, she officially declared this new virus was probably the cause of AIDS, a conclusion dutifully reported by the media.

Before any other scientists could review and comment on Gallo's claim, it had been set in stone. The press conference marked a point of no return. Career-minded scientists immediately dropped all other AIDS research, including work on Epstein-Barr virus, cytomegalovirus, and HTLV-I, as well as all remaining experiments on poppers. From that date forward, every federal dollar spent on AIDS research funded only experiments in line with the new virus hypothesis. Had researchers been politically free to examine Gallo's papers for themselves, they might have pointed out that some of his AIDS patients had never been infected by the virus. They also could have remembered that retroviruses do not kill cells. For that matter, they might have noticed that Montagnier had found the virus first.

But the CDC had now won its victory. The entire world now knew about AIDS and believed it to be contagious. The news media had begun beating the drums for a war on this syndrome. Hundreds of millions, and then billions, of new dollars began flowing into the CDC and other biomedical research institutions. Most importantly, the virus hunters had finally reached center stage; not since the polio epidemic had they revelled in the glory of so much public attention. The fear of infectious disease had now been revived on a mass level for the first time in decades, and the lay public had no choice but to trust their appointed experts for answers.

And on the very day of the press meeting, while the rest of the world was struggling to come to terms with the first infectious plague in many years, Gallo quietly filed his U.S. patent application for the virus antibody test.

Scandal in the Establishment

More than just a politically driven event, the declaration of LAV/HTLV-III as the "AIDS virus" was a sordid affair involving fraud, theft, and cover-up. The story largely centers around Robert Gallo, although it unmasks the character of many leading AIDS researchers today and fulfills the worst expectations of corruption in the over-funded, bloated science bureaucracy. Gallo himself has a long history of false claims thinly veiled as timely scientific discoveries. Given such a track record, the fact that he nevertheless steadily rose to one of the most powerful positions at the NIH serves as an indictment of federally-sponsored research.

Gallo's first notorious attempt to steal the show came in 1970, on the heels of Howard Temin's announcement of finding reverse transcriptase, the retrovirus enzyme that allows it to embed itself in the genetic material of an infected cell. Seeing the chance for a quick and easy way to explain cancer, Gallo soon followed with his own publicity stunt. He declared finding evidence of retrovirus infection in human leukemias. Virus hunters stampeded to confirm his discovery, but, to their dismay, could not. Reflecting on this incident, Gallo's colleague Abraham Karpas later observed that "he probably thought that he could tie himself to Temin and Baltimore's wagon which was going to lead to a Nobel Prize within 5 years. The reason he lost that opportunity to become a Laureate early in the game was because many scientists from around the world, including ourselves, who spent time and efforts [*sic*] trying to reproduce Gallo's 'milestone discovery,' found that it was an uncontrolled artefact."[32] In other words, a false positive.

Gallo further embarrassed himself in 1975 by announcing he had isolated the first known human retrovirus from a leukemia. In his excitement, he did not bother to test his virus carefully. When other laboratories did so, they quickly found it was not a human virus at all, but a mixture of three monkey retroviruses. Caught unprepared, Gallo spent many months trying to argue his way out by insisting that perhaps one of the monkey viruses could cause human leukemia.

In 1980 he was finally credited for discovering a genuine human retrovirus, HTLV-I. In keeping with his one-track thinking, he blamed this virus for a leukemia common to residents of one Japanese island (see Chapter Four). But possibly remembering the 1975 episode with monkey viruses, he avoided performing key experiments to prove that his was truly a human virus. This may have been a clever move, as he ran into troubles trying to find the virus in American leukemia patients. At the same time, a Japanese research team also reported isolating a human retrovirus from leukemic patients, which they named ATLV. After they courteously sent Gallo a sample of the virus to compare with his own, he suddenly became able to run all the tests he should have earlier, including proving HTLV-I to be a human virus and finding it in cells from many leukemic patients. The radical difference in his results after receiving the Japanese virus suggests the possibility that he simply renamed ATLV and claimed it as his own discovery. When Gallo published the genetic sequence of HTLV-I, moreover, it contained a mistake identical to one made by the Japanese group.[33] No formal investigation has probed this incident, and Gallo was awarded the prestigious Lasker Prize as the presumed discoverer of the virus.

Gallo's report of finding a new retrovirus in AIDS patients smacked of similar tactics. Luc Montagnier, of course, was the first to report finding LAV in 1983. Gallo insists he independently found the virus at the same time, but waited nearly a year to test it before releasing his results to the world. The first journalist publicly to question this version of events was Steve Connor, a correspondent for England's *New Scientist* magazine, who wrote an expose of Gallo in 1987.

Both Montagnier and Gallo published the genetic sequences of their viruses in January, 1985, as did a third scientist, Jay Levy, who independently isolated the virus in San Francisco. Several other researchers immediately noticed a suspicious coincidence: the Gallo and Montagnier viruses were so similar to each other that they had probably come from the same patient. Normally a retrovirus isolated from two different people has mutated, if only in trivial ways, enough to mark the two isolates as distinct. But Gallo's virus was almost identical to Montagnier's. The French researcher had generously sent samples of his virus to Gallo on request, and now Gallo was offering an amazingly similar one as his own. When challenged, Gallo failed to produce any of the other virus isolates he claimed to have. To explain away the similarity, he even proposed that the American and French isolates had come from two patients who just happened to be sexual partners. Gallo has since publicly admitted the French virus may have contaminated and taken over his cultures, and has excused his lack of other viruses by weaving tales of laboratory accidents that somehow happened to destroy his dozens of isolates.

Connor's journalistic investigation also revealed a deliberate cover-up. In 1986, Gallo was forced to admit that the photographs of HTLV-III published in his 1984 papers had actually been photos of the French LAV. The switch was discovered after two copies of a letter, written in 1983 by the researcher who photographed the virus with his electron microscope, found their way into the hands of lawyers representing the Pasteur Institute. One copy stated that the virus was indeed LAV, while the other had been doctored to remove that information. Gallo claims to know nothing about the altered letter, and tried to excuse the switched photo as having been "largely for illustrative purposes"—presumably the usual reason photos are published.[34]

But more recently another hidden fact has come to light. Mikulas Popovic, a Gallo lab associate who co-authored the key 1984 paper announcing Gallo's virus, has presented an original draft of the paper to the NIH's Office of Research Integrity. In this earlier manuscript, Popovic gave full credit to the French for first finding the virus , and showed that the Gallo lab had been able to grow LAV soon after receiving the sample. Those admissions were crossed out in the draft, and in the margins Gallo's handwriting scoldingly declares, "Mika, you are crazy… I just don't believe it. You are absolutely incredible."[35] The published version of the paper contained none of the statements giving credit to the French scientists. With this piece of damning evidence, Gallo has now been caught lying about his supposed inability to grow the French virus in his lab.

In 1989, *Chicago Tribune* correspondent John Crewdson joined in the fray with another expose of Gallo, followed by several more articles. That began an avalanche of scientific fraud investigations originating in the NIH itself, in the National Academy of Sciences, and in Congress. As a result, Popovic was convicted of fraud and blocked from working for NIH, and Gallo himself was convicted of scientific misconduct at the end of 1992. The story has since expanded—Gallo apparently also stole the cell line in which he grew the stolen French virus.[36] A sample of the leukemic T cells, originally named HUT78, was sent to his lab for isolating a leukemia virus. Unable to find any retrovirus, Gallo renamed them H9, claimed he developed the cells himself, and used them instead to grow HIV. No prosecutions have yet precipitated over this second misappropriation.

Theft seems to be a common denominator among Gallo lab personnel. Syed Zaki Salahuddin, another researcher in the lab, pleaded guilty and was fired in 1991 for receiving illegal payments. The money had come from Pan Data Systems Inc., a company founded in 1984 by Salahuddin's wife. Salahuddin had used his authority in the Gallo lab to arrange purchases of supplies from Pan Data, paid for by the NIH budget. For this he received compensation from the company. He even stripped Gallo's lab of viruses and equipment that he handed over to Pan Data for use and resale at below-market rates. Authorities are also investigating yet another scientist in the lab, Dharam Ablashi, for involvement in the Pan Data scandal. Salahuddin was a major author on the 1984 Gallo papers announcing the discovery of the "AIDS virus," and had the habit of referring to himself as "doctor" despite having no such degree.

Another co-author on those Gallo papers, Prem Sarin, soon found himself on trial and was fired by NIH for embezzlement. When a German company sent a payment of $25,000 for experimental work performed by the Gallo lab, Sarin deposited the check in a special personal account. He later testified he was simply borrowing the money, although he actually used it to pay off personal debts. The check, originally intended for the hiring of a laboratory technician to conduct the desired experiments, had been made out to the initials of the NIH Foundation for the Advancement of Education in the Sciences (FAES). Sarin's own bank account also had the initials FAES—which he later claimed represented the "Family Account for the Education of the Sarin children." A jury convicted him of criminal charges in July, 1992.

Gallo sank into still deeper trouble in 1990 through a collaborative project with French scientist Daniel Zagury. U.S. rules prevent government scientists from participating in dangerous experiments on human beings. Zagury, with the help of Gallo's lab, tested a supposed AIDS vaccine on nineteen human volunteers, some from Africa. Three of the patients died, a fact that Zagury left completely out of his published paper on the experiment. Word of the disaster and cover-up got out, leading to a major NIH investigation.

Gallo sensed his worsening plight. But as always, whenever he finds himself in a corner, mysterious events take place. A few weeks after the Zagury paper appeared in print, Gallo returned home one August evening from a big dinner to discover the aftermath of a burglary. County police who responded to the call found a baffling scene. "The Gallo family jewelry, silverware, and VCR were in their familiar places, untouched... as police detective John McCloskey told *Science*: 'Not a thing was taken.'"[37] According to Gallo, only one thing had been disturbed—some scientific data sent from Zagury. Gallo eagerly offered John Crewdson, the *Chicago Tribune* reporter, as his first suspect. The police eventually dismissed this idea, and dropped their investigation. Several months later, shortly before Gallo was to appear before Congress in one of many fraud investigations, he once again precipitated an unusual but convenient incident:

... The alarm system Gallo bought after last summer's break-in went off in the night. He phoned the Bethesda police, saying he thought Crewdson was again trying to break into his house. The detective bureau concluded it was a false alarm. Despite Gallo's insistence, the police disregarded the complaint.[38]

Gallo's example has inspired other less-than-honorable scientists, inciting an orgy of greed. English scientist Robin Weiss in 1985 reported independently isolating the same retrovirus—*after* Montagnier had also sent him samples of LAV. A British investigation revealed in early 1991 that Weiss' virus also appeared to be identical to the French virus, and Weiss publicly agreed that he might have accidentally contaminated his cultures with LAV.

Both Gallo and Weiss have managed to cash in on on their incredible series of "mistakes." Gallo secured the U.S. patent rights for the virus test, while Weiss received the British patent. Facing legal actions by a wrathful Pasteur Institute cheated of its patent royalties, they have acted as mutual friends and benefactors. Weiss, according to retrovirologist Abraham Karpas, managed to be the anonymous peer reviewer on a key Montagnier paper in 1983; by trashing it he got it rejected, buying time for Gallo to discover the virus himself.[39]

Other powerfully placed colleagues have rushed to Gallo's defense, either to protect the image of the NIH or because they conduct science in much the same way as he does. Several of these researchers have developed such a close alliance with Gallo that they privately call themselves "the Bob Club." Among its informal members has been Gallo's longtime friend Max Essex, the Harvard retrovirologist who studies the so-called Feline Leukemia Virus and who trained Donald Francis. Essex has publicly supported Gallo's claim to isolating HTLV-III. He also shared the 1986 Lasker Prize with Gallo and Montagnier, in his case for relabeling a monkey retrovirus sent him by another lab and calling it his own.[40] Harvard retrovirologist William Haseltine, another old "Bob Club" insider, was seen copying the genetic sequence of HTLV-II, the second known human retrovirus, from a presentation at a science conference. He then published the sequence, unknowingly including a planted mistake, beating the Japanese research team who had actually done the work.[41] Gallo has also found allies among his bosses and other administrators in high NIH positions, many of them helping to stall or water down the fraud investigations.

Naturally, Gallo's 1984 press conference aroused French ire, and precipitated an international legal fight for almost three years. But with Gallo's support in the federal bureaucracy, a deal was worked out by March of 1987. In a public meeting between President Reagan and French Prime Minister Jacque Chirac, the two governments agreed to share credit for the virus discovery. Montagnier's lawyers were silenced for the sake of political compromise, despite the strong evidence supporting their case. That same year a committee of prominent retrovirus hunters met and chose a new, and therefore more neutral, name for the virus: the Human Immunodeficiency

Virus (HIV). While this name did not discriminate between Gallo and Montagnier, it provided propaganda value by assuming this virus did indeed cause AIDS. The name has stuck, largely because a subsequent letter, published in the journal *Nature* and signed by such names as David Baltimore, Howard Temin, André Lwoff, Jonas Salk, and the director of NIH, backed the decision.

To assure Gallo's place in the science hall of fame, his old friend Hilary Koprowski, the polio vaccine pioneer, launched a campaign in 1987 to elect Gallo to the elite National Academy of Sciences. Koprowski had worked for years alongside Gallo, chasing slow viruses as the director of the Wistar Institute. Citing Gallo's "brilliant discoveries" and "leadership," he succeeded by 1988, when Gallo joined the ranks of the most prestigious scientific body in the nation.

Koprowski himself probably felt a common bond with Gallo, for he was beginning to face his own troubles. The 1984 Nobel Prize for medicine had honored two European scientists for inventing a biochemical tool known as the monoclonal antibody. Upon request, the European researchers had generously sent Koprowski a sample of their cell line, along with a letter warning against any commercial use of the product. In speaking with Cesar Milstein, one of the Nobel laureate European researchers, Koprowski denied seeing the letter, insisting it had somehow been lost. In any case, Milstein directly reminded Koprowski not to use the technique commercially. Yet, after that warning, Koprowski managed to patent the technique himself. To reassure the angered Milstein, Koprowski blandly declared that the money was going entirely into scientific research. It was—in the form of Koprowski's brand new biotechnology company, Centocor, which was reaping the profits.[42] Meanwhile, the Wistar Institute's Board of Directors fired Koprowski as director in 1991. During his last ten years at the helm, he had so mismanaged the Institute's finances that its coffers dwindled from tens of millions of dollars to a several-million-dollar deficit. Centocor fared much better; by the end of 1986, Koprowski's own stock holdings in the company already exceeded $15 million in value.

By 1988 Gallo surely believed his position had been secured. But after the Connor and Crewdson articles, the whole stolen-virus scandal reopened in 1990. His career began tumbling, finally leading, on December 30, 1992, to his official conviction on a charge of scientific misconduct. The Office of Research Integrity found that Gallo had falsely claimed he could not grow the French virus in his own lab.

Gallo appealed the decision to a committee of lawyers under the authority of the Department of Health and Human Services. After months of legal wrangling by both sides, the panel shocked observers by raising the burden of proof on the prosecution. Suddenly the investigators had to prove not only that Gallo had fabricated his results and covered up the evidence, but also that he had consciously planned to do so—as if this scientific review were actually a criminal proceeding. Unable to meet the new standards, the NIH prosecutors were forced to drop the charges, and Gallo was officially "acquitted." Since then, none of the many investigators on the Gallo case have even tried to prosecute the remaining charges, mostly related to the stolen French virus.

But the controversy is not going away. According to columnist Daniel S. Greenberg, "The misconduct case against Robert C. Gallo is showing signs of an afterlife of seething resentment among his detractors and canonization by supporters."[43] Gallo has made many enemies over the years, and many scientists still remember the powerful evidence against him.

The Virus Survives

No amount of controversy over the integrity of leading AIDS scientists has weakened the political support for the HIV hypothesis. The CDC, NIH, and dozens of biotechnology and pharmaceutical companies have invested their full resources in this view, making it unchallengeable for all practical purposes.

In the wake of massive spending increases on HIV research, virus hunters have converged from all fields to stake their claims. Many have taken up HIV research itself, while others have begun reclassifying animal diseases as "AIDS." Animal retroviruses once presumed to cause cancer now suddenly cause immune deficiency, at least in the minds of AIDS scientists. Any young animal that will develop a flu or pneumonia when injected with huge quantities of a retrovirus now becomes an experimental model for AIDS. Virus hunters have transformed one strain of Feline Leukemia Virus into a cause of "Feline AIDS" (FAIDS), isolated the "Simian Immunodeficiency Virus" and blamed it for causing "AIDS" in monkeys (SAIDS), and even indicted a mouse retrovirus simultaneously blamed for leukemia as also causing "Mouse AIDS" (MAIDS).

No virus goes to waste. Even Gallo's original HTLV-I/AIDS hypothesis has not died completely. After stealing credit for HIV, he turned around and proposed that HTLV-I could perhaps serve as a co-factor in causing AIDS, somehow cooperating with HIV when infecting the same victim. Never one to pass up an opportunity, Gallo simultaneously proposed exactly the opposite notion—that HTLV-I might function as the *cure* for AIDS. His logic was simple: if HIV kills T cells, and if HTLV-I makes them grow more aggressively as leukemia, then the two viruses might cancel each other's effects. Few scientists have bought into either of these silly hypotheses, which nevertheless stand mostly unchallenged.

The free-flowing money spent on AIDS has thoroughly reshaped modern science. Virus hunting, nearly discredited by the failed War on Cancer, has now enjoyed a spectacular revival. The CDC has shifted its resources back into managing contagious disease, and masterminds public campaigns for controlling HIV. The NIH has continued to experience an ever-growing budget. In an era with no serious infectious disease in the industrial world, the otherwise healthy population has regained its fear of contagion. The dangerous public hysteria formerly witnessed with scurvy, pellagra, SMON, and other non-infectious diseases now repeats itself, but on a larger scale.

The next chapter will examine how the HIV-AIDS hypothesis shaped this public hysteria, and will present the full evidence against this virus causing AIDS.

Chapter 5 Footnotes

[1] Shorter, *The Health Century*. Doubleday, New York, 1987, p. 100.

[2] Langmuir, Biological Warfare Defense. *American Journal of Public Health* 42:235-8, 1952.

[3] Thomas and Morgan-Witts, *Anatomy of an Epidemic*. Doubleday & Co., Garden City, NY, 1982, p. 105.

[4] Wecht, The swine flu immunization program: Scientific venture or political folly? In: *Legal Medicine Annual*, (ed.) Wecht, pp. 227-244, 1978 (p. 231).

[5] Ibid.; see also Cotton, CDC nears close of first half-century. *JAMA* 263:2579-2580, 1990.

[6] Thomas and Morgan-Witts, Op cit., pp. 5-6.

[7] Ibid., p. 3.

[8] Culliton, Legion fever: Postmortem on an investigation that failed. *Science* 194:1025, 1976.

[9] "Legionnaires' Disease." House Subcommittee on Consumer Protection and Finance, Nov. 23 & 24, 1976, p. 5.

[10] Wecht, Op cit., p. 243.

[11] Shilts, *And the Band Played On*. St. Martin's Press, New York, 1987, p. 63.

[12] Ibid., p. 67.

[13] Gottlieb, Schanker, Fan, Saxon, Weisman, and Posalski, *Pneumocystis* pneumonia — Los Angeles. *Morbidity and Mortality Weekly Report* 30:250-252, June 5, 1981.

[14] Shilts, Op cit., pp. 71, 81, 86-87.

[15] Etheridge, *Sentinel for Health*. University of California Press, Berkeley, CA, 1992, p. 326.

[16] Shilts, Op cit., pp. 132, 147.

[17] Ibid., p. 164.

[18] Ibid., p. 81.

[19] Ibid., p. 135.

[20] Ibid., pp. 138, 171.

[21] Etheridge, *Sentinel for Health*, Op cit., p. 334.

[22] Ibid., p. 334.

[23] Shilts, Op cit., pp. 110, 267-268.

[24] Ibid., p. 267.

[25] Ibid., p. 267.

[26] Ibid., p. 107.

[27] Ibid., p. 118.

[28] Etheridge, *Sentinel for Health*, Op cit., p. 219.

[29] Shilts, Op cit., p. 73.

[30] Ibid., p. 73.

[31] Ibid., p. 74.

[32] Karpas, Letter to Serge Lang, Feb. 3, 1993.

[33] Malik, Even, and Karpas, Molecular cloning and complete nucleotide sequence of an adult T cell leukemia virus/human T cell leukemia virus type I (ATLV/HTLV-I) isolate of caribbean origin: Relationship to other members of the ATLV/HTLV-I subgroup. *J. Gen. Virol.* 69:1695-1710, 1988, as cited in Karpas, Op cit.

34 Gallo, *Virus Hunting — AIDS, Cancer, & the Human Retrovirus: a Story of Human Discovery.* Basic Books, New York, 1991, p. 210.

35 Crewdson, Burden of Proof. *Chicago Tribune*, Dec. 6, 1992, section 4.

36 Rubinstein, The untold story of HUT78. *Science* 248:1499-1507, 1990; Dingell, Shattuck Lecture — Misconduct in medical research. *New England Journal of Medicine* 328:1610-1615, 1993, p. 1613.

37 Culliton, Gallo Reports Mystery Break-in. *Science* 250:502, 1990.

38 Werth, By AIDS Obsessed. *GQ*, August, 1991, pp. 145-151, 205-208 (pp. 207-8).

39 MacIntyre, Scientist looks back in anger as battle rages over the discovery of Aids. *Glasgow Herald*, Jan. 30, 1990.

40 Mulder, A case of mistaken non-identity. *Nature* 331:562-563, 1988, as cited in Karpas, Op cit.

41 Haseltine's copying was witnessed by Kunitada Shimotohno and Norman Letvin, as recorded by John Crewdson in a letter to Abraham Karpas, March 12, 1994; the sequence error (bp 580) was published by Shimotohno, *et al.*, Nucleotide sequence of the 3' region of an infectious human T-cell leukemia virus type II genome, *PNAS* 81:6657-6661 (1984); Haseltine had copied this sequence error (also bp 580) in Haseltine, *et al.*, Structure of 3' terminal region of type II human T lymphotropic virus: Evidence for new coding region, *Science* 225:419-421 (1984); the original error was corrected (now bp 7223) in Shima, *et al.*, Identification of p26Xb and p24Xb of human T-cell leukemia virus type II, *Febs Letters* 209:289-294 (1986).

42 Peter Duesberg, interview with Cesar Milstein, May 24, 1993.

43 Greenberg, Saint or scoundrel? The Gallo controversy goes on. *Science & Government Report*, Feb. 1, 1994, p. 6.

Chapter 6

A Fabricated Epidemic

A frightening specter had been launched. The media buildup around AIDS, combined with the 1984 announcement of an AIDS virus, had finally painted a picture of a twentieth-century bubonic plague capable of ravaging our nation and much of the planet. Now everyone was aware of the deadly disease spreading through the homosexual community.

The scientific and government experts, most prominently including Surgeon General C. Everett Koop, gave the public plenty of reason for fear by predicting an explosion into the heterosexual population. In early 1987, he and the World Health Organization were predicting a staggering 100 million people would be infected with the virus by the early 1990s.[1] Talk of casual transmission became popular once top officials at the CDC and NIH announced HIV could be found in saliva,[2] and evidence that the virus could survive for long periods outside the human body led to nervousness about restaurants and public toilets.[3] Naturally, the fact that HIV was a blood-borne virus spurred much discussion of mosquito transmission, including among top AIDS researchers.[4]

AIDS was such a new syndrome that most of its mysteries remained to be solved; we were fortunate enough merely to have isolated the virus by that point. Certainly no vaccine, and probably no potent therapy, would be available for several years, by which time hundreds of thousands—or millions—of people would already have died.

In the meantime, only public health measures could work. Authorities tried to prevent further spread by discouraging the major risk activities, those routes most easily transmitting HIV—the most obvious threat being sexual intercourse. Official warnings were always accompanied by reminders that, although the virus was now transmitted by homosexual contact, it would soon follow the usual pattern of infectious diseases by spreading among heterosexuals of all walks of life. Common stereotypes of African mystique were exploited to paint a picture of our own future; there, whole villages were disappearing as the new syndrome cut a wide swath of destruction among men and women alike. In the industrial world, heterosexual intravenous drug addicts were already passing HIV around by sharing their used syringes. AIDS officials did confidently reassure the public of their timely screening and protection of the nation's blood supply, but noted they were too late to save most hemophiliacs.

Ominous statistics hit the news: 50 to 100 percent of everyone carrying the virus would die, and the unpredictable latency period between infection and AIDS ranged from five to ten years, during which time the carriers could infect many more people. Once infected, an individual's antibody defense raised against HIV was inexplicably useless, except to alert doctors to the fatal infection. Once the virus was reactivated (for unknown reasons), it proceeded to kill off the body's entire supply of T-helper cells, the white blood cells regulating the immune response against all other microbes. AIDS victims suffered horribly slow, painful deaths, being eaten alive by pneumonias, yeast infections, cancers, uncontrollable diarrhea, and dementia from brain degeneration. No recovery was possible, since the patient was completely defenseless against any disease normally harmless to a healthy person.

To add a further sense of urgency, AIDS experts supplemented their official estimate of one million HIV positive Americans with suggestions of two to three million, and with dire predictions that the number might double every year.

The public response to such news was inevitable. Battle lines rapidly emerged between two political camps—civil rights advocates for the HIV positives, and those championing health rights for HIV negatives.

Under the banner call, "Fight AIDS, not people,"groups ranging from the militant AIDS Coalition To Unleash Power (ACT-UP) to the federal government's National Commission on AIDS insisted that the syndrome be treated basically as a handicap. Although acknowledging that AIDS was contagious, many political activists feared the potential backlash from widespread panic. They preferred instead to mobilize support for the care of AIDS patients, assiduously avoiding any hint of blame on the victims. As the National Commission on AIDS proclaimed, "HIV disease has a devastating impact on those who are already marginalized members of society ... HIV disease could not be understood outside the context of racism, homophobia, poverty, and unemployment ...".[5] Likewise President Bush admonished that "Once disease strikes we don't blame those who are suffering. We don't spurn the accident victim who didn't wear a seat belt; we don't reject the cancer patient who didn't quit smoking. We try to love them and care for them and comfort them."[6]

The Centers for Disease Control and other agencies deeply involved in managing the War on AIDS continued to stir up fear of an imminent heterosexual epidemic, knowing full well their fiscal budgets and prestige depended on public anxiety. Activists for HIV positives were therefore forced to offer some solution to halt the syndrome's spread, but without endangering homosexual liberation; they found an answer in condoms and programs to provide heroin addicts with sterile needles. But many activists, including those in the National Commission, also saw in AIDS much opportunity:

> The HIV epidemic did not leave 37 million or more Americans without ways to finance their medical care—but it did dramatize their plight. The HIV epidemic did not cause the problem of homelessness—but it has expanded it and made it more visible. The HIV epidemic did not cause collapse of the health care system—but it has accelerated the disintegration of our public hospitals and intensified their financing problems. The HIV epidemic did not directly augment problems of substance use—but it has

made the need for drug treatment for all who request it a matter of urgent national priority.[7]

The opposite side of the debate operated on the principle, "Better safe than sorry," viewing AIDS in more grand and threatening terms. This alarmism created strange alliances between such individuals as California Congressman William Dannemeyer and former Marxist activist (head of the U.S. Labor Party) Lyndon LaRouche. Most of these people were convinced the AIDS epidemic was actually far worse than officially acknowledged. They certainly had a rich source of raw material upon which to draw, including frequent quotes and numerical projections by federal officials eager to impress upon the public the immense danger, and therefore the importance of vastly increased funding for their federal AIDS research and prevention programs. A 1985 book written by an investigator at the National Institutes of Health provides a typical example:

> The AIDS virus shows every sign of being just as deadly as the plague during the Middle Ages. We are on a crash course with reality. This is not a practice run. There is no second chance. AIDS may be to the twentieth century what the Black Plague was to the fourteenth century.
> The alarm must be sounded, loudly and persuasively. If it is not, the conclusion is inescapable: millions may die.[8]

Believing the population to be on the verge of total decimation, a variety of alarmists called for strong public health measures by government. Their reaction on behalf of the uninfected took on the strenuous tone of Gene Antonio, whose 1986 book became an underground bestseller: "In the pell mell rush to identify with the plight of AIDS sufferers, compassionate concern for the rest of society has been largely ignored. Permeated with heterophobia, AIDS victim identification hysteria has dangerously impeded compassionate steps being taken to safeguard the health of the rest of society."[9] The alarmists generally insisted on mandatory HIV testing, particularly for health care workers and those in AIDS risk groups, as well as infection contact tracing and reportability to government agencies, and even discussed possible quarantine of infected persons. Over fifty countries, including the United States, adopted immigration or tourism restrictions on infected people, and the Cuban government established a quarantine detention center for its HIV-positive citizens. Alarmists derided the weaker proposals of their opponents, often leaping to the defense of medical workers wanting more safeguards from potentially infected patients.

Yet despite their differences, both sides of the controversy agreed on one thing: more money was needed to fight AIDS, and quickly. Federal AIDS officials were no doubt delighted to hear California Congressman Dannemeyer, in an unusual alliance with Michigan Representative John Dingell for increased medical funding on AIDS, nevertheless declare enthusiastically:

> The AIDS Prevention Act of 1990 is a pathbreaking piece of legislation in many respects. For the first time, the federal government would make re-

sources available to states, hospitals, high risk clinics, and nonprofit health care facilities to provide "preventive health services" to low income individuals afflicted with a specific disease—AIDS.

… This legislation breaks new ground in bringing federal resources to bear on a very specific national health problem—the epidemic of HIV infection. It includes many admirable provisions which, if enacted, would establish sound priorities and provide state and local health officials with appropriate resources to fight this horrible epidemic.[10]

This push for larger AIDS budgets certainly succeeded. Some 5.3 billion dollars were spent by the federal government during 1993, and well over $22 billion since the AIDS epidemic began. What have been the results of this modern day Manhattan Project? A staggering 75,000 scientific papers have so far been published on HIV and AIDS, a number unprecedented for any other virus. But AIDS investigators have yet to demonstrate that even a *single life* has been saved by any of their programs. No vaccine exists; condom and clean needle programs have made no measurable impact on the epidemic; the admittedly toxic drugs AZT, ddI, ddC, and d4T, which do not cure AIDS, are the only therapy substitutes available today; despite projections of wild spread, HIV infection has remained virtually constant throughout the world ever since it could be tested in 1985, whether in the United States, Europe, Africa, or Thailand; the estimated incubation period between infection and disease has been revised from ten months to over ten years; and the predicted heterosexual explosion has failed to materialize. When a disease can neither be treated nor controlled, nor its course even roughly predicted, some fundamental assumption is probably badly askew.

In this case, the false premise lies in the virus-AIDS hypothesis itself. As the literature clearly demonstrates, HIV is not a rampant killer but a benign passenger virus.

Innocent virus

Twenty years of belief in human viruses causing disease after long incubation periods, and the many decades of hunting animal retroviruses, had rendered most biologists utterly incapable of challenging Gallo's 1984 announcement of an AIDS virus. Prestigious awards and new grant moneys awaited scientists who could apply their animal models or "slow virus" concepts to human disease. Researchers also automatically felt insecure upon venturing outside their narrow fields of specialization to raise questions in other areas: epidemiologists assumed clinicians were accurately describing their cases, virologists trusted the statistics of the epidemiologists, the immunologists placed confidence in the virologists' lab experiments, and the computer modelling experts believed them all. Any intrusion into another scientist's domain entailed peer rejection and humiliation.

In this atmosphere of conforming pressures, the lessons of the bacteria hunting era were easily overlooked. Virtually no one thought to test HIV according to Koch's postulates. These time-tested standards apply even more perfectly to viruses, which are nonliving parasites with no behavioral flexibility, than to bacteria, which can sometimes release toxins or adapt to changing environments. The growing mountains of data on HIV were instead interpreted solely to fit the consensus virus-AIDS hypothesis, and researchers forgot the very rudiments of virology itself as they assigned increasingly bizarre properties to this virus. But Koch's postulates do indeed cut to the heart of the issue, exonerating HIV and rendering most AIDS research entirely pointless:

1) The microbe must be found in all cases of the disease.

Robert Koch explicitly stated that a causal germ would be found in high concentrations in the patient, and distributed in the diseased tissues in such a way as to explain the course of the symptoms. In the case of AIDS, the affected tissues include the white blood cells of the immune system, particularly the T-helper cells, as well as the skin cells in lesions of Kaposi's sarcoma and brain neurons in dementia. But no trace of the virus can be found in either the Kaposi's sarcomas or the neurons of the central nervous system. Since retroviruses, in fact, cannot infect nondividing cells, the absence of HIV in these neurons is hardly surprising. However, because Kaposi's sarcoma itself has long been synonymous with AIDS, this lack of virus seriously undermines the HIV hypothesis.

If HIV were actively infecting T cells or other members of the body's immune system, cell-free virus particles, known as virions, should be found with great ease circulating in the blood. This is the case with all classical viral diseases: in a patient suffering from hepatitis B, one milliliter of blood (about five or ten drops) contains approximately 10 million free virus particles. Likewise, flu-like symptoms appear only in the presence of 1 million rhinovirus particles per milliliter of nasal mucous, and 1 to 100 billion particles of rotavirus per gram of feces will accompany diarrhea in the patient. But in most individuals suffering from AIDS, no virus particles can be found anywhere in the body, and the remaining few patients have at most a few hundred or a few thousand infectious units per milliliter of blood. One paper, published in March of 1993, reported two individuals with about 100,000 virus particles per milliliter of blood, out of dozens of AIDS patients with little or no detectable virus.[11] Thus HIV behaves as a harmless passenger microbe, only sporadically coming back to life long after the immune system has been destroyed by something else and can no longer suppress the virus.

Even those patients with some detectable virus never have more than one in every 10,000 T cells actively producing copies of the virus; on average, only one in every 500 or more T cells contains even a dormant virus. The absence of active virus automatically disqualifies HIV as a player in the syndrome. Microbes can only cause serious damage when infecting the host's cells faster than the body can replace them; T cells, the presumed target of HIV, are constantly regenerating at much higher rates.

HIV is not, of course, behaving differently from other viruses. Upon infecting a new host, a typical virus invades its target cells and begins replicating in large quantities, producing new virus particles that spill into the bloodstream and infect more cells; this is the period during which high levels of virus can be isolated from the patient and the symptoms are strongest. The body's immune system responds to the threat by mobilizing to mass-produce the specific antibody proteins that attack and neutralize the virus particles. As this battle heats up, antibodies are produced more rapidly than the virus, ultimately eliminating active virus from the body. Most viruses are thereby completely destroyed, although some herpes viruses can establish chronic infections by hiding temporarily in certain tissues.

Retroviruses, by nature, insert their genetic information into infected host cells, becoming dormant once neutralized by the host's immune system. HIV, like other retroviruses, can achieve high levels of virus when first infecting the body (up to 100,000 particles per milliliter of blood), but in most people is then permanently inactivated by the antibodies generated against it. During this brief period of HIV activity, some newly infected people have reported mild flu-like symptoms at most—but no AIDS diseases.

AIDS patients, on the other hand, have generally been infected by HIV for years, not days, before they deteriorate and die. Thus the virus has long since been neutralized, forcing doctors to test the patient either for the dormant virus or the antibodies against it. This is the operating principle of the "HIV test," which identifies antibodies, and yet ironically stands as proof of the innocence of this virus. HIV can never be found in Kaposi's sarcoma cells, nor in the brain neurons of AIDS dementia patients, and only occasionally in T cells. Despite extensive searches throughout the body, including in the lymph nodes, macrophage cells, dendritic cells, and elsewhere, no reservoir of hidden virus infection can be found.

Not all AIDS patients, however, carry even dormant HIV. Antibody-positive patients usually do have latent virus left over from past infection. But many people dying of AIDS-like conditions, ranging from Kaposi's sarcoma to immune deficiencies and various opportunistic infections, have never been infected by HIV in the first place. The CDC does not include most of these antibody-*negative* cases in its AIDS figures, rendering these people invisible.

According to the CDC's own statistics, at least 25% of all official AIDS cases have never been tested for antibodies against HIV, many of whom might turn out to be negative. Further, the HIV test itself often generates false positive results, particularly in members of AIDS risk groups who have been infected with large numbers of interfering viruses; thorough follow-up testing could reveal HIV-negative cases in the official AIDS tally. And we have already uncovered in the scientific literature some 4,621 confirmed cases of HIV-free people dying of AIDS diseases, including homosexuals and heroin addicts in the United States and Europe, and central Africans. These dozens of studies generally found that, among any group of AIDS patients, the majority test negative for HIV. But because the CDC ignores virtually all HIV-negative patients, counting only those with the virus as AIDS cases, the total number of such cases may never be known.

Even a "slow virus" hypothesis of HIV cannot explain how *uninfected* people would develop AIDS conditions. From every angle, HIV fails Koch's first postulate.

2) The microbe must be isolated from the host and grown in pure culture.

This postulate was designed to prove that a given disease was caused by a particular germ, rather than by some undetermined mixture of noninfectious substances. HIV has been isolated and is now grown continuously in HIV research labs. This rule therefore has technically been fulfilled, but only in some instances.

Since free virus is rarely found in AIDS victims, HIV can only be retrieved from the great majority of them by reactivating the latent form of the virus. Millions of white blood cells must be taken from the patient and grown in culture dishes for weeks, during which time chemical stimulants that shock cells into growing or mutating are added to awaken any dormant HIV from within its host cells. Given enough patience and plenty repeating of such procedures, a single intact virus can eventually be activated, at which point it starts infecting the remaining cultured cells. Yet even this powerful method does not yield active virus from many AIDS cases that have confirmed antibodies against HIV. Gallo himself faced this intractable problem, a frustrating situation that may have led him to steal Luc Montagnier's virus instead.

Often while inserting its genetic information into the DNA of a cell, a retrovirus will make a mistake and thereby leave only a defective copy, one which can never be reactivated. Even this can be detected with incredibly sensitive technology available since the mid-1980s. The polymerase chain reaction is a process of biotechnology that amplifies even the tiniest amounts of any specific DNA sequence, creating enough copies of the desired sequence for detection and analysis. This amounts to finding the proverbial needle of dormant HIV in a haystack of human DNA, but contrary to statements by some HIV scientists this is not an isolation of the actual virus, and does not fulfill Koch's second postulate. Nevertheless, scientists and journalists alike sometimes mislabel such exhumations of dead virus as "new, more sensitive techniques" that somehow prove HIV can be found in an ever-greater portion of AIDS patients.

3) The microbe must reproduce the original disease when introduced into a susceptible host.

The official HIV-AIDS hypothesis declares a 50 to 100 per cent probability of death from infection. In practice, scientists and medical doctors interpret antibodies against HIV as a sure sign of imminent doom. This notion, of antibodies as a prognosis of death, defies all classical experience with viruses and bacteria; virtually every microbe causes disease only in a minority of infected individuals, since the majority are usually healthy enough to mount a rapid immune response. Certainly no fatal viral disease is known to cause death in nearly all infected people—except the paradoxical "AIDS virus." Any microbe killing all its hosts would soon destroy itself, even if such could exist in the first place; any germ must be able to reach new hosts before the previous one dies, lest it go down with a sinking ship. Any universally lethal parasite would be, by definition, a suicidal combination. HIV would face even less chance of survival, since it is so difficult to transmit from one person to another, and would thus usually die with its infected host.

Traditional incubation periods, defined as the time between initial viral infection and the onset of disease symptoms, are measured in days or weeks. During this period the virus multiplies up to concentrations high enough to cause disease. The process is exponential: each virus particle infects a single cell, and eight to forty-eight hours later hundreds of new virus particles begin to be produced, each destined to infect a new cell. Flu, common colds, and herpes simplex infections develop with short incubations lasting between one day and one week; measles, chickenpox, and rubella have longer incubations of ten to twenty days, while extreme conditions such as hepatitis can take two to six weeks. These classical delays occur before the body has launched an immune response against the new virus. But borrowing from their cancer research, virus hunters officially give HIV ten to twelve *years* between infection and the onset of AIDS, during which time antibodies neutralize the virus. Such latency periods have been invented solely to circumvent Robert Koch's postulates; any germ not causing symptoms before being cleared by the immune system should be ruled out as causing disease. The very need to create a latent period for HIV should also throw the virus out of consideration.

Koch's third postulate merely insists on reproducing the disease in at least a few cases, by injecting the allegedly dangerous microbe into a number of uninfected and otherwise healthy hosts. This condition can be tested in one of three ways: infection of laboratory animals, accidental infection of humans (deliberate infection would be unethical), or by vaccination experiments. HIV fails all three tests:

(a) Blood from AIDS patients was injected into several chimpanzees in 1983, before the availability of HIV tests. The animals were infected by HIV, as later evidenced by antibodies against the virus, but in ten years none has yet developed any sickness. Roughly 150 other lab chimpanzees, injected with purified HIV since 1984, have proved that antibodies against the virus are generated within a month of inoculation just as in humans; but again, none has developed symptoms to this very day.

In short, no animal becomes sick from HIV, although monkeys and other test animals do suffer disease from human viruses causing polio, flu, hepatitis, and other conditions.

(b) Accidental infection of health care workers by HIV is judged only by ruling out other possible means of transmission, including sex with other HIV positive people or intravenous drug use. In the absence of these other routes for infection, the medical worker is presumed to have contracted the virus through needlestick injuries, which are surprisingly common, or by some sort of blood contamination. Out of twenty such medical workers, the Centers for Disease Control reported in 1988 that one had developed AIDS, but no confirming data was published; no clue was given as to the specific AIDS indicator disease diagnosed, nor was a case history of the individual's background provided. Later that same year, none of these accidentally infected medical workers was listed as having AIDS, meaning the one had apparently recovered.[12]

By the end of 1992 the CDC had reported some 33 medical workers as most likely having received HIV accidentally, of whom seven were diagnosed with AIDS symptoms. None of these reports has been confirmed with published medical case histories, although an informal editorial in a 1989 issue of *The New England Journal of Medicine* was presumably written by one of them, a doctor. Entitled "When a house officer gets AIDS," the article describes only minor weight loss of ten pounds and a "bit" of fatigue as being the doctor's AIDS "complications."[13] This hardly counts as evidence for Koch's third postulate. Nor has the CDC stated whether any of these medical workers have taken the dangerously toxic AZT, the official AIDS treatment, which itself causes immune deficiency (see Chapter Nine).

During the last decade, over 300,000 AIDS patients have been treated and investigated by a system of five million medical workers and AIDS researchers, none of which has been vaccinated against HIV. Several thousand health care workers have by now been diagnosed with AIDS, but 90 percent of these belong to the same AIDS risk groups as 90 percent of all AIDS cases—homosexuals and intravenous drug users. And although three quarters of all health care workers are female, over 90 percent of these AIDS patients are male, the exact same ratio as with all other AIDS cases. *In other words, medical accidents are not producing the expected AIDS epidemic among unvaccinated personnel in that industry.*

Nor has HIV affected the recipients of blood transfusions, most notably hemophiliacs. Some 15,000 hemophiliacs in the United States—about three-quarters of the total—were infected with HIV before the blood supply was screened in 1984. But also during the last fifteen years, improved medical treatment has doubled their median life expectancy; by this association, one could facetiously argue that HIV has lengthened their lives! Fewer than two percent of these HIV-positive hemophiliacs develop AIDS each year. According to a few small studies, this matches the rate of immune deficiencies and death among HIV-negative hemophiliacs, a phenomenon apparently related to hemophilia itself.

(c) The third postulate can be tested in humans through a reverse method. If vaccines or other techniques can be used to provoke the body into neutralizing the microbe with antibodies, and the disease is thereby prevented, the germ has been proven guilty experimentally. But since AIDS is found in each patient only after his immune system has already suppressed HIV, the virus plays no role. Most AIDS researchers have conveniently forgotten this important principle, and continue to blame the virus when only antibodies against it can be found; others blatantly reverse the logic of the vaccination test, declaring antibodies useless *because* they do not prevent AIDS.

If HIV cannot induce disease in whole organisms, one might at least expect it to kill T cells grown in laboratory culture dishes, where the concentrations of actively replicating virus are enormously high. Robert Gallo, however, has been able to patent the virus by growing it continuously in immortal T-cell cultures since 1984. The French discoverer of the virus, Luc Montagnier, reported occasional cell death in infected cultures that was stopped by adding antibiotics, which do not affect virus replication but do kill undetected bacterial contaminants. Indeed, the HIV antibody test is made from virus that is mass-produced in T cells, which grow continuously rather than die. The reports from other labs and biotechnology companies are consistent: HIV grows harmoniously with the cells it infects. The failure to kill T cells, even under optimal conditions, is the acid test for any supposed "AIDS virus."

4) The microbe must be found present in the experimental host so infected.

No animal or human has yet developed AIDS after receiving only HIV, leaving this postulate irrelevant. The virus can sometimes be re-isolated from infected individuals but, as noted under the second postulate, this can only be done with great difficulty, by reactivating the dormant form of the virus.

To gain some perspective, one should remember that most people carry inactive forms of several viruses, none of which cause disease while the microbes remain hidden and dormant in the body. Two out of every three Americans carry the herpes virus, and an equal number harbor the herpes-class cytomegalovirus; Epstein-Barr virus, causing mononucleosis ("kissing disease") when active, resides in dormant form in four of every five Americans; and an even higher proportion of people host the papilloma, or wart, virus. If these viruses could cause disease while latent, the absurd situation would arise in which virtually no one would be left to treat the hundreds of millions of sufferers.

HIV clearly fails Koch's postulates. However, virologists should have expected this from the beginning. HIV is, after all, a retrovirus, precisely the kind of virus so benign to its host cells that it had inspired such hope in the War on Cancer, since cancer cells grow and behave uncontrollably rather than die. Retroviruses have never been known to inhibit or kill billions of rapidly dividing cells, and could hardly be expected so to affect T cells or otherwise destroy the immune system.

HIV typifies a retrovirus in every measurable way. It has the same biochemical structure and infective properties, benignly stimulating cells to produce more copies of the virus. It has the same amount of genetic information, and the same three basic genes as all other retroviruses. It also has six smaller genes, themselves a normal feature of other retroviruses. Although many HIV researchers focus their efforts on studying these "extra" genes, no one gene is unusual and all are either functionless or needed for virus survival. HIV contains no special "AIDS gene" expressed during the syndrome. However, this does not stop industrious AIDS scientists from endlessly re-examining the genetic sequences for some magical clue to explain AIDS.

To be the cause of AIDS, the virus would require still more miracles. A number of the AIDS indicator diseases are not opportunistic infections preying on an immune-deficient host, including dementia, wasting syndrome, and the various AIDS cancers—Kaposi's sarcoma, the lymphomas, and as of 1993, cervical cancer. HIV would have to kill T cells while destroying brain neurons it cannot infect, and at the same time induce white blood cells and skin cells to grow malignantly. AIDS scientists would therefore like to blame all these diseases on immune suppression, but despite years of research no evidence can be found that the immune system fights cancer cells, which after all are part of the host's own body. In fact, dozens of AIDS patients with Kaposi's sarcoma have been reported to have normal immune systems. So HIV would indeed have to accomplish many incredible tasks at once. Stranger still, infants with AIDS suffer immune suppression from deficiencies in B cells, a subgroup of white blood cells altogether different from the T cells.

No matter how convincing these paradoxes should be, official AIDS scientists cannot be dissuaded from their virus hypothesis. When forced to answer the above arguments, their imaginations run wild.

Defending the low ground

After the polio epidemic ended, no new diseases, and no fundamentally different viruses, were being discovered. In order to maintain a position of medical importance, virologists began connecting known viruses to unexplained diseases—such as cancer or multiple sclerosis. But because these progressive diseases (often of older age) in no way behaved as traditional infectious disease, the virus hunters had to invent new properties for the germs. First the incubation period of viruses, typically between one day and two or three weeks, was allowed to stretch into years. Then antibodies had to be abandoned as a sign of immunity against the microbes. And since the viruses never reappeared during disease, indirect methods of damage had to be postulated.

Nevertheless, all these creative maneuvers merely delayed the inevitable. By the early 1980s, virology was withering from lack of public interest—a fatal weakness when trying to attract new recruits, research money, and federal programs. The public was losing faith in wars on cancer that were never won, or wars on diseases that rarely affected the average person.

But AIDS has changed everything, reviving virus hunting as the most glamorous and rewarding branch of biomedical research. To blame HIV for AIDS, virologists had to employ every invention at their disposal, including an ever-expanding latent period, an antibody test, and plenty of paradoxes to keep tens of thousands of investigators busy for many years. The evolution toward these false assumptions had been so gradual, so favored by consensus politics within science, and so shaped by the increasing sensitivity of biotechnology, that most researchers had been lulled into thinking of such rationalizations as normal science. By the time Robert Gallo and other virus hunters had engraved the HIV hypothesis in stone, anyone who dared to raise serious questions appeared truly radical to the rest of the research establishment.

Peter Duesberg first heard questions about the HIV hypothesis circulating among his colleagues shortly after Gallo's 1984 press conference. These scientists could see two fundamental problems: HIV was a retrovirus, meaning it should not kill the cells it infected, and the virus could barely be detected even in late-stage AIDS patients. The following year the NIH awarded Duesberg its Outstanding Investigator Grant, a special seven-year award officially designed to allow free inquiry and latitude for exploring risky new research directions. He took this mandate to heart. As the discussions over HIV continued quietly, he began exploring the issue as a potentially important shift from his usual work on cancer genes and animal retroviruses.

The editor of *Cancer Research*, hearing of Duesberg's doubts about whether retroviruses could cause cancer in humans or most animals, invited him to write a special review paper in 1985. Duesberg spent many months compiling the evidence from the scientific literature. While he was working on this piece, the questions about HIV began intruding into his thinking ever more prominently. He finally decided to add a section arguing that HIV could not cause AIDS, citing data that showed HIV was inactive in the body, did not kill T cells, and could not possibly have a long latent period before inducing AIDS.

He was still writing the paper in 1986 when he took nine months' leave from Berkeley to work in another retrovirus lab at the NIH facility in Bethesda, Maryland. As chance would have it, he worked in the building that housed Gallo's laboratory, though on a different floor. This afforded him many opportunities to test his growing suspicions of the virus-AIDS hypothesis. Not yet realizing Duesberg's intentions, Gallo invited him to be the featured speaker at one of his regular lab seminars. Gallo seemed to enjoy most of Duesberg's talk, which questioned the importance of cancer genes, and did not even become upset when Duesberg threw in a short criticism of the HIV-AIDS hypothesis at the end. Apparently Gallo thought he was not really serious, merely dabbling for fun.

But the following weeks brought increasingly tense conversations between them in which Duesberg would constantly raise new questions. Often these discussions took place in the elevator, on the way to their respective labs. One time Gallo burst into such incredible anger over Duesberg's persistence that he left the elevator on the wrong floor—where he had worked for many years! Another time Duesberg posted a copy of a review paper Gallo had written that alleged HIV might be found in saliva and warned against "heavy saliva exchange" in kissing. Unable to resist, Duesberg hand-wrote a half-joking question on the copy: how large a volume of saliva was dangerous? The posting had disappeared the following morning. Although Gallo increasingly resisted talking about HIV, several researchers in his lab privately admitted to Duesberg the enormous problem in not finding the virus active in the body. They knew perfectly well something had to give. Rather than abandon HIV, however, they told him they hoped to explain the problem using "cofactors" or other rationalizations. Naturally, these experiences began confirming Duesberg's suspicion he had stumbled onto something profound. Judging from their reactions, no one had previously thought of these questions, nor could they find answers.

Duesberg's long, 22-page review paper appeared in the March 1987 issue of *Cancer Research*. Colleagues found the section on AIDS especially shocking, privately admitting the importance of the questions about HIV. To this very day, not one scientist has come forward to answer the paper.

Traditionally, such deafening silence has always been universally interpreted as a victory for the author, indicating the arguments to be irrefutable. However, despite being unable to find any flaws in the article, no researcher could afford to take on the powerful HIV-AIDS establishment. Unwilling to risk status and career by challenging the growing AIDS research structure, but having no arguments to defend the virus hypothesis, scientists chose the safety of quietly studying HIV. Most even rationalized their stand, convincing themselves they were actually producing beneficial "spin-off" research by studying an "interesting" virus, or that they were furthering science in some vague, undefined way. These researchers became quite sensitive about the virus hypothesis, reacting in anger to any criticisms.

The *Cancer Research* paper nevertheless generated some interest, and upon invitation Duesberg wrote a guest editorial in *Bio/Technology* that November. Again no answer. The wide-circulation *Science* soon ran an article on the emerging controversy, though placing Duesberg in a rather unsympathetic light. Prompted by Duesberg's letter in response, the editor decided to set up an official debate in his journal, which appeared in July of 1988. Duesberg was on one side, opposing Gallo, Howard Temin, and the epidemiologist William Blattner. Each side offered an opening page, and a rebuttal to the opposition's opening page; that was all. *Science* has thereafter refused to publish anything but an occasional letter on the topic, declaring it received as much coverage as it deserved.

Although before this exchange Duesberg still had doubts, after seeing this faltering inability to answer his arguments, he became thoroughly convinced the virus was harmless. As he further immersed himself the AIDS literature, the sheer volume of damning evidence became overwhelming. In a response to the short *Science* debate, he wrote an extended update paper, which after months of fighting he managed to publish in the *Proceedings of the National Academy of Sciences* in 1989. This paper was printed on the express condition that another virologist would respond with an equal rebuttal. Gallo himself promised such, but did not deliver. Once again, no scientist has ever chosen to answer that piece, nor to Duesberg's subsequent review papers in *Research in Immunology* or the *Proceedings*.

Only a few short, general responses to Duesberg have appeared in other journals: the brief debate forum in *Science*, short exchanges in some 1989 issues of the *Journal of AIDS Research*, terse letters in a May, 1990 issue of *The New England Journal of Medicine*, a blatantly *ad hominem* attack in the pages of *Nature* during June of 1990, a few editorials in 1993. From these and excerpts of Gallo's writings, only a tepid defense of the HIV-AIDS hypothesis can be reconstructed. None of the most influential AIDS scientists has ever published another formal apologetic for HIV, yet when confronted with the paradoxes they all answer with similar arguments. Otherwise they prefer to ignore the questions.

The arguments for HIV fall into four categories:

1. The Gallo postulate.

The case for HIV as an AIDS virus depends first on bypassing Koch's postulates. The most complete excuse for this is presented by Gallo in his 1991 book, *Virus Hunting*, where he coolly disposes of these time-tested standards:

> ... Rules were needed then, and can be helpful now, but not if they are too blindly followed. Robert Koch, a great microbiologist, has suffered from a malady that affects many other great men: he has been taken too literally and too seriously for too long. We forget at times that we have made great progress in the last century in developing tools, reagents, and diagnostic techniques far beyond Koch's wildest fantasies...
>
> Koch's postulates, while continuing to be an excellent teaching device, are far from absolute in the real world outside the classroom (and probably should not be in the classroom anymore except in a historical and balanced manner). They were not always fulfilled even in his time. Certainly, they did not anticipate the new approaches available to us, especially in molecular biology, immunology, and epidemiology, or the special problems created by viruses. They were, after all, conceived only for bacterial disease, and even here they often fail. Sometimes they are impossible to fulfill; many times one would not even want to try to do so; and sometimes they are quite simply erroneous standards.[14]

Koch's postulates, of course, consist of elementary logic. Whereas technology is continually being outdated, logic is permanent. Gallo never tries to explain how logic would change over time; indeed, in this age of ultrasensitive biotechnology, such rules take on more importance than ever in sorting out relevant data from mere trivia. Nor does Gallo offer any rigorous scientific rules to replace Koch's postulates, thus exposing Gallo's arguments as a simple ploy to strip science of any standards at all. Koch's rules, after all, simply restate the germ theory itself in experimental terms.

Gallo continues by misstating Koch's postulates, falsely claiming that a germ is required to cause a disease every single time it infects a new host. With all microbes, the majority of infected people or animals experience no symptoms; Koch's test only required that a *few* animals become sick when injected with a disease-causing germ, or that vaccination prevent the illness. Gallo then cites false or misleading examples of germs that supposedly fail the postulates despite causing disease, pretending, for example, that the hepatitis B and flu viruses cause no disease in animals. Or he draws examples from the "slow virus" hypotheses, including measles/SSPE, papilloma/cervical cancer, HTLV-I/leukemia, and feline leukemia virus (see Chapters Three and Four). Or he cites diseases erroneously thought to result from bacteria, such as leprosy and neurosyphilis (see Chapter Two). In reality, all classical viral diseases do fulfill Koch's standards perfectly—yellow fever, measles, polio, chickenpox, herpes, hepatitis A and B, and flu, among others.

Gallo's these-postulates-are-too-old argument is repeated by English retrovirus hunter Robin Weiss and American CDC official Harold Jaffe: "...

what seems bizarre is that anyone should demand strict adherence to these un-reconstructed postulates 100 years after their proposition."[15] Weiss and Jaffe also forget to explain how logical rules could become outdated, and again proceed to misquote Koch and use misleading examples of disease-causing microbes supposedly failing the postulates.

Having persuaded himself to ignore the traditional rules of Robert Koch, Gallo joins with Luc Montagnier in substituting a previously unknown "postulate":

> That HIV is the cause of AIDS is by now firmly established. The evidence for causation includes the fact that HIV is a new pathogen, fulfilling the original postulate of "new disease, new agent."[16]

As far as we know, no one else has ever proposed or defended such a bizarre notion. Would its legal equivalent be "new crime, new criminal"? Its economic equivalent, "new purchase, new customer"? What could this statement even mean?

Gallo, of course, means a new *infectious* agent, preferably a retrovirus. He falsely assumes both AIDS and HIV are, in fact, new; even if this were true, it would have no significance. And he assumes AIDS must be contagious, caused not by a deficiency or a toxin but by a microbe. He has never explained how he knows this. In citing such an odd principle, Gallo stands nearly alone, for most modern virologists blithely abandon Koch without replacing him.

2. Virus models.

Scientists accepted the HIV-AIDS hypothesis so easily precisely because the notion of "slow viruses" had already been built over a period of decades. When confronted with the paradoxes of HIV, its defenders simply reach for their bag of virus hypotheses, pulling out on demand a mixture of invented or misinterpreted models. They usually cite viral precedents of three types.

The first comes from the supposed "slow viruses," which are used to justify the long latency period of HIV, but which also fall apart in light of the evidence.

Chronic viral infections comprise the second model. Herpes simplex virus, for example, can cause lesions even long after antibodies against the virus have been produced; using this model, HIV scientists justify both the latent period and antibody test in one breath. But herpes does produce symptoms upon first infecting the body, and antibodies do neutralize it. Herpes can only recur because it hides in certain nerve cells, waiting until some future opportunity when the host's immune function is temporarily reduced. Once the immune system regains strength, the virus is again suppressed and the sores disappear. HIV, on the other hand, is alleged to kill its host *only* years after being neutralized, and even *without* reactivating.

The third virus model has been created only since the appearance of AIDS. Some animal retroviruses will cause "AIDS" when injected into hosts of the appropriate species. Simian immunodeficiency virus (SIV), a monkey retrovirus, attracts most of the attention. But these animal diseases can only be called "AIDS" by stretching the definition to extremes. They do not include most of the human AIDS conditions such as Kaposi's sarcoma or dementia. Rather, the animal symptoms usually resemble the flu: the animals become sick within days or not at all, without long latent periods, some animals recover by raising an immune response and never suffer relapse, and those that die must be injected with large quantities of the virus while very young, before they have developed any immune system at all. In the wild, their cousins retain antibodies against SIV all their lives without ever becoming sick from the virus. These laboratory diseases are, in all respects, very traditional viral flu-like diseases, but HIV scientists betray their desperation by misnaming them "AIDS."

3. Evasion.

Lacking answers to Koch's postulates, and serious virus precedents, AIDS scientists resort to a variety of excuses. At first glance their responses appear to be genuine arguments, but, in reality, they artfully avoid specific issues altogether while sounding vaguely knowledgeable or authoritative. The standard evasions fall into four general categories: the arguments from unknowns, from speculation, from authority, and from irresponsibility.

The argument from unknowns makes the obvious point that scientists never know everything, and implies that the HIV-AIDS question is therefore somehow unimportant now, since it eventually will be resolved through more research. According to this argument, the issue is not *whether*, but *how*, HIV causes AIDS; paradoxes therefore merely prove that further research is needed and that scientific knowledge will consequently expand, not that the virus is itself in question. William Blattner and Robert Gallo of the National Cancer Institute joined with fellow retrovirologist Howard Temin in using typical arguments from unkowns:

> Biology is an experimental science, and new biological phenomena are continually being discovered... Thus, one cannot conclude that HIV-1 does or does not cause AIDS from Duesberg's "cardinal rules" of virology...
>
> Duesberg's descriptions of the properties of viruses is in error and provides no distinction between knowing the cause of a disease, that is, its etiology ["whether"], and understanding the pathogenesis of this disease ["how"]... There are many unanswered questions about the pathogenesis of AIDS, but they are not relevant to the conclusion that HIV causes AIDS.
>
> ... The CDC definition of AIDS has been revised several times as new knowledge has become available and will undoubtedly be revised again...
>
> It is true that there are two viruses that cause human AIDS, HIV-1 and HIV-2. The origin of these HIVs is an interesting scientific question that is not relevant to whether or not HIV causes AIDS.[17]

Likewise Robin Weiss and Harold Jaffe:

> It is unwise to conclude that because we do not understand the pathogenesis of HIV in molecular detail, it is therefore harmless... So Duesberg

is right to draw attention to our ignorance of *how* HIV causes disease, but he is wrong to claim that it does not.

… One need not harp upon molecular quibbles, important though these are for directing research to the prevention or amelioration of HIV infection. To deny the role of HIV in AIDS is deceptive.[18]

The guardians of HIV dogma never quite mention just which standards *could* prove the virus harmless. Until they suggest a scientific experiment that could disprove the HIV hypothesis, they convey the implicit message that they would accept no evidence at all.

The argument from speculation is used more often than any other. It uses specialized terms that make it difficult for outsiders to understand, and amounts to a "snow job." It responds to any paradox with pure speculation, adding one completely untested assumption after another. For instance, if little or no HIV can be found in the body, scientists propose hidden reservoirs and special routes of infection; if only antibodies against HIV can be found, researchers call them "non-neutralizing" (or ineffective) antibodies and assert that the virus mutates too fast for the antibodies to keep up; if the virus does not make animals sick or kill cells in culture, then researchers claim that the virus somehow makes fine distinctions between humans and chimpanzees, something no other virus can do. All of these hypotheses are constantly being disproved or shown to be irrelevant, but the reservoir of new evasions is everlastingly full.

The argument from authority cites the "overwhelming evidence" for HIV, without becoming too specific. In another form, it rebuffs inquisitive epidemiologists for lacking clinical experience while bypassing medical critics for having no epidemiological training. In other words, unless one is an expert in everything, one may not question anything. This response simply alludes to esoteric scientific data as reason for critics to remain silent. Blattner, Gallo, and Temin provide perfect examples: "In summary, although many questions remain about HIV and AIDS, a huge and continuously growing body of scientific evidence shows that HIV causes AIDS," and "Thus, we conclude that there is overwhelming evidence that HIV causes AIDS."[19]

The argument from irresponsibility serves as the answer of last resort. In the vein of a "better safe than sorry" warning, such HIV defenders as Weiss and Jaffe whip out the weapon of fear:

> … If he [Duesberg] and his supporters belittle 'safe sex', would have us abandon HIV screening of blood donations, and curtail research into anti-HIV drugs and vaccines, then their message is perilous.[20]

The irony, as will be reviewed later, lies in the danger of the officially approved measures to combat HIV, which are themselves costing lives.

4. Epidemiology.

The three basic arguments outlined above clearly answer no questions. The only positive evidence in favor of the virus-AIDS hypothesis is found in epidemiology, the study of disease epidemics. This field operates entirely by correlation: according to AIDS officials, where HIV goes, AIDS follows. Despite all the sophisticated biotechnology and vast investment in virology, the best evidence for HIV is only by correlation. Ironically, the point is made by retrovirologists Blattner, Gallo, and Temin: "The strongest evidence that HIV causes AIDS comes from prospective epidemiological studies that document the absolute requirement for HIV infection for the development of AIDS."[21] Or, as stated by Weiss and Jaffe, "The evidence that HIV causes AIDS is epidemiological and virological, not molecular."[22] Gallo again emphasizes the point in his book, declaring correlation to be "one hell of a good beginning."[23]

What sort of correlations seem so convincing to AIDS officials? The one usually cited first might be called the "geographic overlap." According to Blattner, Gallo, and Temin, "... epidemiological data show that AIDS and HIV infection are clustered in the same population groups and in specific geographic locations and in time. Numerous studies have shown that in countries with no persons with HIV antibodies there is no AIDS and in countries with many persons with HIV antibodies there is much AIDS. Additionally, the time of occurrence of AIDS in each country is correlated with the time of introduction of HIV into that country; first HIV is introduced, then AIDS appears."[24]

Second, a tighter association is recorded for individual people: every victim of AIDS has antibodies against HIV, whereas most healthy people do not. This apparently perfect correlation exists in official CDC records, as well as in selected surveys that follow people at risk for AIDS.

A third argument evokes powerful emotional sentiments without much substance, and works surprisingly well not only on the lay public, but on scientists as well. When challenged that only people with serious health risks develop AIDS, experts answer with anecdotes, even though the same medical officials will consider anecdotes a worthless type of evidence in any other debate. An anecdotal story is one individual case chosen to prove the absence of other health risks, implying HIV was the only factor that could have led to disease. So, for example, epidemiologists will describe a baby contracting HIV and subsequently developing AIDS. But in a nation of 250 million people, a few anecdotal cases can always be found to support *any* medical view.

Fourth, AIDS epidemiologists supposedly trounce the opposition by pointing to their prospective studies, in which the supposedly conclusive proof of the HIV hypothesis can be found. These studies monitor two groups of people over time, one of HIV positive patients and the other of HIV negative people in the same age group. According to such reports, the infected people develop AIDS while their uninfected counterparts do not.

These correlations have proven the most powerful arguments to scientists and laymen alike. Only a more complete picture can expose the misleading nature of this sloppy epidemiology.

The other statistics

In one strange sense, AIDS officials do refer to some genuine correlations between HIV and AIDS. The syndrome, for example, is never found in any nation or individual apart from HIV infection. Indeed, the virus and the syndrome correlate with textbook perfection, ironically illustrating the most fundamental problem with the entire virus-AIDS hypothesis—for the connection was artificially constructed.

AIDS is a syndrome, not a disease. It displays no unique combination of symptoms in the patient; clinically, it is identified by the diagnosis of specific diseases known to medical science for decades or centuries. The CDC has several times modified the official list of AIDS indicator diseases, most recently on January 1, 1993. The list now includes brain dementia, chronic diarrhea, such cancers as Kaposi's sarcoma and several lymphomas, and such opportunistic infections as *Pneumocystis carinii* pneumonia, cytomegalovirus infection, herpes, candidiasis (yeast infections), tuberculosis, and others—some thirty conditions altogether. Even low T cell counts in the blood can now be called AIDS, with or without real clinical symptoms. And cervical cancer has recently been added to the list, the first AIDS disease that can only affect one gender (in this case, women); the purpose behind adding this disease was entirely political, admittedly designed to increase the number of female AIDS patients[25]—which creates an illusion that the syndrome is "spreading" into the heterosexual population. Originally the AIDS diseases were tied together because they were all increasing within certain risk groups, but today they are assumed to derive from the common basis of immune deficiency. The overlap between AIDS and certain risk groups still holds true, but as we have pointed out, a number of these diseases are not products of weakened immune systems.

One might ask how a doctor would distinguish between an AIDS-related tuberculosis and a more traditional one. Clinically, the symptoms are identical, so the CDC has stipulated in its current definition that the tuberculosis must be renamed "AIDS" if antibodies against HIV are also found in the patient. In the absence of previous HIV infection, the disease is virtually always classified under its old name and treated accordingly. AIDS, therefore, can never be found apart from HIV infection—entirely by definition!

AIDS officials neglect to mention this crucial fact partly from ignorance, most never having read the definition carefully, and in some cases precisely because it shines a disturbing light onto their supposedly perfect epidemiological coincidence between the virus and AIDS. The observation that AIDS always follows HIV in each nation becomes trivial, since testing for antibodies is followed by a renaming of indigenous diseases.

The real epidemiological question, then, must be shifted away from any "correlation" between HIV and AIDS to a correlation between HIV and the separate AIDS-diagnostic diseases. Does infection with the virus, independently of any other health risks, lead to an increased risk of contracting pneumonia, cancer, or other diseases? Is HIV new, and found in all recent outbreaks of these diseases? Is HIV infection nearly always fatal?

The latter question can be answered most easily. Since the HIV test has been made available in 1985, the CDC has officially estimated about one million Americans to be HIV positive, a figure that has not changed with the accumulation of testing data or the passage of nine years. Of these, only about 315,000 had been diagnosed with AIDS by the middle of 1993, 121,000 of whom still lived. In other words, two-thirds of HIV-positive Americans have not developed any of the AIDS diseases since 1985 (even including the most recent expansion in the AIDS definition).

Nor will most of them do so. The numbers of new AIDS cases have clearly been levelling off for some time now, although different analysts will place the peak at different times. Michael Fumento, the Colorado-based lawyer who gained some media notoriety with his 1989 book, *The Myth of Heterosexual AIDS*, draws a curve with its peak in 1987; two epidemiologists, in a 1990 paper in the *Journal of the American Medical Association*, point to 1988 as the year of levelling.[26] In any case, a slowly increasing 40,000 to 50,000 new cases of AIDS—four to five percent of the infected subpopulation—have appeared in each of the last few years. The enormous gap between HIV-infected people and AIDS patients has goaded the CDC to play more tricks with the numbers; at the time of this writing, the CDC is considering *lowering* its official estimate of one million HIV-positive Americans, to a new total of 600,000 to 800,000.[27]

Part of the AIDS scare results from the way the numbers are reported. Rather than giving the numbers of new AIDS cases each year, CDC and other officials use the cumulative total for the current year added to the figures for all years previous, including those victims already dead. So where the annual numbers would remain constant in the first case, the number actually reported to the public grows with each passing year. Such calculation gives the overwhelming but false impression that AIDS is spreading, since the cumulative numbers can only go up. Given enough time, such accounting methods will boost the total AIDS count higher than the number of HIV-positive people. If this method were applied to count the American population, the cumulative number of newborns over several decades would eventually exceed the total number of Americans alive.

The commonly cited 50 to 100 percent death rate from HIV has been derived, not from national statistics, but from studies on carefully selected cohorts of people. Several ongoing epidemiological studies have for years been observing hundreds, or at most thousands, of homosexual men at high risk for AIDS. Large proportions of the men in these studies have already been infected with HIV. But virtually all the subjects also admit to years of heavy drug abuse, extremely promiscuous sexual activity, and long histories of venereal diseases. Indeed, one major study was specifically organized around homosexual men with repeated bouts of hepatitis B. Researchers calculate the high fatality rate of HIV infection from these health risk groups, casually extrapolating these numbers to average, heterosexual HIV-positives—thus the discrepancy with the higher survival rate among the nation's one million HIV positives.

The national AIDS figures fall well short of a virus with a nearly one-hundred percent fatality rate. But rather than abandon the hypothesis, the experts have chosen to revise the parameters of HIV infection. The latency period was originally calculated in 1981 on the basis of tracing sexual contacts, finding homosexual men developing AIDS an average of ten months after their last sexual contacts with other AIDS patients. This "incubation period" has since been stretched to a current ten to twelve years between HIV infection and disease. For each year that passes without the predicted explosion in AIDS cases, approximately one more year is added to this incubation time. Even this is insufficient; with only three percent of infected Americans developing AIDS each year, the average latent period would have to be revised up to some thirty-three years for all 100% to become sick. Faced with this gap, the CDC retroactively lowered the estimated number of infected people in late 1989, declaring that only three-quarters of a million people had been HIV positive in 1986. Given the numbers as they stand, the CDC will have to plan on a great deal more revision in the near future.

The increasing numbers of new AIDS cases until 1987 have largely been products of the artificial AIDS definitions. Each alteration in that definition has added, not subtracted, diseases to the diagnostic list. Every time the CDC needs higher rates of new AIDS cases, it expands that definition once again, and more diseases are reclassified into the syndrome.[28] With the stroke of a pen an illusion of the spread of AIDS is created, prominent officials explain the revisions as products of our growing scientific knowledge, and the lay public feels reassured that federal efforts are justified—or perhaps even a little too slow.

A deeper look at the disease risk of infected populations reveals stranger paradoxes yet. The probability of developing AIDS varies radically between different HIV-positive populations. Sub-Saharan Africa, with infection rates approaching thirty percent of the population in some areas, has only reported approximately 250,000 AIDS cases to the World Health Organization in the last decade. This stands against six to eight million Africans infected with HIV since the mid-1980s, whereas more Americans (now over 300,000) have contracted AIDS in a country with only one million HIV positives. AIDS patients in Zaire, with about three million HIV-infected people, number only in the hundreds; Uganda, internationally considered a model for accurate testing and reporting, had by 1990 only generated some 8,000 AIDS cases out of one million HIV positives. Roughly 360,000 infected Haitians have produced only a few hundred AIDS patients. In the industrial nations, homosexuals, heroin addicts, and hemophiliacs face greater probabilities of developing AIDS than do HIV-positive individuals without extraordinary health risks. And infants have a much shorter average latent period—two years, as opposed to the ten years in adults. No virus, including HIV, could possibly discriminate so enormously based on such subtle distinctions between its hosts.

HIV would need to perform other miracles to cause AIDS. Virtually all diagnoses of Kaposi's sarcoma are made in homosexuals, not in the other AIDS risk groups. Intravenous drug addicts disproportionately suffer from tuberculosis, Haitians from toxoplasmosis, and hemophiliacs from pneumonias. African AIDS diseases are basically different, manifesting as tuberculosis, fever, diarrhea, and a slim disease unlike our wasting syndrome. Thus a homosexual with HIV, who may develop Kaposi's sarcoma and yeast infections, can donate blood for a hemophiliac, who is more likely to develop pneumonia if he contracts anything at all; only HIV is common to both victims.

No virus could possibly make such distinctions between its hosts. A more likely hypothesis would blame the health risks specific to each group for their different diseases. If the same diseases can be found on the rise in the same risk groups, but also in people without HIV, then the virus would appear to be a harmless passenger.

The evidence bears this out. Hemophiliacs without HIV develop progressive immune degeneration just like the infected ones; HIV-negative babies of infected mothers develop the same dementia-related symptoms as their HIV-positive siblings; heroin addicts contract the same pneumonias, herpes infections, weight loss, and tuberculosis with or without the virus; and uninfected homosexuals with Kaposi's sarcoma are now being reported. Outbreaks of pneumonias or tuberculosis in recent years have included as many people without the virus as those with it. Thousands of central Africans with "slim disease" have now been tested for HIV, and over half are completely negative; given the relatively high cost of HIV antibody tests, most African cases must be diagnosed by symptoms and remain untested for the virus.[29] In the industrial world, upwards of one-quarter of all AIDS patients remain untested for the antibodies against HIV, with their doctors merely assuming the virus is present. We have already found, in the existing scientific literature, over 4,800 cases of AIDS-defining conditions in people never infected by HIV. With various AIDS-type diseases increasing in the risk groups even apart from HIV, the virus appears ever less relevant.

HIV even violates Gallo's postulate of "new disease, new agent." A virus newly introduced into a human or animal population spreads exponentially, until it achieves saturation of some part of that population. This pattern, observed repeatedly for all infectious diseases, has been known as "Farr's Law" since the 19th century. A new, sexually transmitted virus therefore spreads rapidly among sexually active people, slowing once the remaining uninfected people are only those too sexually inactive to pick up the virus from a newly infected host.

If HIV were truly a new virus, spread mostly by sexual activity, it should also be infecting new victims at an exponential rate. But the CDC estimates show the number of HIV-positive Americans holding at a constant one million during the eight years since the HIV test became available. The well-publicized "explosion" of the virus in various countries turns out to have been an explosion of HIV testing; the actual estimates of HIV infection have remained constant throughout the world since the test has been available. The virus is therefore quite old, having stopped spreading probably long before the 1980s, and thus fails as Gallo's "new agent."

The evidence further argues for HIV as a long-existing virus: for the most part, HIV is not spread sexually. After neutralizing the virus with the immune reponse, an HIV-positive person requires an average of one thousand unprotected sexual contacts to pass along this virus just once, as discovered by testing the wives of HIV-infected hemophiliacs.[30] A pregnant mother is a different story; in effect, she provides her child with a nine-month continuous exposure to her blood, and therefore has at least a fifty percent chance of passing HIV to the baby. HIV, as with any retrovirus, survives by reaching new hosts perinatally (mother to child), this being 500 times more efficient than by sexual transmission.

This would explain why the numbers of HIV-positive people, in America as well as Africa, have remained so constant; HIV is much older than usually supposed. This also reveals the reason for the virus being so widespread and equal between the sexes in Africa—HIV has been passed along from mother to child for many centuries, not through heterosexual sex as commonly assumed. In the industrial world, HIV can be transmitted differently only among the most sexually active homosexuals, among needle-sharing heroin addicts, and through blood transfusions to hemophiliacs, the routes that so easily transmit numerous other microbes. In short, the very people with tremendous health risks *also* more easily pass around HIV, making it a surrogate marker for the real causes of AIDS. A rough correlation between HIV and AIDS diseases therefore exists, but is imperfect.

Any virus, including HIV, that is passed along perinatally cannot possibly be deadly, for it would have killed off its hosts long ago and disappeared with them; pregnant mothers actively infected by a truly harmful virus often face miscarriages or children with deformities. Thus not only is HIV old while the AIDS epidemic is new, but the virus depends for its own survival on not being deadly, because it is passed along maternally in the great majority of cases.

All circumstantial evidence aside, the ultimate epidemiological test for HIV would be a case-controlled comparison. In such a study, a large number of infected people would be monitored over time, and compared with a large number of uninfected people *with precisely the same health risks*. They would not only be matched for age, sex, and income, but for levels of drug use, degree of hemophilia, and other medical complications. If HIV were truly harmful, the infected group would develop much more disease than the uninfected. Honest scientists would conduct this type of study even before testing Koch's postulates, but for HIV as an AIDS virus neither test has yet materialized. Only a few small studies like this have been published, examining fewer than 20 hemophiliacs in each, *and all report no difference in health between those with and those without HIV*.[31]

Defenders of the HIV hypothesis, desperate when confronted with the whole of the evidence against them, will sometimes dishonestly cite studies comparing groups with and without the virus, to show that only those infected will degenerate and die. But none of the vast number of such prospective studies has actually matched two groups for the health risks that might cause

AIDS. They have been designed merely to compare the symptoms of AIDS patients with normal people in the same age group, not to determine the cause of the syndrome. The studies themselves are not dishonest, but are deceptively quoted by some researchers.

No AIDS virus at all

Given that HIV fails all standards of scientific evidence as an "AIDS virus," could another, possibly unidentified, virus cause AIDS instead? Such a microbe would have to possess amazing qualities beyond those ever known, for AIDS does not behave as a contagious disease at all.

The sexual revolution of the last twenty years has caused increases in all the major venereal diseases, including syphilis, gonorrhea, chlamydia, and genital warts. The same has occurred with hepatitis B. All of these infectious diseases have spread far beyond their original reservoirs into the general population, and affect men and women nearly equally.

AIDS, however, has remained absolutely fixed in its original risk groups. Today, a full decade after it first appeared, the syndrome is diagnosed in homosexuals, intravenous drug users, and hemophiliacs some 95 percent of the time, just as ten years ago. Nine out of every ten AIDS patients are male, also just as before. Even the very existence of a "latent period" strongly suggests that years of health abuse are required for such fatal conditions. Among most AIDS patients in the U.S. and Europe, one extremely common health risk has been identified: the long-term use of hard drugs (the evidence for this new AIDS hypothesis will be presented in Chapter Eight). AIDS is not contagious, nor is it even a single epidemic.

Tragic deaths, time and money wasted, hysterical public debate over a harmless virus—these have been the fruits borne of a scientific establishment grown too large for genuine science. The creative pursuit of knowledge has been swallowed to satisfy careerism and its voracious appetite for job security, grant money, financial benefits, and prestige. But the monster is twice guilty, for it also destroys or marginalizes those few scientists daring to ask questions. These dissidents against the HIV hypothesis are the subject of the next chapter.

Chapter 6 Footnotes

[1] Projections show rising worldwide AIDS toll. *American Medical News*, May 8, 1987, p. 40, as cited in McNamee and McNamee, *AIDS: The Nation's First Politically Protected Disease*. National Medical Legal Publishing House, La Habra, CA, 1988, pp. 6-7.

[2] Groopman, *et al.*, HTLV-III in saliva of people with AIDS-related complex and healthy homosexual men at risk for AIDS. *Science*, Oct. 24, 1984, pp. 447-449, as cited in McNamee and McNamee, Op cit., pp. 75-76; CDC announcement, Jan. 11, 1985, as quoted in Antonio, *The AIDS Cover-up?* Ignatius Press, San Francisco, CA, 19486, p. 108.

[3] Antonio, Op cit., pp. 109-115; see also McNamee and McNamee, Op cit., pp. 73-75.

[4] Antonio, Op cit., pp. 105-107; McNamee and McNamee, Op cit., pp. 83-87.

[5] Humphrey (ed)., *America Living With AIDS*. National Commission on AIDS, 1991, p. 13.

[6] Ibid., p. 2.

[7] Ibid., p. 4.

[8] Slaff and Brubaker, *The AIDS Epidemic*, Warner Books, New York, 1985, pp. 162-163, as quoted in Antonio, Op cit., p. 138.

[9] Antonio, Op cit., p. 189.

[10] Dingell, *AIDS Prevention Act of 1990*. Report of the House Committee on Energy and Commerce, May 31, 1990, p. 91.

[11] Piatak, *et al.*, High levels of HIV-1 in plasma during all stages of infection determined by competitive PCR. *Science* 259:1749-1754, 1993.

[12] Duesberg, Human immunodeficiency virus and acquired immunodeficiency syndrome: Correlation but not causation. *Proc. Nat. Acad. Sci.* 86:755-764, 1989.

[13] Aoun, When a house officer gets AIDS. *New England Journal of Medicine* 321:693-6, 1989.

[14] Gallo, *Virus Hunting — AIDS, Cancer, & the Human Retrovirus: a Story of Human Discovery*. Basic Books, New York, 1991, p. 277.

[15] Weiss and Jaffe, Duesberg, HIV and AIDS. *Nature* 345:659-60, 1990.

[16] Gallo and Montagnier, AIDS in 1988. *Scientific American* 259:40-48, 1988 (p. 44).

[17] Blattner, Gallo, and Temin, HIV causes AIDS. *Science* 241:515-16, 1988.

[18] Weiss and Jaffe, Op cit.

[19] Blattner, Gallo, and Temin, Op cit.

[20] Weiss and Jaffe, Op cit.

[21] Blattner, Gallo, and Temin, Op cit.

[22] Weiss and Jaffe, Op cit.

[23] Gallo, *Virus Hunting*, Op cit., p. 292.

[24] Blattner, Gallo, and Temin, Op cit.

[25] Stolberg, AIDS tally to increase due to new definition. *Los Angeles Times*, Dec. 31, 1992, pp. A3, A29.

[26] Fumento, *The Myth of Heterosexual AIDS*. Basic Books, New York, 1989; Bregman and Langmuir, Farr's Law Applied to AIDS Projections. *Journal of the American Medical Association* 263:1522-5, 1990.

[27] Altman, Obstacle-strewn road to rethinking the numbers on AIDS. *New York Times*, March 1, 1994, p. C3.

28 See, for example, Stolberg, Op cit.

29 For the various examples of HIV-free AIDS, see Duesberg, AIDS acquired by drug consumption and other noncontagious risk factors. *Pharmacology & Therapeutics* 55:201-277, 1992; see also Duesberg, The HIV gap in national AIDS statistics. *Bio/Technology* 11:955-956.

30 Duesberg, AIDS acquired by drug consumption and other noncontagious risk factors, Op cit., p. 223.

31 Ibid., p. 217.

Chapter 7

Dissension in the Ranks

In its self-ordained mission to coordinate the War on AIDS, the Centers for Disease Control used its full resources to popularize AIDS as a single, infectious, terrifying plague. But the agency hardly succeeded in monopolizing interest in the epidemic. Other doctors also took notice of the rising numbers of young homosexual men dying of infections and conditions uncommon for their age group. From the time the CDC advertised its first AIDS cases, the apparently new syndrome invited speculation on its cause.

Those medical professionals who bought the CDC's party line scrambled to find an infectious agent. Michael Gottlieb, the first doctor to report AIDS cases, led a number of virus hunters in suggesting cytomegalovirus. Other well-known viruses, including Epstein-Barr, received growing attention. The retrovirus hunters found themselves torn between Gallo's HTLV-I and the search for a new virus. Still other researchers began thinking of bacteria, or even new combinations of several old microbes all causing AIDS together.

The search for the cause of AIDS officially ended with Gallo's 1984 press conference. No American scientist had yet published a single paper on HIV, but most scientists understood the politics and quickly fell into line. Doubts about this virus were relegated to quiet conversations, especially among those researchers whose careers most directly depended on the NIH-CDC medical establishment. Most physicians never even heard any reason to question the official doctrine, and easily bought into it.

For a few people, however, the press conference settled nothing. Doctors who knew something about the methods of scientific research, and who felt a bit more independent of the federal government, continued to raise questions. If anything, the rush to blame HIV for such a complex and varied syndrome, one that struck people with so many obvious health risk factors, seemed simple-minded at best. By throwing its weight behind HIV, the AIDS establishment unwittingly fed some of the alternative thinking it sought to end.

The early days

Joseph Sonnabend became one of the very first to break ranks. Having received a medical degree in his native South Africa, he found his way into basic research upon moving to Great Britain in the late 1950s. There he joined the revived microbe hunting trend, albeit more from the angle of medical treatment, and began studying the body's immune response against viruses. He focused on interferon, a newly discovered protein that seemed to slow virus infections. Scientists have always placed great hopes in this substance, expecting it to serve as their long-sought magic bullet against viruses and cancer. Both of these dreams have died, but scientists are now trying to revive it for use against multiple sclerosis.

The 1970s brought Sonnabend a temporary chance to conduct his research on interferon and viruses at a medical school in New York. After the money ran out, he was forced to practice medicine at a public hospital in Brooklyn. He supplemented his income by working for the city's Department of Health, where in 1978 he briefly became director of the venereal diseases division. In this capacity he encountered many of the "fast track" homosexuals who constantly needed treatment for their recurring diseases.

Later that year Sonnabend lost both positions. Although he preferred laboratory microbiology, he had little choice but to continue medicine. As a compromise, he decided to continue working on infectious diseases by starting his own private practice in Greenwich Village, New York, treating homosexual men for their venereal diseases. By the early 1980s Sonnabend began seeing AIDS cases, just as similar patients were showing up at the UCLA Medical Center on the opposite coast. He recognized the descriptions in Gottlieb's 1981 report of five such men, and immediately conducted research to find the cause. Having seen rising frequencies of venereal disease among homosexual men for years, Sonnabend instinctively reached for the most familiar explanation—that somehow the combination of all these conventional microbial infections caused immune suppression and AIDS.

He went public with his hypothesis by 1982, publishing reports that men with immune deficiencies also had long histories of venereal disease, hepatitis, and even infections by obscure parasites. Meanwhile he started treating his AIDS cases by using antibiotics and other medications directed against the opportunistic infections themselves, including *Pneumocystis carinii* pneumonia. But his views attracted little attention until a publisher suddenly provided Sonnabend the funding to create a scientific journal of his own. *AIDS Research* was thus launched, and the first twelve pages of the first issue, published in 1983, contained a review written by Sonnabend himself. Entitled "The Etiology of AIDS," the article officially proposed what he called the "multifactorial model" of causation. According to this notion, many different infections could have a combined effect that eventually destroys the immune system. He also hypothesized that semen itself—coming in contact with blood when rectal tissues were torn during anal intercourse—might cause immune suppression. Sonnabend opened his review by attacking the Centers for Disease Control viewpoint that AIDS was caused by some new virus, pointing out that no such virus had yet been isolated. Then he turned to his own idea:

> The first issue of this new journal is an appropriate occasion to review an alternative hypothesis regarding the genesis of AIDS. This hypothesis proposes that there is no specific etiologic agent of AIDS, and suggests that the disease arises as a result of a cumulative process following a period of exposure to multiple environmental factors...
>
> Among homosexual men, it appears that the disease has been occurring in a rather small subset characterized by having had sexual contact with large numbers of different partners... Such conditions were met in New

York City, San Francisco and Los Angeles in the 1970's as a result of changes in lifestyle that became apparent in the late 1960's.

The specific factors we propose that interact to produce the disease in homosexual men are: (1) immune responses to semen; (2) repeated infections with cytomegalovirus (CMV); (3) episodes of reactivation of Epstein-Barr virus (EBV); and (4) infection with sexually transmitted pathogens, particularly those associated with immune complex formation such as hepatitis B and syphilis.[1]

In explaining AIDS in Haiti or Africa, Sonnabend argued their diseases might not be new at all, and could reflect such factors as "poverty and malnutrition, some tropical infections," while in the case of blood transfusion recipients "It is well known that blood transfusions are themselves immunosuppressive." In any case, he criticized the CDC assumption of a new AIDS virus in no uncertain terms, specifically taking on their cluster study as not being proof AIDS was a single infectious disease: "That AIDS results from infection with a specific etiologic agent remains a hypothesis... An alternative explanation is that the cases occurred in a relatively small subset of homosexual men who shared a similar lifestyle."

He accurately tore apart the assumptions of the virus-hunting establishment, exposing the lack of evidence for AIDS as a single, contagious disease. But his multifactorial hypothesis completely ignored the drug abuse factor in most AIDS patients. Those homosexuals at greatest risk for the syndrome, who had long records of infectious disease, also had used enormous quantities of recreational drugs, especially the alkyl nitrites. Sonnabend tended to overlook drugs as a risk factor, largely because of his virology background and his experience treating venereal diseases. He forgot that infectious diseases do not affect everyone equally; probably no germ on earth, from the most common flu virus to the deadly cholera bacterium, causes disease in every infected individual. Only those people whose resistance is lowered for some reason—even a temporary immune deficiency from lack of sleep or other causes—become ill; a healthy person's immune system efficiently suppresses microbes and prevents symptoms, regardless of the number of infections. Multiple contagious diseases, therefore, could not *cause* immune suppression in a person, but must rather be the *result* of immune deficiencies for other reasons. Even semen, particularly in the minute quantities that could contact blood in anal intercourse, could not have an irreversible effect on the immune system.

Sonnabend continued making his argument. Soon after launching *AIDS Research* he published a similar review paper in the prestigious *Journal of the American Medical Association*, co-authored with his colleagues and close collaborators, Steven Witkin and David Purtilo. As he stepped up the debate, Sonnabend found himself increasingly crossing paths with Robert Gallo. The two simply did not get along. To counter Gallo's early hypothesis that HTLV-I was the "AIDS virus," Sonnabend tested seventy patients and reported that none of them had antibodies against the virus. He shortly thereafter published a letter to the editor of *Nature* in 1984, following Gallo's press conference announcing "HTLV-III" as the cause, stating that since

HTLV-I, -II, and now -III could each be isolated from some AIDS patients, this "suggests that they are more likely to represent opportunistic infections or reactivations from latency."[2]

He made the same point in a 1985 letter published in the *Wall Street Journal*, suggesting that HIV might only be a harmless, opportunistic virus found in some people after their immune systems had already been destroyed. He also acknowledged "the possible role of drugs in the causation of AIDS," an unusual departure from his multifactorial hypothesis.[3] As late as 1988, while he was working on a chapter for a medical textbook, Sonnabend wrote to Peter Duesberg describing the effects of growing political pressure to swallow the HIV hypothesis: "I just spoke to David Purtilo who does not wish to be on the update—unless a role for HIV can be put in. Steve Witkin also wants a role for HIV, so I'll do it alone."[4] By the time the textbook finally appeared, Sonnabend's longtime collaborators had removed their names.

But eventually even Sonnabend succumbed to the pressure. He had, after all, always occupied a strange but comfortable position within the medical establishment. Dating back years before AIDS appeared, his career had benefited enormously from his connections to the inner circles of power. His research collaborations, his funding, and his influence all came from prominent contacts in the National Institutes of Health (NIH), the Centers for Disease Control (CDC), the Food and Drug Administration (FDA), universities and private foundations, and even political circles.

His prestige had been such that James Curran, head of the CDC's KSOI Task Force that scoured for evidence to prove AIDS an infectious disease, personally consulted with Sonnabend in 1981. Sonnabend takes credit for devising the notion of "safe sex," the use of condoms supposedly to prevent transmission of AIDS or the venereal diseases he believes cause it, which has become wildly popular with public health authorities as their mainstay of AIDS prevention. When a press conference was organized in February of 1985 to announce that Gallo's isolate of HIV was suspiciously identical to that of Montagnier, Sonnabend was the man chosen to make the presentation. The FDA used Sonnabend's unorthodox clinical trial to approve the aerosolized drug pentamidine for treatment of *Pneumocystis* pneumonia, and to set precedent for future licensing (he had dispensed with the time-honored testing rules of double-blind controls and placebos).

His most powerful connection has been Mathilde Krim, a colleague who also studied interferon's effects on virus infection. Krim was more than just another scientist; her husband, a Hollywood veteran who founded Orion Pictures, had also been chairman in charge of finances for the national Democratic Party and therefore a consultant to several presidents. Mathilde herself had been one of the powerful individuals selected for the Senate's Panel of Consultants in 1970, which advised Richard Nixon to launch the War on Cancer. Krim had long befriended Sonnabend, and when he began running out of money to continue his AIDS research in 1982, she stepped in. She organized the American Medical Foundation (AMF) to finance his work, and her clout brought onto the board several important scientists, as well as former president Jimmy Carter's wife Rosalynn. So much money flowed into the foundation that other scientists offered to collaborate with Sonnabend in order to benefit.

Although Sonnabend sometimes enjoyed forays into unfashionable areas of medical research, he clearly stood to lose much by straying too far from the official line. By continuing to question the HIV hypothesis, he unwittingly did precisely that. In 1985, one year after Gallo's press conference, the axe began to fall. The publisher who had financed his journal, *AIDS Research*, suddenly replaced Sonnabend with Dani Bolognesi, a retrovirologist at Duke University. Bolognesi was one of Gallo's closest allies, a member of the informal "Bob Club" and therefore a partisan for the HIV hypothesis. As the new editor, Bolognesi dumped Sonnabend and his supporters, bringing on board his own retrovirus-hunting friends Max Essex and Robert Gallo. The journal's new title became *AIDS Research and Human Retroviruses*, and thereafter it only published papers founded on the HIV hypothesis. Its days of open inquiry were over.

Meanwhile Mathilde Krim was reorganizing the AMF, negotiating a merger with a more glamorous and better-funded foundation under Michael Gottlieb, the scientist who reported the first five AIDS cases. Gottlieb objected to any doubts about HIV, and Krim ejected Sonnabend from the foundation and its support. Sonnabend found himself isolated, having learned a bitter lesson about challenging a view so cherished by the medical powers-that-be.

At this point Krim stepped in again, playing good cop to Gottlieb's bad cop. She helped Sonnabend establish a new organization for sponsoring research on AIDS treatments, the Community Research Initiative. After more than a year of set-up, the group began receiving funds. Sonnabend's criticisms of the HIV hypothesis gradually became muted or were relegated to obscure newsletters. By 1989 he had sufficiently won his way back into good graces that Krim arranged a public meeting at Columbia University with NIH officials. At the luncheon table, Sonnabend was seated between Sam Broder, Gallo's boss and head of the National Cancer Institute, and Anthony Fauci, director of the National Institute of Allergy and Infectious Disease. Both were power brokers of the AIDS establishment, to whom Sonnabend had finally become acceptable.

The sanctions have taken their toll. In 1992, when an interviewer asked, "What if HIV doesn't cause the disease?", Sonnabend responded, "Well, I have reluctance in speaking about this, too, because I am a great believer that safer sexual practices are important and that needle sharing is not a good idea."[5] He continued to evade the interviewer's questions about Peter Duesberg, finally declaring bluntly, "There are good reasons why HIV is a respectable candidate. For Duesberg to say that HIV cannot be the cause would mean that he wouldn't want any research to be done on HIV, and that's kind of ridiculous, too. I'll go to great lengths to make sure that I am not confused with Peter Duesberg."[6]

Indeed he does. He joined Duesberg and other dissidents at a May, 1992, meeting of HIV critics in Amsterdam, Holland. On the final day of the conference, Sonnabend stunned the participants by issuing a press release attacking Duesberg, on official symposium stationery. The man who once argued AIDS was not infectious now lashed out at Duesberg for saying the same thing, and insisted that "his outrageous assertion that safe sex is irrelevant to the spread of AIDS is appalling and may kill people."[7] He even managed to get a few participants to co-sign the release. But AIDS dissident John Lauritsen rallied most of the others at the meeting to Duesberg's defense, issuing their own contrary press release. Some of Sonnabend's co-signers switched sides or publicly apologized. Sonnabend himself was seen by witnesses privately apologizing to Duesberg, although he officially denied it later in print.[8] His public attack may have primarily resulted from worries about attending the meeting in the first place.

Even Sonnabend's private medical practice has been changed. Originally he had been widely known for his vocal opposition to the toxic chemotherapy AZT as AIDS treatment. A 1988 article quoted him as declaring "AZT is incompatible with life," and he refused to prescribe the drug to his own AIDS patients.[9] But the pressures have since changed his mind. He now admits to giving his patients AZT when they request it, and no longer lobbies against it.

He has shifted course so radically that his old nemesis, Robert Gallo, recently invited him to speak at the NIH. Sonnabend accepted, and his talk on interferon was well received by the believers in HIV. But of his old friend Duesberg, Sonnabend could only comment to an interviewer that "on balance I think [Duesberg's] been bad" for the debate over the virus-AIDS hypothesis.[10] Especially for those trying to reconcile with Gallo.

His research group has been reorganized as the New York-based Community Research Initiative on AIDS (CRIA), where he conducts research on AIDS treatments and maintains a relatively low profile on the HIV controversy.

At the same time that Sonnabend was first struggling against the growing AIDS virus hunt, another rebel was emerging nearby in New York City—John Lauritsen. Several years later, he would be described as "one of the heroes of the epidemic" by another medical dissident against HIV. "He is not only a top-notch investigative reporter. In his own way he is also a scientist."[11]

Lauritsen has worked in the survey research field since the mid-1960s, where he performed tasks as a market research executive and analyst. Professional survey research, he explains, maintains much higher professional standards than does its academic sister, epidemiology; questionnaires require careful designing, data must be rigorously checked after it is gathered, tables must show all data clearly and completely, and statistics are analyzed critically. He had also co-authored *The Early Homosexual Rights Movement (1864-1935)* and edited an anthology of writings by John Addington Symonds. Lauritsen the scientist and Lauritsen the journalist were both products of an A.B. degree from Harvard's Department of Social Relations.

He first got involved in AIDS after he learned of Sonnabend's work. His attention was focused on the syndrome in 1983, when he decided to spend a week in the library of the New York Academy of Medicine, reviewing for himself the still small scientific literature on AIDS. The evidence quickly fell into place, strongly suggesting that AIDS was not an infectious disease. Lauritsen certainly had the savvy to interpret the data; his medical logic had been shaped by an uncle who taught public health, and by his athletic father, who involved his family in sports-related activities. He now suspected that some lifestyle environmental factor was killing people, not a microbe.

Shortly thereafter, he stumbled across an article describing Hank Wilson, a well-known homosexual rights activist in San Francisco. Wilson was waging a one-man crusade against the use of "poppers," the nitrite compounds inhaled almost entirely by "fast track" male homosexuals as bathhouse aphrodisiacs and muscle relaxants. The volatile drugs made anal intercourse easier by relaxing the anal sphincter, but also had toxic effects on the blood and other parts of the body. Wilson had taken up this cause after friends who used poppers heavily began suffering swollen lymph nodes, which had led him to research the chemical nature of the nitrites. He founded the Committee to Monitor Poppers in 1981, warning homosexuals of the dangers and lobbying for legal bans on the substance.

Lauritsen began corresponding with him, and soon concluded that poppers and other recreational drugs being used in the bathhouses played some role in AIDS and other sickness. As a member of the New York Safer Sex Committee, Lauritsen began circulating warnings about poppers, prompting the group to include the following ending in a 1984 brochure: "Avoid drugs. Shooting up kills. Uppers and downers put a real strain on your system. Pot and alcohol confuse your judgment. Poppers are also dangerous."[12] But the advice fell on deaf ears. No one wanted to give up the popular drug. He then turned to Wilson, and the two of them began organizing a small but nationwide educational campaign that helped push Congress into outlawing poppers a few years later. By February of 1985, Lauritsen was able to publish his first article on AIDS, exposing the CDC's statistical tricks in hiding the association between poppers and the syndrome (as the CDC had been doing since the first reported AIDS cases, part of its campaign to paint AIDS as infectious). The piece appeared in the *Philadelphia Gay News*. As he soon discovered, the widespread hostility to his message meant that he could only publish in the homosexual press, and then only in a small subset of that.

Lauritsen found a journalistic niche freelancing for the *New York Native*, self-billed as the largest independent homosexual-interest weekly in the country. Independent it certainly was. Its publisher and editor, Charles Ortleb, had infuriated the CDC and other public health and medical officials when he switched from promoting AIDS as an epidemic to probing virtually any alternative explanation of its cause, no matter how bizarre. Whether he was promoting the mythical African Swine Fever Virus or a hidden strain of syphilis as causes of AIDS, Ortleb knew he could not believe in the HIV hypothesis. Lauritsen provided him with properly credentialed reporting, and in exchange

Lauritsen wrote about his own drug-AIDS hypothesis alongside the unfolding story of the HIV debate.

By 1986 Lauritsen had left full-time survey research to allow himself to focus on AIDS. That year he and Hank Wilson produced a small self-published book, *Death Rush: Poppers & AIDS*. In it he made his complete case for the role of poppers and other drugs in causing AIDS, impressively documented with the dozens of scientific papers on the subject. He also thoroughly exposed the conflicting interests of homosexual publications and academia in their ties to the poppers industry. And he even included two pages citing Koch's postulates to argue against HIV as the cause of AIDS.

His articles continued to reflect his own research. In March of 1987, for example, he wrote a devastating attack on a National Academy of Sciences report, pointing to their own admission that HIV is neutralized by antibodies as evidence against the virus hypothesis. But two months after his article was published, he read Peter Duesberg's original *Cancer Research* article. To Lauritsen, it was a stunning confirmation of everything he had suspected. As he later told Bryan Ellison (one of the authors of this book), "I had never heard of such concepts as 'biochemical activity,' and it clicked. I no longer had any doubt that HIV was not the cause."[13]

The following June an article by Chuck Ortleb appeared in the *Native*, excitedly reviewing Duesberg's paper. Ortleb tracked Duesberg down, finding him near the end of his stint at the NIH. Lauritsen immediately caught a train to Bethesda, becoming the first journalist to interview Duesberg. They spent several hours talking, everything faithfully recorded on Lauritsen's tape machine.

In preparing for the interview, Lauritsen had phoned the CDC and NIH to pester officials with questions about HIV. Confronting the National Cancer Institute's press officer, he pressed for the definitive proof that the virus caused AIDS. She was unable to answer and deferred until the following day, returning the call to read off a hastily prepared response. Nothing she said directly answered Duesberg's arguments, so Lauritsen raised the obvious issue of Koch's postulates. Her reply serves as the perfect picture of modern virus hunting:

> What are those? I've never heard of them. How do you spell that? Kock? What did you say? Koch? When were those made? [Lauritsen: About a century ago.] Oh, well then, would you say that those apply now?[14]

The approval of AZT as AIDS therapy pushed him to take on a new fight. He read the evidence, and concluded that such a toxic chemotherapy could do nothing but worsen an AIDS condition, since the drug destroyed the immune system. His investigation led him through a maze of sloppy scientific papers, federal bureaucracy in trying to release documents under the Freedom of Information Act, and uncooperative researchers. A critical letter to the editor of the *New England Journal of Medicine*, which had published the original AZT trials in humans, yielded Lauritsen nothing but a private response that dodged his facts and airily declared, "I don't know of any noteworthy clinical investigator in the AIDS field who takes your position."[15] Fed up with the closed doors and establishment arrogance, Lauritsen wrote several articles on AZT for the *Native* and compiled his information into another book, *Poison by Prescription: The AZT Story*, self-published in 1990. The book remains the most comprehensive critique of AZT available today.

He and Sonnabend do not always see eye-to-eye. Where Sonnabend was compromised through his ties to the medical establishment, Lauritsen has kept himself independent. Both have faced discouraging hostility from all sides, but Lauritsen accepts this as the price for intellectual honesty. And unlike Sonnabend, Lauritsen maintains his uncompromising stand on the drug-AIDS hypothesis and against AZT.

Still, he cannot feign perpetual optimism. He has just self-published another book, *The AIDS War: Propaganda, Profiteering, and Genocide from the Medical-Industrial Complex*. The angry tone reflects his years of struggle. A mix of new material and previously published articles, its 480 pages cover topics ranging from AZT to the death of ballet superstar Rudolf Nureyev from AIDS. Most of his first interview with Duesberg is printed, along with exposures of the cozy relationships between AIDS organizations and the pharmaceutical industry. Portions even discuss a "program of recovery" from AIDS, focusing on the health risks Lauritsen implicates in causing the syndrome. Mostly the book is a personal story, documenting the fight against HIV as seen by someone on the front lines.

Alternative views

In the wake of challenges against the HIV hypothesis by Sonnabend, Lauritsen, and Duesberg, other medical doctors and scientists gradually began joining the chorus of opposition. Some were encouraged to find their open doubts shared by prestigious figures, others had previously felt intimidated in speaking out alone, and a few simply had never given thought to possibilities other than HIV. Not all of these people volunteered their own alternative hypotheses, but all were united in questioning the HIV monopoly in AIDS research and treatment.

For those who did propose alternative causes, the temptation lay in imitating Sonnabend's mulitfactorial model. AIDS patients not only carried a multitude of opportunistic diseases, but also engaged in extremely promiscuous sexual activity or needle-sharing, behaviors that gave the patients long histories of venereal and parasitic infections. Thus a researcher could easily blame any of those microbes for AIDS, purely on the basis of a heavy overlap between almost any germ and the syndrome. Some, like Sonnabend, chose to blame many or all of the microbes simultaneously, creating a cumbersome and largely untestable notion of AIDS as the consequence of some undefinable combination of diverse germs. Others preferred to implicate one or two specific microbes, sometimes as "cofactors" with HIV; according to this view, AIDS was still a truly contagious disease for which the wrong microbe had been identified.

For a few years, syphilis became the most popular alternative hypothesis. Some superficial associations made this idea seem plausible. The syphilis bacterium, for one thing, had the old reputation as the "Great Masquerader," supposedly being able to imitate symptoms of diverse and unrelated diseases. Neurosyphilis—brain rot—had achieved legendary proportions in this regard, and seemed to parallel the symptoms of AIDS dementia. The standard test for syphilis infection, moreover, turned out to be less reliable than previously thought, generating false negative results in people who had been infected. Improved testing revealed high percentages of AIDS patients with prior syphilis. And common wisdom held that AIDS could not be a clearer example of a sexually transmitted disease, just like syphilis.

On the other hand, a hard look at AIDS quickly dispels any connection between the two. Neurosyphilis, as we discussed previously, most probably never really had anything to do with syphilis (see Chapter Two). It never appeared during the original syphilis infection, instead manifesting only after the common treatments of the day—mercury, antimony, and arsenic (Mozart is said to have been one person so treated until his early death). Poisoning has often been blamed for late-stage "syphilis" symptoms, including the many conditions that earned syphilis its image as a masquerader. Indeed, carefully monitored syphilitics have proven to have normal lifespans in the absence of toxic treatment. Exotic symptoms aside, syphilis behaves no differently from any other microbe, in that the disease itself results from, not causes, immune deficiency; as we have noted, healthy immune systems easily suppress any microbe and prevent sickness. Even the syphilis bacterium can do little damage in an otherwise healthy person. This microbe, further, has no latent period between infection and disease, which contrasts the years required for AIDS to develop. Finally, AIDS is not a contagious disease, as evidenced by its tight restriction to risk groups.

The syphilis school of AIDS started in the United States with Joan McKenna. Based in Berkeley, California, she personifies the town's colorful reputation for strange varieties of alternative healing. She is not licensed to practice medicine, but she does advise clients through her Institute for Thermobaric Studies on diet and lifestyle, many of them AIDS patients. Upon hearing in 1981 about the new syndrome, she decided the official search for a new virus had to be misguided. As she put it in a 1987 interview, "We've known for a long time that the gay community is subject to a lot of chronic inflammatory conditions. And that they use a lot of drugs which are immunosuppressive."[16] Without knowing what the cause of AIDS might be, she began recommending changes in diet and drug-taking habits for her patients.

Not until 1984 did McKenna make a connection between AIDS and syphilis, based on reading scientific literature and finding supposed parallels between symptoms. Though still admitting that, with AIDS, "we're looking at multiple assaults of disease and drugs—not one cause with one effect," she increasingly turned her attention toward syphilis.[17] She corresponded and traveled around the United States and even Europe to contact physicians who also suspected a link between AIDS and classical venereal diseases. Like McKenna, several doctors leaned toward a syphilis hypothesis. She even managed to publish a paper describing her idea in a relatively small medical journal.

Her aggressive promotion of the syphilis hypothesis eventually led to an ironic alarmism reminiscent of CDC press statements. In response to an article we wrote for a 1990 issue of *Policy Review*, a letter to the editor from McKenna appeared in the next issue. She admitted seeing "street drugs" and "malnourishment" in her AIDS patients, but instead drew the logical conclusion of her own view: "We believe that AIDS is the tip of an iceberg of immune-suppressive disorders in our country, which if combined with syphilis could lead to a major human die-off by the end of the century."[18]

While she was rounding up support, a more mainstream, if somewhat flamboyant, medical doctor was moving toward similar conclusions on the opposite coast. In 1982 Stephen Caiazza, not terribly long out of medical school, had opened his private practice for homosexuals in New York City. His energies were soon absorbed by the AIDS epidemic, and he became involved in medical campaigns to create "safe sex" guidelines for public health and to get AZT approved for therapy. Questions about HIV had never occurred to him. Then, inadvertently, he discovered that some of his patients with AIDS-like conditions showed temporary remissions with antibiotics, especially penicillin. However, he payed little attention until he received a phone call from Switzerland in September, 1986. Joan McKenna had heard of his results with antibiotics and suspected he was treating an underlying syphilis. She was in Europe to meet with two doctors who treated their AIDS patients with enormous doses of penicillin. Caiazza instantly became fascinated, and flew out within days to the small German town of Augsburg to compare notes.

Whatever else might be said of him, Caiazza exuded a colorful personality. Although he was essentially convinced of the syphilis hypothesis, he felt he had to conduct one experiment to settle the matter. He injected himself with the syphilis bacterium, trying to develop AIDS. In fact, he quickly became deathly ill with syphilis, a condition that plagued him for weeks. Upon recovering, he began treating his own AIDS patients aggressively with penicillin and other antibiotics. Somehow the point that he had recovered, that his disease had no latent period, and that his symptoms hardly resembled AIDS was lost on Caiazza, who now thoroughly believed syphilis was a major cause. He also largely ignored the suggestion that his antibiotic treatments only temporarily suppressed some of the opportunistic infections without curing the underlying immune deficiency, as confirmed by the fact that he had to keep his patients on the regimen indefinitely.

Caiazza's temperament made him a natural spokesman, and he soon led the charge for the syphilis hypothesis, and for treating AIDS with penicillin. He wrote papers or short commentaries for several medical journals, was interviewed for *SPIN* magazine, and published his autobiographical account of the controversy. He also ran into trouble from medical authorities, who now resented his outspoken criticism of the HIV hypothesis. He spoke with Bryan Ellison in December of 1989, describing some of the political fallout:

Virtually the day I announced that I was closing my practice and going off to Germany to do some work with some other investigators on the subject, I get a registered letter from Albany saying that because of an administrative infraction I committed in 1981 (which is true), they're going to have a hearing September 17th. So I have my lawyer call. He said [to them], "This is 1986! The thing was in 1981. Give him a couple of months."

"No."

So they had the hearing without me. I was absent. They found me guilty, of course. I came back from Germany, immediately got hit with a review of my work on a regular basis.[19]

He was still under review at the time of the conversation.

Unfortunately, Caiazza never had the chance to continue his vocal opposition to the AIDS establishment. Within weeks of the interview, he passed away quite suddenly. Although he was young and HIV-positive, his death was not attributed to AIDS. According to friends he died, ironically, of a cocaine overdose.

Another bacterial hypothesis of AIDS was evolving at the same time the syphilis proposal was gathering supporters. In 1986, a virologist named Shyh-Ching Lo first reported finding a new virus in several AIDS patients. He performed some of these experiments at the National Cancer Institute, where colleagues scoffed. In a noble attempt to meet Koch's postulates for causing AIDS, Lo went on to grow the "virus" in cultured cells and then infected four monkeys—all of which died of a wasting disease within months. But at that point he ran into trouble. "Lo had a tough time getting his findings published. 'I forget how many journals turned us down,' he says. One colleague put the figure at more than half a dozen."[20]

The HIV establishment had little use for anything but their favorite virus. Lo had some protection from other virus hunters because he worked at the Armed Forces Institute of Pathology, a military research facility entirely independent of the NIH-funded establishment. Nevertheless, he could not publish his results until 1989, and then only in a relatively obscure journal. By that time he had further identified the nature of his "virus," discovering he had actually been working with a mycoplasma, a tiny bacterium that prefers to hide inside cells rather than grow on its own. He named his find *Mycoplasma incognitus*, reflecting the fact he had originally confused it with being a virus. Lo finally began receiving applause for his discovery the following year, once it was endorsed by Luc Montagnier, the French discoverer of HIV.

Although Lo tested his mycoplasma using Koch's postulates, his microbe-hunting enthusiasm overran his scientific sense. The mycoplasma had in reality failed the test. He could not find the bacterium in many AIDS patients, thereby falling short of the first postulate. And the infected monkeys, while wasting away and dying, developed nothing like the wide spectrum of AIDS diseases, nor did their conditions have a latent period. Thus the third postulate also eliminated the mycoplasma as a candidate. Mycoplasmas have become textbook subjects for decades; they cause roughly one-third of all human pneumonias, and frequently contaminate the cell cultures of unsuspecting researchers. Mostly these microbes function as opportunists, preying on people with weakened health. And since AIDS, as we have argued, is not infectious at all, it could not be caused by this mycoplasma or any other microbe.

With regard to Gallo and the HIV dogma of AIDS, Lo did have poignant comments. Responding to our *Policy Review* article in 1990, he and his supervisor wrote the editor that "to commit oneself exclusively to a particular agent and completely rule out any other possible role of a different microbe, may... result in a greater loss of AIDS victims."[21]

Spreading doubts

Peter Duesberg's entry into the HIV debate in 1987 suddenly changed its scope, particularly with his insistence that the virus clearly had nothing whatsoever to do with AIDS. Faced with such a compelling and uncompromising argument, scientists could no longer easily ignore dissension. Several prominent researchers chimed in with their own doubts about HIV, although they cautiously avoided naming alternative causes for AIDS, preferring simply to question official dogma. Despite their own impeccable credentials, some of them quickly ran into the same political pressures that had plagued other dissenters.

Albert Sabin became the first to follow Duesberg into the fray. Following his days working on the polio vaccine, he had retired to the National Institutes of Health (NIH) as a consultant with his own office. The position was granted to him because of his honored status, having been a member of the National Academy of Sciences since the early 1950s and one of the most respected virologists in the world. His sometimes gruff and forceful personality had even helped enhance the respect his peers afforded him.

In 1987, while still on leave at the NIH, Duesberg was asked to give a lecture in honor of the Fogarty fellowship supporting his NIH research; he chose to speak about his recent paper in *Cancer Research* criticizing the HIV hypothesis. Sabin was one of many NIH people filling the lecture room. Duesberg had barely finished his speech, which had stunned the audience for its audacity in questioning a sacred cow, when Sabin lept to his feet. He headed straight for the microphone, seizing the podium as if to throw it.

"I think the views of a person like Dr. Duesberg are terribly, terribly important," he bellowed, "and we must pay attention to them."[22] Turning to the whole question of whether AIDS would actually spread to the general population, his voice took on an angry tone. He denounced the panic-ridden projections of a heterosexual epidemic. "This is not the population where you find AIDS. We have known this for almost 10 years and the pattern has not changed. I am astonished by the hysteria. This is absolute madness." He thundered along, no one in the room daring to interrupt. "These are irresponsible statements without any scientific foundation... I don't want to be a psychiatrist and try to figure out why these things are said in the absence of evidence, but unfortunately they are receiving a great deal of publicity."[23]

Sabin's years of virus hunting now came into play. He had worked with truly disease-causing viruses, including polio, which induced symptoms only when flooding the body in high numbers. "Presence of virus doesn't mean anything in and of itself," he reminded the audience, "because virologists know that quantities count." This meant, he concluded, that HIV itself should be difficult to pass along between people. "The basis of present action and education is that everybody who tests positive for the virus must be regarded as a transmitter and there is no evidence for that." Finally he threw barbs at the virus hunters who spent all their time investigating the genetic details of HIV, never asking whether it had been proven to cause anything. "Up to the present time, all that beautiful knowledge about the molecular biology of the virus isn't helping us at all to deal with it."[24]

Sabin spent twenty minutes at the microphone, nearly as long as Duesberg himself. The added comments touched off excited rounds of questions and discussion, Sabin's own personality magnifying the charged atmosphere. He was now fired up enough to fight back against the one-sided media coverage of AIDS, and arranged a press conference the following month at the Third International AIDS Conference in Washington, D.C. Duesberg was asked by Sabin to participate, but had not been invited to the AIDS Conference and thus could not attend. Sabin therefore held the meeting himself.

But after that occasion, he was never again heard defending Duesberg or questioning HIV. Having no tenure or other protection, Sabin's position at the NIH was subject to the whims of intolerant superiors, ones who did not enjoy being embarrassed by a scientist with his prestige. Duesberg worked at a university, a more difficult target for NIH retaliation; Sabin was more directly vulnerable. Until he passed away in 1993, Sabin rarely again spoke out on AIDS, and then only to criticize the bizarre HIV vaccination project of his longtime competitor, Jonas Salk.

Duesberg's next outspoken supporter did retain a safer university position. Walter Gilbert, a professor of molecular biology at Harvard, had won the Nobel Prize for chemistry in 1980. Considered one of the more important Nobel awards in recent years, Gilbert had won it for inventing the modern technique for sequencing, or reading, the genetic material DNA.

Upon reading Duesberg's *Cancer Research* paper in 1987, Gilbert was immediately fascinated. He told a reporter, "It is good to have it [the HIV hypothesis] questioned and argued. I absolutely do consider it a valid debate."[25] Specifically, he argued from the time-tested principles of virology that Duesberg "is absolutely correct in saying that no one has proven that AIDS is caused by the AIDS virus. And he is absolutely correct that the virus cultured in the laboratory may not be the cause of AIDS. There is no animal model for AIDS, and where there is no animal model, you cannot establish Koch's postulates."[26] The arguments against HIV are so strong, according to Gilbert, that "I would not be surprised if there were another cause of AIDS and even that HIV is not involved."[27]

Gilbert has made the *Cancer Research* paper required reading for his graduate students, using it as an illustration of how skeptical thinking ought to work in science. This he considers his most important message. As he sees it, "The community as a whole doesn't listen patiently to critics who adopt alternative viewpoints, although the great lesson of history is that knowledge develops through the conflict of viewpoints, that if you have simply a consensus view, it generally stultifies, it fails to see the problems of that consensus; and it depends on the existence of critics to break up that iceberg and to permit knowledge to develop."[28]

With his honors and awards, Gilbert remains fairly immune from political repercussions of his public statements. Thus he can continue to criticize HIV for all who ask, though he does not take an activist role in the debate.

An even more prominent Nobel laureate joined the ranks of HIV dissidents in 1991. Having received the Prize in the early 1980s, Barbara McClintock was finally vindicated after decades of scientific isolation. She had discovered transposons, small genes that periodically jump from one spot to another in the DNA of various organisms. Her long struggle to gain acceptance for the concept has since become legend, her findings hailed as one of the momentous discoveries of biology since World War II. Even in the popular literature, she now stands as a symbol of tireless dissent against an intolerant scientific establishment.

McClintock's years of pioneering research were performed at the Cold Spring Harbor research labs in New York, headed by Nobel laureate James Watson, where she remained all her life. This placed her in the right spot to meet Duesberg in 1991. That May, shortly before Duesberg left for the Cold Spring Harbor facility to attend Watson's annual conference on retroviruses, he received a telephone call from the elderly McClintock. She said that a colleague at Harvard, asked by Duesberg to review the draft of an update paper on AIDS, had sent her a copy. She loved it, and even thought he should make it stronger and more forceful. Would he meet with her at the conference?

After arriving, Duesberg found an opportunity one morning to break away. He found McClintock in her office, and the two of them hit it off immediately. She told him stories about her own conflict with majority scientific opinion. In those days, she laughed, her observations on "jumping genes" were dismissed by her male colleagues. "Isn't it just like a woman," they would say, to propose such a silly idea?

She agreed that science itself had become huge and thoughtless. Most researchers, she emphasized, prefer "knitting" together raw data rather than interpreting it. Thus a "deluge of information" tends to swamp out genuine science. Such people are perfectly happy merely gathering data, and they uncritically accept "tacit assumptions" that force real thinkers to fight an uphill battle. Having come to realize this political nature of modern science, she had little enthusiasm for the honors researchers bestowed upon one another. She found that the Nobel Prize "pushes you into the limelight" and becomes such a nuisance that she actually turned down another prize offered her. "They keep giving awards to the same people," she lamented. "They should find some new people who have done something different."

Turning to Duesberg's paper, she offered some minor points of advice but agreed wholeheartedly that the epidemiology of AIDS did not fit the pattern for a contagious disease. By the end of their two-hour conversation, she had wished him the best of success.

But her own energies were already failing. The following year, Duesberg saw her again at the same retrovirus conference. This time McClintock suffered from a weakened condition, a consequence of her advanced age. Walking with a crutch, she had little time except to say hello and mention that she was seeing a doctor, though still in her friendly way. She would never have the opportunity to speak out publicly against HIV, for she passed away that fall. The same research establishment that she had to bypass throughout her life now felt obliged to honor her in death.

James Watson himself took up an interest in the HIV debate at the 1992 retrovirus meeting. He had won his own Nobel in 1962 for discovering the structure of DNA, the genetic material, and had parlayed that award into his position as director of the Cold Spring Harbor laboratories. Always one to recognize changing fashions in science, he had started the tumor virus meetings at Cold Spring Harbor in the late 1960s, just as the War on Cancer was about to emerge. Sensing the growing popularity of genetic engineering, he managed to secure a spot as a leader in the human genome project during the 1980s. Back when Barbara McClintock had been unfashionable, Watson had sneered; as soon as her star rose, he led everyone else in praising her brilliant work.

Watson had the habit of making transient appearances at his conferences, greeting colleagues according to their unofficial social status. This time he spoke with Duesberg, and the two struck up a conversation about the HIV debate. On this subject Watson was short-tempered; he had previously told a reporter that Duesberg had no "convincing evidence" against the HIV hypothesis.[29] Now he confronted Duesberg with his skepticism: if AIDS is not infectious, why do hemophiliacs get it? Duesberg pointed out that hemophiliacs actually began living longer since roughly the time HIV infected three-quarters of them. Watson was startled. "If that's true, I'll call a special meeting here at Cold Spring Harbor," he declared. His curiosity aroused, he invited Duesberg for a private meeting at his office.

Again Watson demanded answers, still suspicious. "Where is your evidence? You always say things without data." Duesberg objected, mentioning some of the evidence he had uncovered in the scientific literature. Watson then wanted to know why he had not published in the *Proceedings of the National Academy of Sciences*, the journal in which all members of the Academy have an automatic right to publish. At that point Watson learned about a paper Duesberg had failed to get printed in the *Proceedings*, one that reviewed the evidence that drug use causes AIDS.

Thoroughly shocked on learning this, Watson now wanted copies of all the correspondence between Duesberg and the journal's editor. "Send me everything," he insisted at the close of their half-hour meeting. He promised to look into the matter without delay, planning to exert whatever influence he could to stop this unbelievable act of censorship. But although Duesberg sent the material, he has not heard back from Watson to this very day, and his paper remains unpublished.

Duesberg had a brief written exchange with another dissident of sorts, Manfred Eigen, one of Germany's most revered Nobel laureates. Based at the prestigious Max Planck Institute, Eigen decided in 1989 to set himself up as the arbiter of the argument over HIV. In a paper entitled "The AIDS Debate," he reviewed existing evidence and formulated mathematical models in his analysis.[30] In the end, he chose a compromise solution—according to him, HIV did help to cause AIDS, but also needed some sort of co-factor to finish the job. Even this modest concession proved too much for the AIDS establishment. Allegedly, Eigen originally submitted his review to the prestigious journal *Nature*, from which it was rejected; certainly, Eigen's stature was too great normally to publish in the less-known German journal *Naturwissenschaften*, where his paper finally appeared. Duesberg's response was published a few months later in the same journal, taking issue with Eigen's attempt to save a role for HIV. Eigen countered with a series of rationalizations to explain away the puzzles of the HIV hypothesis. Then on a suggestion from Ellison, Duesberg added a short answer pointing out that the difference in viewpoint was philosophical:

> Eigen feels that in the absence of scientific proof for the hypothesis, "It is dangerous to state 'This ends the fear of infection'. . . because it may trigger wishful thinking."
>
> By contrast I will not accord the virus-AIDS hypothesis any more respect or concern than I would any other unproven hypothesis, as for example, the hypothesis that we are going to be invaded by the Martians and hence must build an interplanetary defense system. The burden of proof... is on those who propose a hypothesis, not on those who question it.[31]

Eigen has not publicly spoken further on the HIV debate.

But perhaps the most spectacular defection from the orthodox HIV establishment has been the discoverer of HIV himself, Luc Montagnier. He dropped his announcement in the midst of the Sixth International Conference on AIDS, the huge gathering of scientists and reporters in June of 1990. That year the meeting was held in San Francisco. To everyone's surprise, he used his allotted presentation to declare that HIV could not itself be enough to cause AIDS. The virus needed a co-factor, and he had already chosen a candidate—Shyh-Ching Lo's mycoplasma!

That evening, television broadcasts carried the news internationally. Headlines screamed the new hypothesis the following morning. "Almost all researchers working on AIDS said Montagnier was out on a limb," recalled *Science* a few months later.[32] Robert Gallo's reaction was particularly furious: "Since 1984 we've established enough evidence that there is a single cause for this disease. There is no evidence that anything else is needed."[33]

Gallo's book, published the next year, bore down hard on Montagnier for breaking ranks. "This surprising view, which has been chiefly presented in press conferences, has given, and may do so for a while, added longevity to confused and confusing (to others) arguments that HIV is not the primary cause of AIDS... In short, he has lent *some* support to Duesberg."[34] [emphasis in original]

A 1991 *Science* article mentioned one of the direct consequences of such unapproved behavior:

> But Montagnier has had difficulty getting his new work published. One paper, for example, was rejected last year by *Nature*.
>
> "I have high resistance from the virologists, and high enthusiasm from the mycoplasmologists," Montagnier says.[35]

The reasons behind his sudden shift, however, never made the news. The story actually began several months before the announcement, in the fall of 1989. A Canadian scientist had brokered an arrangement between Duesberg, Montagnier, and *Research in Immunology*, a journal published by the Pasteur Institute. The journal would print a complete debate about the HIV hypothesis between the two scientists. The two sides would volley arguments back and forth by facsimile machine, stopping at a maximum of 2500 words each. Duesberg was chosen to submit the opening round.

In November, after several revisions, Duesberg launched his first install-ment. He had used 1400 words, over half his total, defining as many of the is-sues as possible. Summoning arguments from virology and epidemiology alike, he raised such points as the absence of active virus in AIDS patients, the long latent period, and the extreme bias of AIDS for males. Having laid out a rather overwhelming case, he ended the round with two very tough questions: "What proves that AIDS is infectious? If so, what proves that it is caused by HIV?" Then he, and the journal, waited for a response.

And waited. And waited. Attempts to contact Montagnier only received the brush-off, the French scientist constantly claiming to be preoccupied with other temporary matters. Finally *Research in Immunology* decided to wait no longer. They published a slightly modified version of Duesberg's original in-stallment in their January issue, with a written promise to publish Montagnier's answer at whatever future date he would submit it. But no such response has ever arrived.

Instead everyone found out what Montagnier had been up to by March, when he published a startling and obviously rushed paper in the Pasteur Institute's other journal, *Research in Virology*. This paper actually marked the first time he announced his co-factor hypothesis of AIDS, preceding the San Francisco AIDS Conference by three full months. He had miraculously discovered that cultured cells infected with HIV, which normally died in his laboratory, grew perfectly well when given the antibiotic tetracycline. HIV itself was unaffected by the treatment, so he inferred that some undetected bacterium had been killing the cells. In fact, he concluded the hidden microbe must have been a mycoplasma. He may well have been right, for mycoplasmas commonly contaminate cell cultures, cannot easily be seen, and are killed by tetracycline. Indeed, this sort of contamination is so common that no laboratory ever publishes such a trivial observation as a scientific paper.

The paper smelled more of politics than science. It became his opportunity to announce his co-factor hypothesis, a point he drove home in the last sentence of the paper: "Further experiments are presently being undertaken to isolate and identify the microorganism and to investigate its role in HIV-induced pathogenicity."[36] For those who knew about his abortive debate with Duesberg, Montagnier indirectly gave away the reason for his sudden change of direction—Duesberg's arguments had apparently changed his mind about HIV. Articles and interviews covering Montagnier's June surprise at the AIDS conference quoted him repeating several of Duesberg's arguments, including the low levels of HIV in the bodies of AIDS patients, the latent period, the large number of infected people who never develop AIDS, even the inability of retroviruses to kill cells. But Montagnier never mentioned Duesberg's name, acting instead as if he had thought up the issues himself.

More recently, Montagnier privately admitted to a colleague that he has tested hemophiliacs, finding the same immune suppression in HIV-negative individuals as in their HIV-positive counterparts.[37] But Montagnier has neither published nor officially announced this study, presumably because of political pressures.

The decision to back a co-factor hypothesis also seems political, a position that can allow Montagnier to move easily toward or away from the HIV hypothesis at any time. Depending on the pressures exerted, he has indeed vacillated. In any case, Shyh-Ching Lo has enjoyed a revival of his fortunes, now that Montagnier has chosen to work with him on his *Mycoplasma incognitus*. And AIDS officials have been forced to handle one more annoying dissident.

The dissidents organize

The ranks of HIV dissidents continued growing steadily. Inevitably, they united to present their common message, a move that took place in the spring of 1991. The man who organized this opposition, Charles Thomas, had all the right credentials. As a professor of biochemistry at Harvard University, he had pioneered studies of how the body synthesizes proteins. But he found the years of NIH-financed science too intellectually restrictive. Thomas was motivated by his libertarian political values to leave the government-funded academic setting, opting to use his personal finances to conduct research. He moved to San Diego, California, and started the non-profit Helicon Foundation, as well as his own small biotechnology company, Pantox.

He heard about Duesberg and was intrigued. By May of 1991, he had decided the growing ranks of dissidents should not go to waste. He especially deplored the lack of controlled studies comparing HIV-infected people with those uninfected. Amidst writing a steady stream of letters to editors and prominent individuals, he drafted a statement that remained carefully neutral with respect to alternative hypotheses of AIDS, yet conveyed the skepticism of many scientists about HIV:

It is widely believed by the general public that a retrovirus called HIV causes the group of diseases called AIDS. Many biomedical scientists now question this hypothesis. We propose that a thorough reappraisal of the existing evidence for and against this hypothesis be conducted by a suitable independent group. We further propose that critical epidemiological studies be devised and undertaken.

Thomas aggressively recruited scientists to affix their names to the statement. Within weeks, he already had over two dozen signatures of biomedical researchers with solid credentials garnered from the United States, Europe, and Australia, as well as a smattering of professionals in other fields. Most held academic positions. The membership, however, did reflect the political pressures inside science: most had some form of protection from the virus-hunting establishment, whether because they worked in entirely unrelated fields, were near or past retirement, or were self-employed—like Thomas himself.

By early June, Thomas had sent the statement as a letter to *Science*; the editor responded within days, reassuring him that "If we decide to publish it, we will be in touch with you before publication."[38] Don't call us, we'll call you.

The statement fared no better at such prestigious journals as *The New England Journal of Medicine* and *Lancet*. The editor of *Nature* did call back, promising to print it, but nothing ever happened. Only *Christopher Street*, an independent homosexual-interest monthly run by the *New York Native*'s Charles Ortleb, was willing to print the letter. Realizing this would be a long-term fight, Thomas established a group around this statement and its implicit purpose. Corresponding with Duesberg and a few other outspoken dissidents, he first suggested the sarcastic name "Friends of HIV," which was soon replaced with the "Group for the Scientific Reappraisal of the HIV/AIDS Hypothesis." The Group had grown to some forty members by the end of 1991, and swelled to more than one hundred signatories after the 1992 International AIDS Conference, at which cases of AIDS without HIV infection were announced. By the beginning of 1994, over four hundred people had joined, mostly scientists and physicians.

Of the dissidents so far discussed in this chapter, only John Lauritsen joined the Group. But others who did sign on brought some rather impressive credentials. One of the best known for speaking out on the HIV debate, Robert Root-Bernstein, independently developed his suspicions about the virus shortly after Gallo's 1984 press conference, years before Duesberg published his *Cancer Research* paper. Barely out of graduate school with a degree in the history of science, Root-Bernstein was awarded the MacArthur Prize fellowship—a five-year "genius grant"—in 1981. This afforded him the opportunity to work alongside polio vaccine pioneer Jonas Salk, followed by a professorship at Michigan State University in physiology.

Inspired by Duesberg's outspoken challenge against HIV, Root-Bernstein eagerly added his own energies to the debate. He had always shown a rebellious streak in his science, the very reason for his MacArthur Prize. His

1989 book, *Discovering*, revolved around the theme that large, well-funded science tends to stifle genuine innovation. By early 1989 he had begun corresponding with Duesberg and other critics of the HIV hypothesis. Scouring the scientific literature, Root-Bernstein found hundreds of cases of AIDS-like diseases dating back throughout the twentieth century. This data he extracted into a letter published in the *Lancet* in April, 1990, showing that Kaposi's sarcoma had not been as rare as supposed before the 1980s. The next month he fired off in rapid succession several more papers on the history of other AIDS diseases, all of which the same journal now rejected. Ultimately he was forced to compile the remaining data into a paper in a smaller French journal.

He also began documenting the explosive increases in immune-suppressive risk factors since the 1960s, including venereal and parasitic diseases, and drug abuse. This material, and a bevy of arguments against the HIV hypothesis, formed the basis of several more papers submitted to an amazing array of biomedical journals. His major 1990 paper, "Do we know the cause(s) of AIDS?", clearly laid out the stakes: "It is worth taking a skeptical look at the HIV theory. We cannot afford—literally, in terms of human lives, research dollars, and manpower investment—to be wrong… the premature closure of inquiry lays us open to the risk of making a colossal blunder."[39] By 1993 he had written a book incorporating all of his extensive research, entitled *Rethinking AIDS*. He was also a founding member of Charles Thomas' Group.

Nevertheless, peer pressure left its mark on Root-Bernstein. In a 1990 interview taped for a television documentary, the following exchange took place:

> Q: Do you think HIV causes AIDS?
> A: I don't—absolutely not… I believe that HIV by itself cannot cause AIDS.[40]

But by the 1992 meeting of HIV dissidents in Amsterdam, he had somehow been maneuvered into signing Joseph Sonnabend's press release condemning Duesberg, a move for which Root-Bernstein later seemed apologetic. His book, *Rethinking AIDS*, also contained a different tone than in the past:

> I believe that Duesberg is wrong in ignoring the role of HIV in AIDS…
> I posit that at the very least, HIV. . . can have just as serious and potentially as deadly effects as cytomegalovirus, toxoplasmosis, or *Pneumocysits carinii* pneumonia.[41]

All this said without any scientific justification, perhaps intended more as self-protection from repercussions. His book makes a special acknowledgement of Sonnabend, whose multifactorial model of AIDS as a product of repeated venereal infections has begun shaping Root-Bernstein's own view. The book, however, delves further into his own developing hypothesis of AIDS, the autoimmune model. According to this idea, specific combinations of microbes, if they infect the body all at once, might trigger a chain reaction in which the immune system is fooled into attacking itself. Root-Bernstein includes HIV as one of the infections that might start the process.

The autoimmunity hypothesis, however, suffers several fatal flaws. For one thing, autoimmune reactions have been poorly documented in any disease, not to mention AIDS. In fact, they may never occur in an otherwise healthy person. Moreover, the immune system works so well precisely because it has built-in (but poorly understood) safeguards that prevent it from attacking its own host body; the immune system's inherent function is to attack only foreign particles. For an invading microbe to induce a self-destructive immune response would be a contradiction in terms. Even if an autoimmune reaction *could* somehow take place, AIDS would have a latent period of days, not years. Further, the AIDS diseases against which the immune system provides no defense anyway, including the cancers, dementia, and wasting disease, cannot be explained by this model, or any other, that only accounts for destruction of the immune system. And if AIDS did result from autoimmunity, it would have spread out of its original risk groups into the general population years ago, rather than striking men nine times out of ten. Root-Bernstein himself admits these problems.

Harry Rubin, the retrovirology pioneer, Lasker Prize recipient, and member of the National Academy of Sciences who trained Howard Temin and who has been a close friend of Duesberg since the 1960s, has spoken out against the HIV hypothesis since 1987. Rubin's instincts about retroviruses had been shaped by his changing views of biology over the years; since the early 1970s he had drifted away from the field, precisely because simple agents such as viruses hardly seemed to contain the answers to complex problems such as cancer. He told the interviewer in a 1990 British television documentary:

> I don't think the cause of AIDS has been found. I think [in] a disease as complex as AIDS that there are likely to be multiple causes. In fact, to call it a single disease when there are so many multiple manifestations seems to me to be an oversimplification.[42]

Always cautious, Rubin nonetheless clearly stated that "I don't necessarily agree with everything that Peter is saying. But I *do* support his questioning the simplistic idea that this very complex syndrome is caused by this one virus."[43] Writing in Duesberg's defense, he sent letters to both *Science* and *Nature* in 1988, both of which were printed. Since that time, Rubin has not been able to have similar letters published. He also rallied to Duesberg's side at a 1988 "conference" sponsored by Mathilde Krim's American Foundation for AIDS Research (AmFAR). The two Berkeley colleagues faced an ambush of hostile virus hunters and media reporters at the Washington, D.C. meeting, yet they boldly made their points. Rubin himself leans toward a multifactorial hypothesis, one that includes drug abuse as one of many potential health risk factors that could cause AIDS over time.

British epidemiologist Gordon Stewart, another founding member of the Group, has run into roadblocks against questioning the HIV hypothesis. Stewart also favors a multifactorial model of AIDS, but his argument with HIV focuses on the failure of AIDS to spread out of its original risk groups, an indication that no one microbe causes the syndrome.

After a struggle, he was able to place a letter in the *Lancet* in 1989. But virtually all attempts to speak out thereafter failed, despite Stewart's predictions of the size of the AIDS epidemic continually proving far more accurate than the wildly exaggerated estimates of AIDS officials. The *Lancet* itself rejected two more letters by Stewart. A paper sent to *Nature* in early 1990 took months of review before the editors rejected it. As Stewart's predictions began coming true, *Nature* went on to refuse publication three more times, an embargo that continues today. A paper submitted to the *British Medical Journal* met with instant rejection, though with the suggestion that they might print a shorter letter. Stewart complied, but his second attempt met with equal indifference.

Harvey Bialy, the research editor of *Nature* subsidiary *Bio/Technology*, is a graduate of the University of California, Berkeley, an associate professor at the University of Miami, and another early member of the Group. Bialy's interest focused on Duesberg's arguments after the 1987 *Cancer Research* paper, and he invited Duesberg to publish an editorial in *Bio/Technology* late that year. When *Science* attacked Duesberg a few months later, Bialy wrote a forceful letter to the editor demanding fairer coverage; this led to a news article that revived interest in the controversy—just when many virus hunters were hoping Duesberg would fade away. Duesberg then wrote a letter to the editor, but *Science* instead published a brief written debate between Duesberg and Blattner, Gallo, and Temin (see Chapter Six). Bialy has sometimes opened the pages of his own journal to other AIDS dissidents, and has given lectures critical of the HIV dogma. He explained his own view of the epidemic to the *Sunday Times* of London:

> The [HIV] hypothesis has become all things to all people. It violates everything we previously knew about virus disease, and allows any kind of therapy, any kind of research, to generate research bucks. What kind of science continues to place all its marbles, all its faith, all its research bucks, in such a theory? The answer I keep coming back to is that it has nothing to do with science; the reasons are all unscientific. We have taken sex and equated it with death, and into that mixture we have thrown money. What an ugly stew.[44]

Bialy has faced uphill battles, even at his own job, to keep dissent alive. In 1993 he invited Duesberg to write a standard-length paper for publication in *Bio/Technology*. Bialy was partly overruled, and the paper was cut down to a small fraction of its former length. When the paper finally appeared in August, it had been relegated to the back pages, printed alongside an unnecessary and bizarre disclaimer that "The views expressed here are the author's own, and not necessarily those of *Bio/Technology*."[45] Even the column by editor Douglas McCormick expressed distaste for publishing Duesberg's carefully documented paper, admitting that "we enter the fray reluctantly" because "we think that Duesberg is wrong in his conclusions" and because of Duesberg's debating style.[46] Bialy could not persuade the editor to moderate those antagonistic comments.

Other top names have joined the Group, many criticizing the HIV hypothesis before Charles Thomas began organizing. Beverly Griffin, Director of the Virology Department at London's Royal Postgraduate Medical School, wrote a review in a 1989 issue of *Nature* arguing that "the burden of proof for HIV as a deadly pathogen" rests squarely on "those who maintain that HIV causes AIDS." She also unflinchingly brought up "the pressures of silence imposed by the establishment (including journalists and journals)."[47]

The editor of *American Laboratory*, Frederick Scott, seconded Duesberg's questions in an April, 1989, editorial. There he proposed that nutritional deficiency might contribute to causing AIDS, particularly zinc deficiency. Citing the microbe-hunting mania that once controlled research and treatment of scurvy, beriberi, and pellagra, he argued that AIDS might prove to be a tragic parallel, another non-contagious syndrome falsely blamed on a microbe.

Kary Mullis, another former graduate student from Berkeley, achieved his international fame for inventing the polymerase chain reaction (PCR) a few years ago. This, ironically, is the sensitive detection technique used by AIDS officials to claim they can find HIV in almost every antibody-positive AIDS patient. Mullis refuses to buy this argument: "I can't find a single virologist who will give me references which show that HIV is the probable cause of Aids... If you ask a virologist for that information, you don't get an answer, you get fury."[48] As he points out, the PCR method only finds dormant, inactive HIV.

For his PCR invention, Mullis has since won the 1993 Nobel Prize for chemistry, making him the third Nobel laureate to question the "AIDS virus" and the first to belong to the Group for the Scientific Reappraisal of the HIV/AIDS Hypothesis. Many scientific colleagues had not previously realized that Mullis questioned HIV's significance, and are now becoming seriously unnerved by his comments. Although many journalists refuse even to mention his dissenting view, Mullis continues to hammer the AIDS establishment with his outspoken criticisms:

> Where is the research that says HIV is the cause of AIDS? We know everything in the world about HIV now. There are 10,000 people in the world now who specialize in HIV. None have any interest in the possibility HIV doesn't cause AIDS because if it doesn't, their expertise is useless.[49]

Hundreds of other professionals have now lent their names to Thomas' statement, all agreeing on the need to re-open the HIV hypothesis for testing. Many of the scientists propose their own ideas of what causes AIDS. But to us, by far the most compelling case can be made for the notion that long-term drug use is the culprit in most AIDS. We review the growing evidence for this hypothesis, which can easily be tested, in the next chapter.

Chapter 7 Footnotes

1 Sonnabend, The Etiology of AIDS. *AIDS Research* 1:1-12, 1983.
2 Sonnabend, Caution on AIDS viruses. *Nature* 310:103, 1984.
3 Sonnabend, Letter to the editor. *Wall Street Journal*, Nov. 18, 1985.
4 Sonnabend, Letter to Peter Duesberg, May 24, 1988.
5 Hopkins, Dr. Joseph Sonnabend. *Interview Magazine*, Dec., 1992, pp. 124-6, 142-3 (p. 126).
6 Ibid., p. 142.
7 Stewart, Root-Bernstein, Luca-Moretti, Brands, Callen, Sonnabend, Eleopolis, Bastide, and Leiphart, Press Release. International Symposium: AIDS — A Different View, May 16, 1992.
8 Sonnabend, Letter to the editor. *New York Native*, June 29, 1992, p. 4; Lauritsen, Letter to the editor, same issue.
9 Lauritsen, AZT: Iatrogenic Genocide. *New York Native*, March 28, 1988, pp. 13-17.
10 Callen, A dangerous talk with Dr. Sonnabend. *QW*, Sept. 27, 1992, pp. 42-6, 71-2.
11 Lehrman, Endorsement for Lauritsen, *Poison by Prescription: The AZT Story*, Asklepios, New York, 1990 (back cover).
12 Lauritsen, Letter to Bryan Ellison, May 28, 1993.
13 Ellison, Interview with John Lauritsen, April 21, 1993.
14 Lauritsen, Notes on conversations with CDC/NCI people (unpublished), June 11-12, 1987.
15 Relman, Letter to John Lauritsen, July 11, 1988.
16 Coulter, *AIDS and Syphilis: The Hidden Link.* North Atlantic Books, Berkeley, CA, 1987, p. 78.
17 Ibid., p. 85.
18 McKenna, Letter to the editor. *Policy Review*, Fall 1990, pp. 77-8.
19 Ellison, Interview with Stephen S. Caiazza, Dec. 13, 1989.
20 Wright, Mycoplasmas in the AIDS Spotlight. *Science* 248:682-3, 1990.
21 Lo and Wear, Letter to the editor. *Policy Review*, Fall 1990, pp. 76-77.
22 Rapoport, Dissident scientist's AIDS theory angers colleagues. *Oakland Tribune*, Jan. 31, 1988, p. B-1.
23 Regush, AIDS risk limited, studies suggest. *Montreal Gazette*, Aug. 15, 1987, pp. B-1, B-4.
24 Ibid.
25 Rapoport, AIDS: The Unanswered Questions. *Oakland Tribune*, May 21, 1989, pp. A-1, A-2.
26 Hall, Gadfly in the Ointment. *Hippocrates*, Sept./Oct., 1988, pp. 76-82 (p. 80).
27 Liversidge, Heresy! Modern Galileos. *Omni*, June, 1993, pp. 43-51 (p. 48).
28 Meditel Productions, *The AIDS Catch.* (Documentary), Dispatches, Channel Four Television, London, June 13, 1990.
29 Liversidge, Op cit., p. 50.
30 Eigen, The AIDS Debate. *Naturwissenschaften* 76:341-50, 1989.
31 Duesberg, Responding to "The AIDS Debate." *Naturwissenschaften* 77:97-102, 1990.

172   *Why We Will Never Win the War on AIDS*

[32] Balter, Montagnier Pursues the Mycoplasma-AIDS Link. *Science* 251::271, 1991.

[33] Cotton, Cofactor Question Divides Codiscoverers of HIV. *Medical News & Perspectives* 264:3111-12, 1990.

[34] Gallo, *Virus Hunting — AIDS, Cancer, & the Human Retrovirus: a Story of Human Discovery.* Basic Books, New York, 1991, pp. 286, 297.

[35] Balter, Op cit.

[36] Lemaitre, Guetard, Henin, Montagnier, and Zerial, Protective activity of tetracycline analogs against the cytopathic effect of the Human Immunodeficiency Viruses in CEM cells. *Research in Virology* 141:5-16, 1990.

[37] Cramer, letter to Peter Duesberg, July 8, 1991.

[38] Koshland, Letter to Charles A. Thomas, June 11, 1991.

[39] Root-Bernstein, Do we know the cause(s) of AIDS? *Perspectives in Biology and Medicine* 33:480-500, 1990.

[40] Meditel Productions, *Interview with Dr. Root-Bernstein.* (Transcript), April, 1990.

[41] Root-Bernstein, *Rethinking AIDS: The Tragic Cost of Premature Consensus.* The Free Press, New York, 1993, p. 343.

[42] Meditel Productions, *The AIDS Catch,* Op cit.

[43] Miller, AIDS Heresy. *Discover,* June, 1988, pp. 63-68 (p. 66).

[44] Hodgkinson, Experts mount startling challenge to Aids orthodoxy. *The Sunday Times of London,* April 26, 1992, pp. 1, 12-13.

[45] Duesberg, The HIV gap in national AIDS statistics. *Bio/Technology* 11:955, Aug. 1993.

[46] McCormick, Right of reply. *Bio/Technology* 11:859, Aug. 1993.

[47] Griffin, Burden of Proof. *Nature* 338:670, 1989.

[48] Hodgkinson, Op cit.

[49] Carroll, The weird way to win a Nobel Prize. *San Francisco Chronicle,* Oct. 21, 1993, p. E9.

Chapter 8

So What Is AIDS?

Los Angeles, California, 1980: The man of thirty-three years being examined by Dr. Michael Gottlieb is deteriorating quickly. His fever refuses to go away, as do an active cytomegalovirus (CMV) infection and liver problems. Soon his immune system collapses to the point that native microbes, ones that have lived at peace with him for over three decades, begin eating away at his body. *Pneumocystis carinii* and *Candida*, germs that normally reside in all humans and most mammals, now take over the patient; the former grows into a severe pneumonia, the latter establishing itself as a thick yeast infection that begins choking his throat. By May 3 of the following year, the young artist has died, the autopsy revealing traces of a CMV pneumonia previously hidden by the *Pneumocystis* pneumonia.

This patient gained the dubious distinction as being the first officially recorded AIDS case in history, one of the five reported by the Centers for Disease Control in June, 1981. Gottlieb had dutifully noted the man was an active homosexual who admitted using "poppers," the aphrodisiac drug so popular in the homosexual bathhouses and discos of major cities.

Kenya, Africa, several years later: The hospital that the foreign woman enters is considered better than the few clinics in surrounding areas. She needs the best care medicine can provide. Only thirty-nine years old, she has just arrived from Zaire desperate to find treatment for her lung condition. It had begun with a relatively innocent cough and an unexpected drop in weight. Soon her coughs began bringing up blood. Tuberculosis is the diagnosis of the Kenyan doctor, but the patient has a strong allergic reaction to the drugs he prescribes. Her condition progresses from bad to worse, adding diarrhea, uncontrollable fever, swollen lymph nodes, and anemic blood disorders to her list of symptoms. But while the tuberculosis takes over, the *Pneumocystis* and *Candida* microbes also residing in her body remain perfectly hidden, causing no complications. She represents in every way the typical African AIDS patient.

The woman's husband, staying in the same hospital, suffers something entirely different and more unusual. Doctors assume he must have transmitted AIDS to his wife, though his diseases bear no similarity to hers. He has some sort of pneumonia, as well as a *Candida* yeast infection in his mouth and lesions of Kaposi's sarcoma, a blood vessel tumor, on his now irregularly pigmented skin. For African patients, this tumor appears so rarely as to be almost totally unknown. He loses weight to a relentless diarrhea, and is constantly fighting off episodes of gonorrhea. He knows he is in his death bed.

173

Oddly enough, their children have no such medical troubles.[1]

According to the public health officials directing our War on AIDS, the male homosexual in Los Angeles and the Zairean couple all suffered the same disease. But did they? Each person was affected with radically different diseases—a *Pneumocystis* pneumonia, a tuberculosis, a Kaposi's sarcoma—conditions that in the past would never have been connected by medical doctors. The only common factor between these patients was the presence in each of antibodies against HIV. At least, that is the presumption; Gottlieb's first AIDS case was never actually tested, since the virus had not yet been discovered.

A glance at AIDS statistics reveals that this syndrome encompasses several totally different epidemics under one banner. Each risk group can be defined by a different spectrum of diseases and a different probability of developing sickness. Some of these groups face surges of previously rare diseases, while others find their standard diseases reclassified as AIDS simply because of HIV infection.

The above examples illustrate the unbridgeable gap between "AIDS" in America and in Africa. Since 1985, official estimates have placed the number of HIV-positive Americans at around one million, of which some 315,000 have developed AIDS (by mid-1993). Nine of every ten cases occur in men. Most AIDS victims are older than twenty years and a few are infants, but virtually no teenagers have been affected. Male homosexuals make up 62% of AIDS patients, intravenous drug users and their children another 27%, and hemophiliacs or other blood transfusion patients remain at 3%. While nearly two-thirds of American AIDS diseases do fit the popular image of opportunistic infections taking advantage of decimated immune systems, the remaining third do not. Kaposi's sarcoma, dementia, wasting disease, lymphoma, and cervical cancer can even strike people with healthy immune systems.

The African picture stands in sharp contrast. Also tested for HIV since 1985, six to eight times as many Africans are infected, yet the entire continent has produced fewer AIDS cases—about 250,000. Women overall are diagnosed as often as men, although reports indicate that in certain tribes, *only* women get AIDS. No age group seems particularly to be singled out by the syndrome, nor can risk groups be easily defined by sexual activity or identifiable health risks. Despite the universal presence of *Pneumocystis* and *Candida* microbes in Africans, as in all world populations, these germs do not dominate the African AIDS statistics as they do in the industrial world. Instead tuberculosis, and the fevers and diarrheas associated with parasitic infections, show up most commonly. Even their "slim disease" appears to be a different sort of wasting condition than found in the United States or Europe. And Kaposi's sarcoma, which now strikes ten percent of American AIDS victims, only appears in one percent of African cases.

To find the causes of AIDS, therefore, one must define the health risks common to each separate group. Since this syndrome is not spreading outside of any AIDS risk group, the causes must be non-infectious; a contagious disease, by definition, spreads into the general population, as all microbes do. As witnessed in the past, noncontagious causes can include medically prescribed drugs (as was the case with SMON), vitamin or other nutritional deficiencies (as with scurvy, pellagra, and beriberi), or long-term abuse of substances, such as the smoking hypothesis of lung cancer and the alcohol hypothesis of liver cirrhosis.

As we shall argue, AIDS in the Third World is not new and is not necessarily increasing. The same can be said of hemophiliacs and blood transfusion recipients. But in the United States and Europe, most AIDS does reflect a genuine increase in opportunistic diseases, one that has coincided tightly with the explosion in heavy drug use in certain risk groups.

Drug use and AIDS—The same epidemic?

Virtually everyone's life has been directly impacted by the drug use epidemic. Most people in the industrial world have either tried an illicit drug or know others who have. Just one or two generations ago, high schools spent their time trying to control cigarette smoking in the restrooms; today's students can find almost anything they wish for smoking, swallowing, snorting, or even injecting in those same restrooms.

The 1960s gained the reputation as the decade of freely available drugs, especially marijuana and psychedelics. But in reality, the widespread escalation in drug use began largely at the end of the Vietnam War, about a decade before the appearance of AIDS. Much of the explosion has only taken place in recent years; overall drug arrests in the United States totalled approximately 450,000 in 1980, according to the Bureau of Justice Statistics, up to 1.4 million by 1989.

Heroin-related arrests roughly tripled during the 1970s, corresponding to a jump in the number of heroin overdose victims. In the decade from 1976 to 1985, the number of addicts admitted to hospitals doubled, and then doubled again. During 1985, some 580 injection drug addicts died in hospitals, increasing to 2,483 such deaths by 1990.

The situation with cocaine looks even more grim. A little over 5 million Americans had ever tried the drug by 1974, but eleven years later this figure had jumped to 22 million. The Drug Enforcement Administration confiscated about 500 kilograms of cocaine in 1980, 9,000 kilograms in 1983, 80,000 in 1989, and 100,000 in 1990—a total increase of 20,000 percent in one decade. During that same time the number of cocaine overdose victims admitted to hospitals also exploded, from just over 3,000 in 1981 to over 80,000 in 1990, a 2,400 percent jump. And direct cocaine-related deaths increased over tenfold during that period.

Law enforcement agencies seized some 2 million doses of amphetamines in 1981, but caught some 97 million doses just eight years later.

Alkyl nitrites, used primarily as aphrodisiacs, became so popular during the 1970s that the "popper craze" was born.[2] The National Institute on Drug Abuse estimated that by 1980 some 5 million Americans were inhaling the drug at least once a week. By 1978, the once-tiny poppers industry was already grossing $50 million in annual profits, a figure that continued to climb.[3] Poppers manufacturers even became the largest source of advertising revenue to such homosexual magazines as the *Advocate*, which in turn ignored the efforts of some public health authorities and activists to warn homosexual men of the dangerous effects of poppers.[4]

Naturally, one might expect major health problems in the wake of this drug explosion. If the timing of the AIDS epidemic—following on the heels of the drug epidemic—was no coincidence, then one should also find the spread of AIDS following the spread of drug use.

Not only did the drug use epidemic take off shortly before AIDS appeared, but it hit hardest among precisely the same risk groups. The parallels are astounding. Both AIDS and drug use, for example, are concentrated in younger men. Between 1983 and 1987, the death rate among American men 25 to 44 years old increased by about 10,000 deaths per year, the same as the average number of AIDS deaths per year in that time period. But also during the 1980s, deaths from drug overdoses doubled in men of exactly the same ages, while deaths from blood poisoning—an indirect consequence of injecting drugs—quadrupled. During that same period, AIDS deaths sharply increased among New York injection drug addicts, as did deaths from blood poisoning or other pneumonias—both at exactly the same rate. No one can quite sort out how much overlap exists between these AIDS- and drug-related deaths in young men.[5]

Ninety percent of all AIDS cases occur in men. But nine of every ten people arrested for possession of hard drugs are also male. Even the age distributions coincide perfectly: men between the ages of 20 and 44 make up 72 percent of AIDS cases, just as they make up 75 percent of people arrested or treated for use of hard drugs.[6]

What can be said of drug use in the AIDS risk groups?

The fact that injection drug users comprise one third of American AIDS cases should give pause for thought. Consider how that number breaks down. This figure includes three-quarters of all heterosexual AIDS cases and over two-thirds of all female AIDS. Over two-thirds of all babies with AIDS are born to mothers who inject drugs. Even ten percent of the hemophiliac AIDS cases inject drugs. These statistics only incorporate self-reported drug injection, for they cannot confirm such illegal habits in people who will not admit to them. And more importantly, most drugs are inhaled or taken orally, not intravenously. The Centers for Disease Control, however, does not ask AIDS patients about non-intravenous drug use, but is more concerned about possible HIV contamination on the injection equipment.

Perhaps the heroin itself is more dangerous than the dirty needle through which it passes.

The remaining AIDS cases occur mostly among male homosexuals, the group that originally defined the epidemic. But the homosexuals who get AIDS form a special subset of homosexuals in general—the heavily promiscuous men, the so-called "fast-track" homosexuals who emerged from the closet during the 1970s and entered the bathhouses, discotheques, and sex clubs. There they picked up dozens of sexual encounters in a single evening, often anonymously. These men accumulated hundreds or even thousands of sexual contacts within just a few years. Venereal diseases and exotic parasites spread like wildfire, prompting Joseph Sonnabend's multifactorial hypothesis of AIDS. Infectious diseases ranging from the flu to hepatitis B became commonplace, and heavy doses of antibiotics were taken by many each night before sex, just to prevent unsightly sores or acne.[7]

Such extreme sexual activity cannot be done on a cup of coffee. The "fast-track" lifestyle required liberal drug use—stimulants to get going, poppers to allow anal intercourse, downers to unwind afterwards. Several drugs, combined with alcohol and marijuana, became par for the course of an evening, a routine that would go on for years. One homosexual man, a math professor in New York who has witnessed the fast-track scene, described the situation in a 1993 letter to Duesberg. We reproduce a good part of the letter here as a testimony, a window to the high-risk lifestyle behind AIDS:

> From my experience in the New York City and Fire Island gay communities I can testify that more than 1000 (an ever increasing number) of my acquaintances have been diagnosed HIV/AIDS over the past decade. Unfortunately some 250 (an estimate, it could be greater) of these are now prematurely dead...
>
> I have a list of my friends and acquaintances who died under the HIV/AIDS diagnosis. There are 150 names on the list... The remarkable thing about the people on this list and the hundreds of people living with an HIV diagnosis who presently come in and out of my life, sometimes daily, sometimes weekly, is that they almost all have a drug (recreational and medical) and an alcohol history of duration of often more than ten years...
>
> Most of the people on my list abused some, if not all, of the following drugs used recreationally: alcohol, amyl nitrite, barbiturates, butyl nitrite, cocaine, crack, ecstasy (XTC), heroin, librium, LSD, Mandrex, MDA, MDM, mescaline, methamphetamines, mushrooms, PCP, purple haze, quaalude, secanol, special K, THC, tuinol, and valium.
>
> Most of the people on the list hosted many diseases and some of these diseases more than once. The following microbial diseases or microbes were common: candida albicans, chlamydia, cytomegalovirus, cryptosporidiosis, Epstein-Barr virus, gonorrhea, giardia, hepatitis A or B or C or D, herpes simplex (both 1 & 2), herpes zoster, gay bowel syndrome, scabies, venereal warts and other parasites. In almost all of these cases the diseases were contracted before an HIV$^+$ diagnosis.
>
> ... I know that my acquaintances ingested large amounts of various antibiotics, antifungals and antiparasitics. Some used antibiotics before going out for sex as prophylaxis against sexually transmitted diseases. These antibiotics were routinely given to them by gay doctors familiar with the fast-lane scene. Of course, after HIV diagnosis the overwhelming majority of these people used antibiotics, antifungals, antivirals (AZT, ddI, ddC, d4T, acyclovir, gancyclovir, etc.), as a matter of course, in various combinations over varying intervals of time...
>
> At gay discos, both in New York City and on Fire Island, the use of recreational drugs is prevalent. The most common drugs are cocaine, ecstasy, poppers, and special K. On weekends on Fire Island drug dealers hawk their goods on the beach and on the walks as well as announce their

hotel room numbers. Drug consumption among the fast-track gays is "de rigeur."

I emphasize that my remarks on drug usage are my observations or they were related directly to me by the individuals involved. They are not judgments...

As a result of these observations I am inclined towards the Duesberg drug-AIDS hypothesis.[8]

One Texas doctor, while studying AIDS risk factors among his patients in the early 1980s, discovered some of the dangerous practices in the bathhouses. "As an example, one of the drugs used was the readily available ethylene chloride," he wrote. "I was curious as to how this could be utilized for a 'high' until it was explained to me that a group formed a circle, saturated a towel, and then passed it from person to person for deep inhalation, which certainly seemed an excellent way to transmit disease to me!"[9]

On the west coast, AIDS activist William Bryan Coyle now battles the HIV dogma. He has painted a similar picture of the fast-track life:

> These were the gayest of years! But the question is: Were they a bit too gay? In deciding to "party" and celebrate our newly obtained freedom, where would the limits be set? How much partying? How many cocktails? Would that be just on the weekends or seven days a week? These decisions were, of course, up to each individual, however the tendency by most to want to be social and sexual would lead most gay men to either a gay bar, a gay dance club, or "the baths"... For many the choice became regular visits to the infamous bathhouses, whether it was the main plan for an evening or the finale to an assorted night of gay bars and discos. Whatever the case, it was usually routine to use one or more "mood-elevating substances" to enhance this social/sexual experience. Substances frequently chosen included cocaine, quaaludes, amphetamines, LSD, MDA, amyl nitrite, and, of course, marijuana and alcohol. The combined "recipe" for an evening might possibly involve four or five of these, and in this depressed state the sexual exposure to one or more person's germs would occur and an increased tendency towards indiscriminate additional promiscuity due to distorted judgment capabilities...
>
> Some men would use poppers 30 to 40 times while dancing and then additionally at home or at the baths during their post-disco sexual liaison. As the market grew and "boot-leg" amyl nitrite was now available in half-ounce screw-top glass bottles, it was not uncommon to be in a disco where someone had either accidentally or deliberately spilled a quantity on the dance floor, intoxicating everyone in reach...
>
> So many of the poor souls deteriorating so rapidly with AIDS had gone from illegal/recreational drug abuse, directly into multiple daily prescribed drug abuse [such as AZT]... I, for one, will not be another statistic.[10]

Coyle is HIV-positive and was once diagnosed with AIDS. He credits ending his drug use, and paying careful attention to his diet to help control yeast infections, for his gradually improving health. He has even found the energy to write his own book, currently in progress.

Larry Kramer, the volatile homosexual rights and AIDS activist who founded the AIDS Coalition To Unleash Power (ACT UP), has himself criticized the excesses of "fast-track" living. A playwright and author by profession, he used his 1978 novel *Faggots* to lament the emptiness of anonymous homosexual activity. His book described the intense sexual promiscuity in the bathhouses, a lifestyle that could never be separated from the endless drug use on which it depended. Indeed, Kramer specifically listed many of the most popular drugs, which author Jad Adams later paraphrased as "sixteen varieties of marijuana" and the following:

MDA, MDM, THC, PCP, STP, DMT, LDK, WDW, Coke, Window Pane, Blotter, Orange Sunshine, Sweet Pea, Sky Blue, Christmas Tree, Mescalin, Dust, Benzedrine, Dexedrine, Dexamyl, Desoxyn, Strychnine, Ionamin, Ritalin, Desbutal, Opitol, Glue, Ethyl Chloride, Nitrous Oxide, Crystel Methedrine, Clogidal, Nesperan, Tytch, Nestex, Black Beauty, Certyn, Preludin with B-12, Zayl, Quaalude, Tuinal, Nembutal, Seconal, Amytal, Phenobarb, Elavil, Valium, Librium, Darvon, Mandrax, Opium, Stidyl, Halidax, Calcifyn, Optimil, Drayl.[11]

Years passed before AIDS forced the homosexual community as a whole to acknowledge, however grudgingly, Kramer's point.

Medical physicians and researchers have also described the drug problem rampant among many homosexuals. A surprising guest editorial appeared in a 1985 issue of the *Wall Street Journal*, co-written by a journalist and a Washington, D.C. doctor, Cesar Caceres. The two authors cited official CDC AIDS statistics, as well as Caceres' own patients, to argue that drug use was so universal among AIDS patients that HIV could not be considered the syndrome's primary cause. AIDS patients, they protested, have "pre-existing immune damage" from years of drug use, without which AIDS cannot occur. In a direct challenge to the AIDS research establishment, they rhetorically asked, "Since drug abuse can severely damage the immune system, why has AIDS been identified primarily with sex, especially sex among homosexuals?"[12]

Joan McKenna, a leading advocate of the syphilis-AIDS hypothesis (see Chapter Seven), nevertheless described similar drug use patterns among 100 homosexual men in her medical practice: "We have found... nearly universal use of marijuana; a multiple and complex use of LSD, MDA, PCP, heroin, cocaine, amyl and butyl nitrites, amphetamines, barbiturates, ethyl chloride, opium, mushrooms, and what are referred to as 'designer drugs'."[13]

John Lauritsen and Hank Wilson noted that "Leaders of People With AIDS, who have known hundreds of PWA's, state that most of them were heavily into drugs, and all of them used poppers," and that the owner of a prominent homosexual sex club candidly admitted, "I really don't know anybody who's had AIDS who hasn't used drugs."[14]

Large-scale studies confirm these descriptions. An early CDC study, interviewing over 400 homosexual men recruited from venereal disease clinics, counted 86 percent of them as using poppers frequently. Another study of 170 such men found that 96 percent admitted inhaling poppers regularly, while most had also used cocaine, amphetamines, lysergic acid, and methaqualone; many had also taken phenylcyclidine, ethyl chloride, barbiturates, and heroin. A study of over 350 homosexual men from San Francisco discovered that over 80 percent used cocaine and poppers, with a majority simultaneously consuming other hard drugs. And a similar Boston study of over 200 HIV-infected homosexual men revealed that 92 percent inhaled poppers and three-quarters used cocaine, in addition to the usual laundry list of drugs. Among male homosexual AIDS patients, over 95 percent typically admitted to popper inhalation; by comparison, fewer than one percent of all heterosexuals or lesbians used poppers. In these and other studies, HIV-positive men had always used more drugs than had uninfected men, and sexual activity was tightly linked to heavy drug use.[15]

Drugs have also brought babies into the AIDS epidemic. A small percentage of the total cases, infants tend to suffer their own peculiar spectrum of AIDS symptoms such as bacterial infections and mental deficiencies. This reads like the profile of "crack babies," and is no coincidence. In his book *And the Band Played On*, Randy Shilts revealed which babies were getting AIDS. "Whatever the homosexuals had that was giving them Kaposi's sarcoma and *Pneumocystis*," he noted ominously, "it was also spreading among drug addicts and, most tragically, their children."[16] Except that these young victims did not get Kaposi's sarcomas, lymphomas, or various other diseases common to homosexual AIDS cases. Two-thirds of these children have had mothers who inject drugs; some large percentage of the rest have mothers snorting cocaine or otherwise using non-injected drugs. A few studies have reported identical syndromes among babies of drug-using mothers, regardless of HIV infection.[17] Yet the news media has endlessly exploited these AIDS babies as proof the syndrome is contagious, ignoring the drug connection in these unusual infants.

Injection drug addicts and male homosexuals, and the children of drug-injecting mothers, have contributed 94 percent of all AIDS patients. Thus the correlation between heavy drug use and AIDS is far better than between HIV and AIDS, a relationship underscored by the evidence that AIDS is not a contagious disease. And although thousands of HIV-free AIDS cases have been described in the medical literature, possibly indicating hundreds of thousands more, no study has ever presented a group of AIDS patients genuinely free of drug use or other AIDS risks (such as hemophilia).

Taken together, these facts imply a central role for drug use in AIDS. But there is also strong experimental reason to indict these drugs on the basis of their chemical properties. Indeed, each of the major AIDS-risk drugs shows evidence of toxicity that could destroy the immune system or cause other AIDS diseases.

AIDS through chemistry

Medicine first pioneered the use of alkyl nitrite compounds in the 1860s. Because the substances relaxed muscles and dilated blood vessels, they helped patients with heart diseases such as angina. These liquids were carried in tiny glass vials that would be broken open to inhale the powerful fumes, and thus gained the nickname "poppers." Using only these tiny amounts, terminal heart patients never lived long enough to report dangerous health effects.

During the 1960s, male homosexuals discovered the aphrodisiac effects of nitrites. Receptive anal intercourse became less painful because the anal sphincter (muscle) would relax, and therefore receptive men used far more of the drug than did their insertive partners.[18] Nitrites also helped maintain erections and intensified orgasm, and some users even claimed a euphoric "high." The cost at first seemed little more than a brief rush and often a headache. The interest in poppers for sexual purposes soon turned into a stampede, the drug becoming a staple of bathhouse and discotheque life. Bottles of the drug could be purchased in sex shops under such brand names as "Rush," "Ram," "Thunderbolt," "Locker Room," "Climax," "Discorama," and "Crypt Tonight."[19] As described in one research paper, "Common settings in which these agents are used include the bedroom, parties, backrooms of pornographic bookstores, pornographic theaters, bars, and dance floors. Some users have told us that a few discotheques use special lighting effects to indicate that they are about to spray nitrite fumes over the dance floor."[20] According to John Lauritsen and Hank Wilson, "With regular use, they become a sexual crutch, and many gay men are incapable of having sex, even solitary masturbation, without the aid of poppers."[21] Nitrite manufacturers, however, managed to sidestep most federal controls by labeling the substance as a "room odorizer," and the "popper craze" took off during the 1970s.[22]

But not very many chemicals are more toxic than nitrites. Sodium nitrite, a much weaker related compound used in tiny amounts as a preservative in meats, has been regulated for years as a potential cancer-causing agent (if ingested at much higher concentrations). The alkylated nitrites (poppers), on the other hand, react more violently with almost anything. Upon mixing with water, as in the human body, these nitrites form the unstable nitrous acid, which in turn destroys any biological molecules within reach. The nitrites and their breakdown products have long been known to scientists for their ability to mutate DNA, a point recently verified by direct experiment, and in combination with other substances they can form nitrosamines, some of the most powerful cancer-causing chemicals in existence.

The reactivity of nitrites easily compares with such toxins as carbon monoxide, the gas that suffocates its victims when a car engine is allowed to run in a closed garage. Carbon monoxide destroys the hemoglobin in blood, preventing oxygen from reaching the body despite normal breathing. Nitrites do the same, a process that can be fatal if too much is inhaled at one time. At the height of the "popper craze," for example, a number of overdose victims arrived in hospital emergency rooms with as much as two-thirds of their hemoglobin chemically destroyed. Or to look at nitrites from another angle, a single dose can saturate the person using it with up to ten million nitrite molecules per cell in the body, leaving plenty of opportunity for damage.[23]

But the important question is whether inhaling the drug at sub-lethal doses for several years can eventually destroy the immune system, or cause cancer. Recognizing the universal popularity of nitrites among homosexual

men in 1981, the CDC was forced to offer this drug as one possible explanation of the emerging AIDS epidemic. However, the infection-minded CDC
officials sabotaged the hypothesis by only searching for a single "bad batch"
of poppers that might have temporarily caused a few sicknesses. They also
assumed the effects would show immediately after using poppers, not
following ten years. Naturally, no such batch could ever be found, and the
CDC thereafter focused its search entirely on infectious agents.

Not all scientists dropped the idea so easily. Some continued testing the
proposal that long-term exposure to all nitrites might cause AIDS, and found
some suspicious associations. Kaposi's sarcoma, the blood vessel tumor,
grabbed some attention for its direct link to the poppers. This AIDS disease
almost entirely affected homosexuals, leaving heroin addicts, hemophiliacs,
and other AIDS victims untouched, just as homosexuals were by far the
major consumers of nitrite inhalants. Often the Kaposi's tumor appeared on
the faces and upper torsos, and in the lungs, of its victims, precisely where the
nitrite fumes concentrated the heaviest during use.[24] Researchers also discovered that the risk of the tumor was directly proportional to an individual's total lifetime exposure to poppers, regardless of how many venereal or other
contagious diseases the person had caught. Interestingly, they estimated that
seven to ten years of exposure would, on average, produce AIDS—roughly
the same as the supposed "latent period" of HIV.[25]

Time has born out the nitrite hypothesis of Kaposi's sarcoma. Early public health warnings about the drug's potential effects convinced many homosexual men to stop inhaling it. By 1984, only 58 percent of homosexual men
in San Francisco said they used the drug on a regular basis, dropping to less
than half that number by 1991. In parallel, the incidence of Kaposi's sarcoma
also steadily dropped as a proportion of AIDS cases, from half of all AIDS
reports in 1981 to only 10 percent by 1991. This has been the only AIDS disease to decrease this way, a change so shocking that the CDC itself briefly
considered the possibility, in early 1991, that Kaposi's sarcoma might be a
disease completely independent of AIDS and not caused by HIV. In the end,
they retained this tumor in the list of AIDS diseases, correctly assuming few
people would pay attention. Reports have now also emerged of young homosexual men with this tumor who have never been infected by HIV, but who
do admit having used poppers.

Intrigued by the poppers connection, researchers in several laboratories
began independently testing long-term exposure in rats or mice to see if the
drug could also cause immune deficiency. One CDC research team deliberately used a low dose and carried out the experiment for only a few weeks,
finding some side effects but no damage to the rodents' immune systems. But
several other labs used higher doses that resembled the heavy recreational use
by homosexuals, their experiments all showing clear destructive effects on
the immune system, especially after a few months. In 1983, however, the
CDC publicized only its own mouse study, claiming this as proof nitrites
were really harmless. The later studies remained obscure and mostly
forgotten.[26]

Even today, most scientists have not heard of the later nitrite research, and in various conversations we have encountered curiosity or amazement that human beings would inhale such chemicals. The editor of *Science* magazine, the most popular journal among researchers, privately expressed to us his astonishment at the pervasive use among homosexual men with AIDS, a group he previously thought only had HIV as a risk factor.

Heroin is another AIDS-risk drug with a long history of serious health effects, though not as well studied as the nitrites. Some of this information even dates back to the time opium was smoked, rather than injected as heroin. Descriptions of health troubles in drug users date back as far as 1909, often following waves of addiction. Persistent drug users have showed loss of white blood cells, the cornerstone of the immune system, as well as lymph node swelling, fever, rapid weight loss, brain dysfunctions and dementia, and a marked vulnerability to infections—in other words, immune deficiency. Addicts who inject heroin have classically died from pneumonias, tuberculosis, and other opportunistic infections, as well as from wasting syndromes, all precisely the same "AIDS diseases" they suffer today.

In fact, modern studies that look at heroin addicts with such diseases typically find that half of them, or more, have never been infected by HIV, yet all are dying of the same conditions. Sampled from places as diverse as New York and Baltimore, as well as France, Germany, Sweden, and Holland, injection drug users manifest pneumonia, tuberculosis, T cell depletion, and death even without HIV. Some studies have found the death rates of HIV-positive and -negative addicts to be the same, and others have found the percentage of addicts with HIV to be the same among those who died and those still alive. In these dozens of scientific papers published over the last decade, the only truly common denominator has been the drug use itself, irrespective of HIV infection.[27]

Even among addicts with HIV, only the drug use seems to affect rates of AIDS and death. Those who stop injecting drugs at some point consistently develop less AIDS and survive longer than those who continue to inject.[28] And babies born to drug-injecting mothers have more suppressed immune systems and worse deformities than babies born to mothers who stopped injecting before pregnancy, independently of whether the babies were infected with HIV or not.[29]

The steadfast belief in the HIV hypothesis by public health authorities has created problems in trying to control AIDS. The Swiss city of Zurich recently learned the hard way when city officials reserved a park in the center of the city, Am Platzspitz, as a free zone for heroin addicts. Each drug user was provided sterile needles for injection on a daily basis, in order to prevent the spread of HIV. Much to the surprise of government officials and the news media, the heroin addicts have continued to develop their standard pneumonias and other diseases at the usual rate. If anything, the provision of sterile needles actually encouraged further drug use, thereby promoting AIDS. But public health officials, convinced they had done their job in fighting the epidemic, referred to the continued pneumonias as "AIDS-like diseases" so as to imply the drug addicts were now dying of something entirely different.[30]

Cocaine has also become a popular injection drug, although it is mostly inhaled or smoked. Less is known about its long-term health effects, but it does suppress the growth of T cells in the culture dish. Babies born to cocaine-using mothers have severe mental retardation and other problems. Cocaine addicts often develop lung problems, and have proven unusually susceptible to tuberculosis, an AIDS disease. A new epidemic of tuberculosis has even emerged among cocaine and "crack" addicts within the last few years. In its press statements, the CDC first assumed the outbreak resulted from the spread of HIV.[31] But upon testing these new tuberculosis cases, it found only a minority of them infected with the virus. Backed into a corner, the CDC smoothly turned the tables by announcing that a new tuberculosis epidemic, parallel to AIDS, was now surfacing—and would soon threaten the general public! For decades, however, a significant percentage of the population has been infected by the tuberculosis bacterium, over ninety percent of whom never become ill. Populations in the industrial world no longer develop symptoms from tuberculosis, whereas cocaine users seem to have a special inability to fight off the disease.

Amphetamines are also becoming a popular recreational drug among AIDS risk groups, particularly homosexuals. Swallowed as pills in the past, the drug is making new rounds in a crystal form that can be smoked—"ice." Complete with all the addictive problems of "crack" cocaine, these amphetamines are causing a range of symptoms, from the loss of motor coordination found in Parkinson's disease to psychoses and sudden, radical weight loss. The latter qualifies as the wasting disease of AIDS.

But even "ice" cannot begin to compare with the devastating effects of "crystal," the street name for methamphetamine. One of the cheapest and most powerful stimulants available, "it raises sexual cravings to new, superhuman levels," and is now becoming an uncontrollable epidemic in the homosexual community. "Crystal is a gay person's drug and a gay community concern," states one official at a Los Angeles drug treatment facility. Many snort the drug in powder form, while others inject it intravenously or as an enema. Crystal drives its users to unparalleled heights of intense sexual excitement and frenzied behavior, coupled with periodic crashes of equal horror and the gradual development of psychoses. Overdose victims are beginning to show up. "We're just starting to see heavy usage types in our emergency rooms in New York City," says one medical worker, who also notes that "life expectancy for those intravenously injecting crystal is two years." What about those who last longer on the drug? According to the head of a French AIDS foundation, "There is ample evidence to suggest that crystal accelerates premature progression to full-blown AIDS in people dealing with HIV infection. Studies have shown that crystal eats T-cells for breakfast, lunch and dinner."[32] The crystal epidemic is so new that its impact on the AIDS epidemic is probably just beginning to be felt.

Science, however, has little working knowledge on the long-term effects of heroin, cocaine, amphetamines, and other common recreational drugs. Ultimately, we can determine whether these drugs truly cause AIDS only by exposing animals, such as mice, to these drugs for several months at a time.

Except for the nitrites, no such experiments have ever been done. AIDS research dollars have been plowed entirely into studying HIV, leaving the comparatively tiny field of drug toxicity with virtually no support at all. Most illegal drugs have only been given to mice or rats in a single dose, looking for the short-term effects. Until researchers can perform long-term experiments, the role of drugs in AIDS will never be proven. Certainly the evidence above strongly implies drugs could more easily cause AIDS than could any microbe.

Two more potential risk factors also need to be investigated.

As increasing numbers of homosexuals entered the "fast-track" during the 1970s and 1980s, infections by viruses, bacteria, and other parasites skyrocketed. Antibiotics became the panacea; pop a few pills, and one could return to the bathhouses to catch another infection. "A typical medical history would include dozens of cases of VD [venereal disease] in the decade before the 'AIDS' diagnosis," writes John Lauritsen. "Each case of VD would be treated with stronger and stronger doses of antibiotics. Some doctors gave their gay patients open prescriptions for antibiotics, advising them to swallow a few before going to the baths. One popular bath house in New York (now closed) sold black market tetracycline on the second floor, along with all kinds of street drugs."[33]

Tetracycline certainly topped the list of favorite medical drugs, both for treatment and even to prevent new infections—often being taken before visits to the discotheques or sex clubs. Perhaps the only survey of this phenomenon, which "interviewed the patrons of a gay bar in Memphis, Tennessee," found that "over 40 percent of the men surveyed responded that they 'routinely' treated themselves with prescription antibiotics."[34] In some cases this would reach an extreme, as seen in certain of Joan McKenna's patients: "I have histories of gay men who have been on tetracycline for 18 years for the possibility of a pimple! I guarantee you their body chemistry isn't normal."[35] A less specific antibiotic than penicillin, tetracycline interferes with the body's normal metabolism. Doctors include with prescriptions a warning to stay out of the sunlight, for this antibiotic stops the skin from repairing sunburns. Used over the long term, it can also cause immune suppression.[36] The same holds true for corticosteroids and erythromycin, also widely prescribed to treat or prevent venereal disease in homosexual men.[37] Possibly the worst side effects of these antibiotics result from killing helpful bacteria, such as *E. coli*, residing in the body. Many people using antibiotics for long time periods find yeast or other fungal infections moving in to replace the dead bacteria.

The more toxic drugs came into play when treating diarrhea caused by intestinal parasites, such as ameobae. Homosexual men would receive such compounds as flagyl and diiodohydroxyquin, the latter related to clioquinol, the drug that caused SMON (see Chapter One).[38] And to prevent *Pneumocystis carinii* pneumonia, such sulfa drugs as bactrim and septra are now prescribed, which certainly have serious side effects.

Malnutrition, another potential AIDS risk factor, also plagues the drug addict, who spends money on drugs rather than on a complete diet. Protein and zinc deficiencies have been described among many drug users, but the nature and importance of these dietary problems has never been researched. In general terms, malnourished people do face a high risk of immune deficiencies and pneumonias. Protein- and vitamin-deficient diets are found in much of the Third World, and existed throughout Europe immediately following the havoc of World War II. Under such conditions, opportunistic infections do run rampant.

If recreational drug use and its associated risks have produced 94 percent of the American AIDS epidemic, how can we explain the remaining 6 percent? Half of these extra AIDS victims caught HIV through blood transfusions, a point that fuels the popular belief in AIDS as a contagious disease. But a closer look at these patients reveals some surprising facts, ones that confirm AIDS is neither infectious nor a single epidemic.

AIDS and the blood supply

Tax rebellion dominated the late 1970s, and Paul Gann epitomized that theme. Working with his long-time friend Howard Jarvis, a sometimes-crusty California state legislator, he organized the citizens' crusades against rising tax burdens. The years of relentless warfare against the political establishment finally paid off in 1979, when California voters overwhelmingly passed Proposition 13 to limit property taxes. Excitement spread around the country, and dozens of states began following suit.

Gann had achieved folk hero status in the eyes of millions of taxpayers. Yet even his fighting spirit could not withstand the ravages of age. A worsening heart condition forced him into the hospital by 1982, when he was seventy years old. His heart disease was so bad that doctors made the decision to operate, creating five separate bypasses of the heart during the long operation. Large volumes of blood had to be transfused to make up for the losses. Gann slowly recovered enough to leave the hospital, but by the following year he returned with blocked intestinal arteries. Again bypass surgery was required.

Gallo's patented test for finding antibodies against HIV became universally available by 1985, after which HIV-positive blood was screened out of the nation's supply. Several years later, ongoing complications and increasing political pressure to find AIDS in heterosexuals[39] prompted doctors to test Gann. As chance would have it, he was positive, probably having received the virus in one of his previous transfusions. The announcement devastated Gann psychologically, who now believed he must inevitably die of AIDS. Dismay and anger fired up his old combativeness, and despite old age and ailing health he launched yet one more campaign, the last of his life. Hordes of loyal supporters gathered signatures, placing Proposition 102 on the 1988 California ballot. The measure called for stronger public health controls to prevent the spread of HIV. But in a close vote that November, the proposal went down to defeat.

Gann himself fared little better. The next year he again wound up in the hospital with a broken hip, a poor candidate for recovery at seventy-seven years of age. He was immobilized for several weeks, his condition steadily deteriorating. A severe pneumonia took over his lungs, refusing to disappear, until he finally died.

Media headlines blared the news that Gann had succumbed to the "deadly AIDS virus," reminding the public that the disease could strike anyone, homosexual or heterosexual alike, including the otherwise healthy Gann. Few news reports bothered describing his decidedly unhealthy condition, including cardiovascular disease. Nor did they remind readers that his seventy-seven years precisely equalled the average life expectancy of American men.

Gann's death typified the health situation for blood transfusion recipients. Amazingly, even health care workers rarely seem to know the survival statistics of such patients: half of all blood recipients die within the first year after transfusion.[40] Naturally, this risk does not apply equally to all patients. The very old, the very young, and the most severely injured bear the brunt of death. Transfusions, after all, are not given to normal, healthy people. These patients have undergone traumatic medical problems requiring the blood in the first place, generally followed by equally traumatic surgery and the attendant anasthesia using potentially immune-suppressive drugs. In the case of an organ transplant, the patient is given special drugs designed specifically to suppress the immune system and thereby reduce the possibility of organ rejection. And blood itself is foreign material, overloading an already-stressed immune system in proportion to the amount transfused. Transfusion recipients die of many complications, not the least being opportunistic infections preying on weakened immune systems, as for example pneumonia.

Among AIDS patients, those who caught HIV through blood transfusions do not suffer Kaposi's sarcoma, dementia, or several other major diseases found in the homosexual or injection drug-using cases. Instead they develop the pneumonias and other conditions typical of such patients as Paul Gann, with or without HIV. No evidence has shown that death rates from blood transfusions ever increased from HIV transmission, nor has anyone demonstrated that death rates declined again once the virus was screened out of the blood supply. One 1989 study reported that among hundreds of transfusion patients, those with HIV died no more often than the uninfected during the first year—the official "latent period" between HIV infection and AIDS for such patients! In short, no new epidemic of disease has affected transfusion recipients in recent years, nor do their diseases belong under the same heading as AIDS in homosexual men or heroin addicts. In 1981, the CDC's KSOI Task Force searched frantically for transfusion recipients to reclassify as having AIDS (then known as "KSOI") only for the propaganda value, as a truly contagious disease would have spread through the blood supply. AIDS has not. But by redefining the standard diseases of transfusion patients as "AIDS," the CDC has left the specter of infection as an indelible impression on the public mind.

Hemophiliacs present a similar picture. Lacking key components that allow blood to clot, these people have long faced poor prognosis. Depending on the severity of the disorder, any damage could potentially cause unstoppable bleeding, externally or internally. Hemophiliacs constantly needed blood transfusions, which only added to the problem, although the difference could hardly be noticed against the background of early death. As recently as 1972, hemophiliacs had a median life expectancy of only eleven years. Then an innovative product changed their lives permanently; scientists invented a method of extracting from normal blood the missing proteins. Known as Factor VIII, this blood component can be injected by hemophiliacs, and restores most of the clotting ability they lack. Fewer blood transfusions are now needed, and their median life expectancy has more than doubled, reaching twenty-five years by 1986.

The clotting factor brings a price tag, not just paid in financial terms. Where hemophiliacs once died from internal bleeding, they now gradually develop immune deficiencies as they get older. Factor VIII itself seems to be part of the problem: with or without HIV infection, hemophiliacs lose immune competence according to the cumulative amount of Factor consumed. However, when the clotting factor is purified, the immune system remains rather healthy. Cost, unfortunately, bars many hemophiliacs from using the purified factor. Hemophiliacs consequently develop some opportunistic diseases. Those with HIV, who are counted as AIDS cases, get these same pneumonias, while being unaffected by the Kaposi's sarcoma, lymphoma, wasting disease, and dementia that afflict homosexuals or heroin addicts with AIDS. And as would be expected if these hemophiliac diseases are not caused by HIV, those with AIDS are on average at least ten years older than the rest—ten extra years of clotting factor and blood transfusions.

Ryan White provides a case in point. The young Indiana teenager became a national symbol of heroic battling against AIDS after his school expelled him as a threat to the other students. His family's lawsuit eventually prevailed, and a court order forced the school to accept him back into the classroom. The ruling was based on the fact that HIV is difficult to transmit. The news media kept a periodic spotlight on White's life, and when he became sick and was hospitalized by 1990, the story splashed across the front pages as implicit proof the deadly virus could kill even the healthiest of people. White's death in April drew so much attention that entertainers Elizabeth Taylor and Michael Jackson attended his funeral. Although the news media portrayed the death as the tragic end to White's long fight with AIDS, the doctor never publicly confirmed that the death certificate actually attributed the cause to AIDS.

In the process of writing an article on the HIV hypothesis, Bryan Ellison phoned the Indiana Hemophilia Foundation to check the details. The voice at the other end of the line connected him with a representative who confirmed she was directly familiar with White's case. What specific AIDS diseases did he die of? She listed only internal bleeding and hemorrhaging, liver failure, and collapse of other physiological systems. These conditions match the classical description of hemophilia, none being listed as an AIDS condition, but she did not seem to know that. She then acknowledged that White's hemophilia condition was more severe than the average, requiring him to take clotting factor every day near the end. On top of all that, White had taken AZT, the former cancer chemotherapy now prescribed as AIDS treatment.

Hemophiliacs, needless to say, are particularly vulnerable to the internal ulcerations induced by such chemotherapy. Only media hype transformed White's death from a severe case of hemophilia, exacerbated by AZT, into AIDS.

Those hemophiliacs whose diseases are reclassified as AIDS tend to have the severest clotting disorders in the first place, needing more Factor VIII and transfusions to stay alive. On the other hand, hemophiliacs have less to worry about than ever before. Of the 20,000 in the United States, some three-quarters were infected by HIV through the blood supply a little more than a decade ago. Yet during that same time period, clotting factor has doubled their life expectancies, and very few are diagnosed with AIDS each year. HIV has made no measurable impact on the well-being of hemophiliacs.

AIDS in the Third World

Public health officials never cease predicting the spread of AIDS out of these narrow risk groups into the general population. This line has become less believable with each year-end CDC report showing no such spread. So the public health experts resort to an old standby. For a picture of our future, they say, look to the Third World, where AIDS has already spread into the heterosexual population.

For instance, Thailand. The last few years have brought headlines and news stories on the impending doom in that poor country, where 300,000 people are infected with HIV. A disaster for Thailand, but bad for us as well. Several Thai cities host a flourishing sex industry, where men from Europe and the United States meet to indulge themselves in the abundant prostitution. This sex tourism supposedly could bring the AIDS epidemic back to our countries in force, finally triggering the long-awaited explosion out of the risk groups.

News photographers cannot publish enough pictures of Thai prostitutes, and no estimate of the potential danger is considered too large. In all the hustle, however, reporters forget to mention the grand total of AIDS cases in that country: as of 1991, only 123 individuals had been so diagnosed, rising to 1,569 cases by the middle of 1993. This amounts to only one-half of one percent of the 300,000 HIV-positives. Even more shockingly, these Thai AIDS victims fall into very strict risk groups. Half of them are either male homosexuals or injection drug users. The other half hold down jobs as "sex workers," more commonly known as prostitutes, among whom drug use is hardly uncommon. Tuberculosis and pneumonia rank as the most common AIDS diseases in this handful of people. So much for an explosive Thai epidemic.

Africa, on the other hand, has been touted as a disaster already in progress, the ultimate example of what can happen in the industrial world if CDC guidelines are not heeded. In a continent with six to eight million HIV positives, whole villages are said to have disappeared while burdened economies are strained to the breaking point by massive death. Hospitals allegedly can no longer handle the AIDS load.

Careful inspection yields a different picture. For one thing, African population growth is higher than for any other continent—three percent per year—a figure that belies the supposed devastation of AIDS. Since the AIDS epidemic began, the entire continent of Africa has reported only 250,000 cases, fewer than in the United States. This reduces to an annual AIDS rate of about 0.3 percent of the HIV positives developing the syndrome, compared to ten times that rate in the United States. Nor is this a product of extreme under-reporting. The Ugandan AIDS surveillance system, considered internationally a model for the rest of Africa, provides similar numbers. And medical clinics seeing many HIV positives commonly find very few AIDS cases. Another confirmation comes from Felix Konotey-Ahulu, a medical physician and scientist visiting London's Cromwell Hospital from Ghana. In early 1987 he toured dozens of cities throughout sub-Saharan Africa, trying to size up the AIDS epidemic. Upon returning, he wrote a scathing editorial for the *Lancet*, criticizing news media coverage of the situation:

> If one judges the extent of the AIDS in Africa on an arbitrary scale from grade I (not much of a problem) to grade V (a catastrophe), in my assessment AIDS is a problem (grade II) in only five, (possibly six, since I was unable to obtain a visa for Zaire) of the countries where AIDS has occurred...
>
> The phrase "possibly a considerable underestimate" has appeared many times in articles and broadcasts all over the world whenever a colossal figure is attached to the extent of AIDS in Africa...
>
> If tens of thousands are dying from AIDS (and Africans do not cremate their dead) where are the graves?[41]

Konotey-Ahulu made a point of visiting hospitals featured in the Western press as hotbeds of the AIDS epidemic, but consistently found very few AIDS cases. Nevertheless, many African doctors themselves participate in building the myth of the AIDS pandemic. *Spin* reporter Celia Farber discovered the reason during a recent trip to Africa:

> Many believe that the statistics have been inflated because AIDS generates far more money in the third world from Western organizations than any other infectious disease. This was clear to us when we were there: Where there was "AIDS" there was money—a brand-new clinic, a new Mercedes parked outside, modern testing facilities, high-paying jobs, international conferences. A leading African physician... warned us not to get our hopes up about this trip. "You have no idea what you have taken on," he said on the eve of our departure. "You will never get these doctors to tell you the truth. When they get sent to these AIDS conferences around the world, the per diem they receive is equal to what they earn in a whole year at home."
>
> ... In Uganda, for example, WHO [World Health Organization] allotted $6 million for a single year, 1992-93, whereas all other infectious diseases combined—barring TB and AIDS—received a mere $57,000.[42]

To a large extent, the myth of an African AIDS epidemic grew out of a report in the late 1980s, entitled *Voyage des Krynen en Tanzanie*. Written by French charity workers Philippe and Evelyne Krynen, it dramatically summarized their findings of devastated villages, abandoned homes, growing numbers of orphans, and a sexually-transmitted AIDS epidemic that threatened to depopulate the Kagera province of northern Tanzania. As the heads of *Partage*, the largest AIDS charity for Tanzanian children, the Krynens told a story that the news media could not resist, one that is still repeated today. The vivid images helped shape the Western impression of an AIDS problem out of control.

But after spending a few years working with the people of the Kagera, the Krynens changed their minds. To their own disbelief, they discovered no AIDS epidemic in the region at all. The "sexually transmitted" disease somehow completely missed the prostitutes while killing their clients; the exact same prostitutes work the towns today. Then the Krynens discovered that over half their "AIDS" patients tested negative for HIV. The empty houses turned out to be additional homes owned by Tanzanians who had moved to the city. And the final blow came from the "orphans" themselves, who turned out to be the consequences of the Tanzanian social structure; the parents typically moved to the cities to earn money, leaving the grandparents to care for the children. "There is no Aids," Philippe Krynen now states flatly. "It is something that has been invented. There are no epidemiological grounds for it; it doesn't exist for us."[43] He also describes how the epidemic is created for media consumption:

> Families just bring [children] as orphans, and if you ask how the parents died they will say Aids. It is fashionable nowadays to say that, because it brings money and support.
> If you say your father has died in a car accident it is bad luck, but if he has died from Aids there is an agency to help you. The local people have seen so many agencies coming, called Aids support programmes, that they want to join this group of victims. Everybody claims to be a victim of Aids nowadays. And local people working for Aids agencies have become rich. They have built homes in Dar es Salaam, they have their motorbikes; they have benefited a lot...
> We have everybody coming here now, the World Bank, the churches, the Red Cross, the UN Development Programme, the African Medical Research Foundation, about 17 organisations reportedly doing something for Aids in Kagera. It brings jobs, cars, the day there is no more Aids, a lot of development is going to go away...
> You don't need Aids patients to have an Aids epidemic nowadays, because what is wrong doesn't need to be proved. Nobody checks; Aids exists by itself.[44]

Exaggeration involves more than the numbers; the epidemic itself is manufactured. None of the African AIDS diseases is new. Many common Third World diseases are confused with AIDS even if they are not part of its official definition. The WHO definition for African AIDS includes "slim disease," a composite of weight loss, diarrhea, and fever, plus such conditions as persistent coughing, skin problems, swollen lymph nodes, and some opportunistic infections like tuberculosis. This list reads like a summary of indigenous African health problems. Malaria, the leading killer in the Third World, produces fever and other symptoms frequently misdiagnosed as AIDS. Tuberculosis, also a common killer, presents another problem, as described by a Nigerian medical professor: "The serologic demonstration of HIV infection in patients with tuberculosis in Africa is very important because it aids the separation of seropositive from the seronegative patients since such a separation may be impossible in all cases on clinical grounds."[45] According to an Ugandan doctor treating AIDS cases, "A patient who has TB and is HIV positive would appear exactly the same as a patient who has TB and is HIV negative. Clinically, both patients would present with prolonged fever; both patients would present with loss of weight, massive loss of weight, actually; both patients would present with a prolonged cough, and in both cases the cough would equally be productive. Now, therefore, clinically I cannot differentiate the two."[46]

Konotey-Ahulu has illustrated what a complete mess has been made by the AIDS definition:

> Immunosuppressive diseases, of course, there always have been in Africa and elsewhere before antiquity was born... I have clinical photographs from 1965 of a Ghanaian man who looked exactly like some of the AIDS patients I saw in Africa recently. The man who was like a skeleton (from gross weight loss) has severe non-bloody diarrhoea (more than twenty bowel actions a day); he had what looked like fungus in the mouth (candidiasis), skin changes (dermatopathy), periodic fever and cough—all the classical features of African AIDS... The patient (according to relatives) had literally consumed on average one and a half bottles of whisky every single day for the previous 18 months before admission. We found it difficult to believe the story but there are photographs today showing a complete reversal in 1966 of the physical signs and symptoms, including the diabetes, when hospitalisation cut short his alcohol supply and active treatment was administered, with gradual protein calorie build up and pancreatin supplements.[47]

He had also seen the effects of reclassifying traditional diseases under the AIDS umbrella. From his medical practice in Africa, he recalled that "Before the days of AIDS in Ghana there was a death a day (more in the rainy and harmattan seasons) on my ward alone of thirty-four beds." Listing dozens of fatal diseases ranging from tuberculosis to various cancers, he remarked sarcastically, "Today, because of AIDS, it seems that Africans are not allowed to die from these conditions any longer."[48]

In a 1989 letter to the *Lancet*, four Tanzanian doctors reported examples of another source of confusion—the misdiagnosis of diabetes as AIDS.

> Some of the reasons why diabetes may be confused with AIDS are illustrated in these case histories. Weight loss is often marked in newly presenting diabetic patients in Africa, fatigue may be a prominent feature, frequent visits to the toilet may be misinterpreted as indicating diarrhoea... Skin lesions, especially fungal infections, boils, and abscesses, are often present in newly presenting diabetic patients, and these could also mislead observers.

In tropical Africa febrile illnesses are frequently attributed to malaria. Now in certain places AIDS is the fashionable diagnosis, made by the public and doctors. Many patients with treatable and curable illnesses may now be condemned without proper assessment. Public and medical education on AIDS should stress that symptoms such as those described are not unique to AIDS, and that even if a person presents with clinical AIDS the possibility of coexisting problems such as diabetes should not be overlooked.[49]

So how can doctors tell the difference between AIDS and other conditions? Only by testing for antibodies against HIV! Thus HIV has no connection with disease, and no new epidemic exists. Several large studies recently published findings that among thousands of randomly selected Africans with standard AIDS diseases, fewer than half were HIV positive.

As one nurse working in Tanzania put it, "If people die of malaria, it is called AIDS. If they die of herpes, it is called AIDS. I've even seen people die in accidents and it's been attributed to AIDS. The AIDS figures out of Africa are pure lies, pure estimate."[50]

Like everywhere else, AIDS in Africa seems to encompass at least two independent epidemics. Konotey-Ahulu and some other doctors insist that one major risk group is composed of urban prostitutes. As in Thailand, these women supply the goods for a "sex tourism" market. European and American men bring money to such countries as the Ivory Coast to purchase time with these "international prostitutes," who themselves travel from surrounding countries to compete for customers. The same modern jet travel that has made such trade possible has also brought another plague to African cities: recreational drugs. Authorities are becoming frustrated with the rising levels of cocaine and other substances being imported into the cities, creating all the attendant problems since the mid-1980s. Injection drug use remains uncommon, but cocaine and heroin are commonly smoked. The little evidence that emerges from Africa indicates that only those urban prostitutes sinking into the drug epidemic are developing AIDS.[51] Certainly this is true of Thailand.[52]

A completely separate epidemic seems to affect rural Africans, this one with no identified risk group at all. Some reports suggest a correlation between AIDS and malnutrition, which has long been known to cause such conditions. Doctors observe that AIDS patients who eat least often, or whose diets are skewed by food availability, suffer the most rapid decline in health. Other doctors attribute some of the sickness to "voodoo death" syndrome, the term for illnesses induced psychologically. According to one nurse, "We had people who were symptomatically AIDS patients. They were dying of AIDS, but when they were tested and found out they were negative they suddenly rebounded and are now perfectly healthy."[53] Needless to say, sanitation rarely exists in rural Africa, and clean water supplies are often little better than a fantasy. Whatever does cause early death among Third World populations, nothing appears to be new in Africa.

Both sorts of AIDS epidemics may have affected Haitians as well. The country hosts an active sex trade in the cities, while virtually all of the

Haitians who arrived in the United States suffered some degree of malnutrition. Tuberculosis has topped the list of their AIDS diseases; Kaposi's sarcoma can hardly be found. Although Haitians still form a risk group for AIDS, the CDC has for years reclassified them under other AIDS risk categories, the reason they are no longer mentioned as a separate group in AIDS statistics.

The widespread belief in the HIV hypothesis has yielded tragic ironies. AIDS control programs in African nations, funded by outside governments, provide little but fear. Konotey-Ahulu's 1989 book reproduces a photograph of an Ugandan child, his filthy clothes ripped in tatters and his bony frame revealing the rampant hunger in his war-torn land, holding up the condoms given him by public health experts. With solutions like this, Africa's burdens are likely to continue crushing the little hope that remains.

Only one group of AIDS victims has not been explained thus far. Three percent of American AIDS patients fall under the CDC's "other" exposure category, having no identifiable risks for catching HIV. This hardly rules out hidden drug use, but some of these cases must result from the expansive definition of AIDS. Each year, a fairly random background of people develop an occasional pneumonia, yeast infection, or hepatitis, any of which will be rediagnosed as AIDS if the person is coincidentally also infected by the virus.

Many HIV-positive people, whether they have symptoms or not, would normally not die of AIDS, but do so anyway. The reason lies in their treatment, AZT, one of the most toxic substances ever chosen for medical therapy. This politically chosen drug is now creating a scandal that may soon explode as the most embarrassing in the history of medicine. The evidence that AZT actually causes AIDS, and the story behind its unethical approval, are told in the next chapter.

Chapter 8 Footnotes

[1] Konotey-Ahulu, *What Is AIDS?* Tetteh-A'Domeno Co., Watford, England, 1989, p. 109.

[2] Newell, Spitz, and Wilson, Nitrite inhalants: Historical perspective. *in* Haverkos and Dougherty, *Health Hazards of Nitrite Inhalants*, Research Monograph 83, National Institute on Drug Abuse, Rockville, MD, 1988, p. 5; Lauritsen, *The AIDS War*. Asklepios, New York, 1993, p. 104.

[3] Lauritsen and Wilson, *Death Rush: Poppers and AIDS*. Pagan Press, New York, 1986, pp. 6, 15.

[4] Ibid., pp. 48-53.

[5] Duesberg, AIDS acquired by drug consumption and other noncontagious risk factors. *Pharmacology & Therapeutics* 55:201-277, 1992, especially p. 237.

[6] Ibid., especially p. 237.

[7] Root-Bernstein, Do we know the cause(s) of AIDS? *Perspectives in Biology and Medicine* 33:480-500, 1990, p. 484; Lauritsen, *The AIDS War*, Op cit., pp. 197-199; Coulter, *AIDS and Syphilis — The Hidden Link*. North Atlantic Books, Berkeley, CA, 1987, p. 47.

[8] Buianouckas, Letter to Peter Duesberg, April 29, 1993.

[9] Hill, Letter to Peter Duesberg, June 4, 1992.

[10] Coyle, "In memory of... The way it was" (an open letter, unpublished), Jan. 14, 1992.

[11] Adams, *AIDS: The HIV Myth*. St. Martin's Press, New York, 1989, p. 129.

[12] Krieger and Caceres, The Unnoticed Link in AIDS Cases. *The Wall Street Journal*, Oct. 24, 1985.

[13] McKenna, *et al.*, Unmasking AIDS: Chemical immunosuppression and seronegative syphilis. *Medical Hypotheses* 21:421-430, 1986, as quoted in Coulter, Op cit., pp. 47-48.

[14] Lauritsen and Wilson, Op cit., p. 11.

[15] Duesberg, AIDS acquired by drug consumption and other noncontagious risk factors, Op cit., pp. 238-239.

[16] Shilts, *And the Band Played On*. St. Martin's Press, New York, 1987, p. 104.

[17] Duesberg, AIDS acquired by drug consumption and other noncontagious risk factors, Op cit., pp. 237-238, 241, 247.

[18] Ibid., p. 240.

[19] Lauritsen and Wilson, Op cit., pp. 5, 33.

[20] Sigell, *et al.*, Popping and snorting volatile nitrites: a current fad for getting high. *American Journal of Psychiatry*, Oct., 1978, pp. 1216-1218, as quoted in Lauritsen and Wilson, Op cit., p. 46.

[21] Lauritsen and Wilson, Op cit., p. 5.

[22] Newell, Spitz, and Wilson, Op cit., p. 5; Lauritsen, *The AIDS War*, Op cit., p. 104.

[23] Duesberg, AIDS acquired by drug consumption and other noncontagious risk factors, Op cit., pp. 248-249.

[24] Duesberg, AIDS epidemiology: inconsistencies with human immunodeficiency virus and with infectious disease. *Proc. Natl. Acad. Sci. U.S.A.* 88:1575-1579, 1991. See especially references #24-26.

[25] Duesberg, AIDS acquired by drug consumption and other noncontagious risk factors, Op cit., pp. 248-249.

26 Lauritsen and Wilson, Op cit., pp. 29-43; Haverkos and Dougherty, Op cit., pp. 50-74.

27 Duesberg, AIDS acquired by drug consumption and other noncontagious risk factors, Op cit., pp. 246-248.

28 Ibid., p. 240.

29 Ibid., p. 247.

30 Amendt, *Sucht, Profit, Sucht,* Rowohlt Taschenbuch Verlag GmbH, Hamburg, Germany, pp. 299-324; Weber, *et al.,* Progression of HIV infection in misusers of injected drugs who stop injecting or follow a programme of maintenance treatment with methadone. *Br. Med. J.* 301:1361-1365, as cited in Duesberg, AIDS acquired by drug consumption and other noncontagious risk factors, Op cit.

31 Cocaine use linked to tuberculosis, *San Francisco Chronicle,* July 26, 1991, p. A19; Craffey, A killer returns. *San Francisco Examiner — Image,* June 14, 1992, pp. 6-13.

32 Sadownick, Kneeling at the crystal cathedral. *Genre,* Jan. 1994, pp. 40-45, 86-90.

33 Lauritsen, *The AIDS War,* Op cit., p. 197.

34 Root-Bernstein, *Rethinking AIDS: The Tragic Cost of Premature Consensus,* The Free Press, New York, 1993, p. 228.

35 Coulter, Op cit., p. 86.

36 Root-Bernstein, Do we know the cause(s) of AIDS?, Op cit., p. 484.

37 Coulter, Op cit., pp. 47, 86-87.

38 Lauritsen, *The AIDS War,* Op cit., p. 199.

39 Stolberg, AIDS tally to increase due to new definition. *Los Angeles Times,* Dec. 31, 1992, pp. A3, A29; see also Chapters Nine and Ten.

40 Duesberg, AIDS acquired by drug consumption and other noncontagious risk factors, Op cit., p. 214.

41 Konotey-Ahulu, AIDS in Africa: Misinformation and disinformation. *The Lancet,* July 25:206-7, 1987.

42 Farber, Out of Africa, part I. *Spin.* March, 1993, pp. 61-3, 86-7.

43 Hodgkinson, African Aids plague 'a myth.' *Sunday Times* (London), Oct. 3, 1993; Hodgkinson, The plague that never was. *Sunday Times* (London), Oct. 3, 1993.

44 Ibid.

45 Williams, *AIDS: An African Perspective.* CRC Press, Boca Raton, Florida, 1992, p. 238.

46 *AIDS and Africa.* Meditel, March 24, 1993. Television documentary.

47 Konotey-Ahulu, *What is AIDS?* Op cit., pp. 56-7.

48 Konotey-Ahulu, 1987. Op cit.

49 Konotey-Ahulu, *What is AIDS?* Op cit., p. 119.

50 Farber, Op cit.

51 *AIDS and Africa,* Meditel, Op cit.

52 Duesberg, AIDS acquired by drug consumption and other noncontagious risk factors, Op cit., p. 221.

53 Farber, Op cit.

Chapter 9

With Therapies Like This, Who Needs Disease?

Cheryl Nagel felt excited, her dream on the verge of becoming tangible reality in that late October of 1990. She and her husband Steve had wanted a child of their own for a long time, and now her flight was arriving deep in the heart of eastern Europe, in Romania. Steve could not take off the time, so her mother accompanied her to the remote city of Timisoara. Cheryl felt out of place, having travelled so far from her suburban home just ouside Minneapolis; back home Steve cooked for a restaurant, while she worked as a realtor's assistant. But when they heard the news of turbulence in that country, and then of the orphanages full of desperate children, the Nagels knew in their hearts where they had to go.

Arriving turned out to be the easy part. Touring the entire surrounding area, Cheryl and her mother soon met Lindsey, a baby girl only several days old. She had been born in the small coal-mining town of Petrosani, nestled deep in the Transylvanian Alps. She had been given up by her impoverished mother, who was already burdened by caring for three older daughters. But Cheryl found the adoption process absurdly difficult, not to mention the desperate economic and social condition of the country. Constant shortages of the littlest things, even light bulbs, could cause delays, and a phone call overseas took four hours to connect before she could hear the reassuring sound of her husband's voice. Two weeks of paperwork, bureaucratic stalling, and struggling with a strange language in a still-socialist economy forced her back to the United States to recover. Returning within a few weeks, however, she passed the final hurdles and retrieved the two-month-old baby.

Lindsey was a happy, healthy child, her slightly small size reflecting the norms for her original family. The Nagels took her for a complete check-up with a clinic near Minneapolis. The doctor's battery of tests included one for HIV. To everyone's astonishment, Lindsey was confirmed positive. Upon investigation, the Nagels discovered that Lindsey's birth mother did not have the virus. This left only one possible source—the blood transfusion Lindsey had received (despite having had nothing more than a brief ear infection) in Romania's backward medical system, where the method was carelessly used as a treatment for almost any illness. Lindsey still seemed a picture of health. However, the Nagels were now told she had the deadly "AIDS virus." It was only a matter of time.

Then the nightmare began. Naturally Steve and Cheryl agreed to treat Lindsey prophylactically, to delay the onset of symptoms as long as possible. They were referred to a specialist at the Children's Hospital in Minneapolis, where the doctor examined Lindsey and found no symptoms at all. No infections, no abnormalities, nothing. "She is [a] very bright, smiling and happy girl," noted the doctor, who nevertheless decided to head off a potential AIDS pneumonia immediately. Lindsey was prescribed Septra to be taken three times each week.

The drug is known by dozens of brand names, including Bactrim. Septra is a sulfa drug, a remnant of the era before penicillin and the other antibiotics. Sulfa drugs do not target invading microbes as narrowly as the antibiotics, and so have become notorious for their side effects. According to the *Physician's Desk Reference*, Septra can cause "nausea, vomiting, anorexia" and "bone marrow depression," and also includes "rash, fever, [and] leukopenia" among its side effects.[1] Even the drug's manufacturer, Burroughs-Wellcome, strongly recommends against using Septra for more than two weeks, in children or adults. Young Lindsey, however, would take the drug for some nine months.

When the Nagels brought their daughter back a week later, the specialist announced that Lindsey's T cell count was perfectly normal. Nor had any infections shown up. But given the HIV infection, the doctor wanted to slow the presumably inevitable appearance of AIDS. This time she prescribed the only drug approved for AIDS therapy—AZT. Lindsey began swallowing a total of 120 milligrams of the drug every single day, in addition to her Septra.

AZT stands for azidothymidine, a drug often marketed under the names Zidovudine or Retrovir. As with Septra, AZT is produced by the pharmaceutical giant Burroughs-Wellcome. Both have toxic effects. But compared to the sulfa drug, AZT amounts to poison. The doctor herself admitted some of the effects in her medical report of the visit, stating that Lindsey's "Mother was explained the side effects of Zidovudine which are primarily bone marrow suppression with anemia, sometimes nausea and vomiting and rarely the cause of other symptoms like skin rash."[2] If anything, this understated the effects. AZT kills dividing cells anywhere in the body—causing ulcerations and hemorrhaging, damage to hair follicles and skin, wasting away of muscles, and the destruction of the immune system and other blood cells. Children are affected more severely, for they lose their normal growth patterns. Amazingly, AZT was first approved for treatment of AIDS in 1987, and then even for prevention of AIDS in 1990.

Totally unaware of the toxicity of this controversial drug, the Nagels faithfully fed their daughter the AZT syrup four times a day. At their next visit the following month, the doctor strangely began praising Lindsey's "improvement."[3] Upon reflection, the Nagels grew puzzled. What "improvement" could the doctor have meant, since Lindsey had suffered no medical problems at all before the treatment began? In fact, their daughter was already changing for the worse. Despite gaining slightly in weight, she was beginning to fall behind the proper growth rate for her five months of age. She was also losing her appetite, feeling too sick to drink her milk.

This process continued for months. Lindsey developed no infectious diseases, but her appetite continued to decline. The doctor barely acknowledged that the child was falling further behind the normal growth curve. By the time Lindsey reached her first birthday on October 15th, her adoptive parents began to lose patience. The doctor had finally noticed the developing problem the month before, but seemed to believe the lack of growth had more to do with HIV infection than with any drug effects of Septra or AZT. As the Nagels began reading up on the officially recognized "side effects" of these drugs, their uneasiness turned to outright anxiety when they found perfect descriptions of their daughter's condition. Becoming suspicious of their doctor for not admitting or discussing these side effects, Steve and Cheryl took Lindsey to Dr. Margaret Hostetter at the University of Minnesota clinic. They felt overwhelmed and wanted clearer advice.

Dr. Hostetter possessed all the poise and confidence of her twin appointments as a university professor and director of the clinic's infectious disease program. Exuding an urbane but authoritative charm, she at first appeared much more professional and much friendlier than the other physicians. "Thank you for referring this lovely family to me," she wrote to Lindsey's first pediatrician after her November visit.[4] Running a complete battery of tests, she decided to take Lindsey off the Septra immediately. But the Nagels did notice that the doctor seemed to blame Lindsey's weight loss on HIV, rather than on drug side effects.

As soon as the Septra prescription ended, Lindsey began rebounding. Within one month her weight had again increased, though hardly back to normal, and her appetite recovered slightly. Amazingly, Dr. Hostetter completely missed the point. She had increased Lindsey's AZT dosage at the same time as ending the Septra, so at the Nagels' next visit she credited the baby girl's improvement to the AZT. In fact, she discussed plans to increase the AZT yet again. Even the experimental drug ddI, another powerful drug similar to AZT and just approved by the Food and Drug Administration, started cropping up among the doctor's suggestions.

After the rapid side effects of the sulfa drug had disappeared, the slower toxicity of the extra AZT began taking over. Lindsey stopped improving, and her weight, though still rising slowly, could no longer keep up with the normal growth rate for her age. She remained at the bottom end of the healthy weight range. By March she virtually stopped growing altogether. Her parents, fending off an increasing nervousness with each passing month, nevertheless kept up the daily syrup-feeding routine. The doctor carefully managed the Nagels' reaction, praising Lindsey's nonexistent progress at each visit.

The tension finally erupted a few days after Lindsey's second birthday. Steve and Cheryl woke up one night to the tormented screams of their daughter. Racing into her room, they found her sitting up and tearfully clutching her legs. The muscle pains were unbearable. Leg massages, Tylenol—they used anything that would allow Lindsey to sleep again. The same thing happened the next evening. And the next one. Night after night, the pain returned with ruthless consistency to deprive the entire family of sleep. The Nagels recognized precisely what was happening to their daughter: based on their own study, they had already learned that AZT produces muscle wasting as one of its "side effects."

That was the last straw. A few weeks earlier, the doctor had stretched their patience by pressuring them to put Lindsey on ddI. The young girl's T cell levels were dropping, she said, and new drugs might help combat the deadly HIV. Investigating for themselves, the Nagels discovered that all children normally start with over 3000 T cells per microliter at birth, declining to about 1000 before adulthood. Lindsey's counts were coming down at the standard, healthy rate. Naturally the Nagels had refused ddI therapy. But now they were reconsidering AZT as well.

By chance they stumbled across an article discussing Peter Duesberg's dissent against AZT treatment for AIDS. Upon tracking down his phone number and calling, they received an earful about the drug's toxic effects. From there the Nagels talked with several other scientists dissenting against the HIV hypothesis. By early November the picture had become clear, and the Nagels stopped feeding their daughter the drug. A nutritionist helped with her diet. Lindsey's changes took even her parents by surprise:

> After Lindsey was off AZT, she became a "new" child almost overnight.
> She started sleeping much better, including longer hours... Her muscle cramps went away.
> She started eating at least 2-3 times as much every day as she had ever eaten before.
> She would now drink milk, and especially around other youngsters, would drink as much as 6 ounces at a time. She would never drink milk before unless we added chocolate syrup, not a very nutritious drink...
> She displayed a much calmer demeanor. Lindsey was almost described as "hyperactive" by several people, including maternal grandparents who babysat a lot. This was a night and day difference! Lindsey, before, could not sit still for 5 minutes, and was seemingly agitated all the time...
> ... after seeing our nutritionist for only 2 months, and ridding Lindsey's body of toxic effects of being on AZT and Septra, Lindsey, now at 27 months, had an upswing on the chart. Her weight has been going up ever since. Now for the first time in 21 months, Lindsey is at 24 pounds, and is back on the chart at the 10th percentile...[5]

Dr. Hostetter knew nothing about Lindsey being off AZT. The Nagels contacted the physician to demand an open discussion about the drug's merits at their next visit, to take place in early December of 1992. They were caught completely off guard by the doctor's reaction.

> Dr. Hostetter looked very tense... we were verbally attacked, as if we were 5 years old, and how dare we question her opinion, let alone the use of AZT! She told us how lucky we were that Lindsey had tolerated AZT so well, and had not needed to go on ddI up until now. Then, Dr. Hostetter drew a large diagram on the black board, and told us (as she reminded us that she had told us all of this before) which cells AZT affects and which ones it definitely does not affect. If one of AZT's main side effects is bone marrow toxicity, how does a doctor know which cells the AZT will affect? (How does the AZT know?)... After our "lecture," Dr. Hostetter gave us her 20 minute sales pitch for AZT.[6]

The parents felt too intimidated by the meeting to let the doctor know they had ended the AZT treatment. In a letter written one week afterward to the Nagels' private physician, Hostetter noted that Lindsey had grown remarkably well during the previous two months, and warned that "we, unfortunately, might well see a return of Lindsey's previous failure to thrive were we to discontinue this drug."[7]

When the Nagels finally informed the doctor in writing and switched Lindsey to a chiropractor and nutritionist, Hostetter's mood turned downright ugly. Her response letter thundered a stream of dire warnings:

> As we have discussed repeatedly, AIDS is a fatal disease... To take Lindsey off Retrovir now will, I am afraid, hasten her decline and death.
> As parents, you are responsible for your child's health and life... Running away from qualified medical care will not help you, and it will certainly jeopardize Lindsey's life. You must take Lindsey to a qualified M.D. immediately.[8]

Hostetter followed up the letter with an angry call to the Nagels' chiropractor—on New Year's Eve. "She wanted to warn our chiropractor that she had no right to be seeing Lindsey," recalled Cheryl. "She also said that there are 'foster homes to provide care for children who were in Lindsey's predicament!' (Living with parents who wouldn't give their daughter AZT.)"[9]

Hoping to stall Dr. Hostetter and to get a second opinion, the Nagels took their adopted daughter to another physician referred by Hostetter. But all he gave them was the same opinion. He recommended they restore Lindsey's treatment, and his nurse-practitioner called AZT a "wonder drug," a term even its manufacturer, Burroughs-Wellcome, has never dared use.

Now three years old, Lindsey remains off AZT and all other toxic drugs. Her healthy growth pattern continues, she suffers no unusual diseases, and she is developing normally. According to public health officials she should already have died of AIDS, for babies with HIV are only supposed to survive about two years.

Not everyone is so fortunate. In 1987, three years before Lindsey was born in far-away Romania, Doug and Nancy Simon brought their daughter Candace into the world, in a town slightly south of Minneapolis. Their daughter certainly seemed healthy enough, but by the time she reached one and a half years of age, the doctor discovered she had HIV. Investigation traced the infection to her mother, who had contracted the virus from her husband. He, in turn, had contracted it from a blood transfusion several years earlier. None of them suffered from AIDS.

The Simons took Candace to the Minneapolis Children's Hospital, the same one where Lindsey Nagel would be given Septra and AZT a couple of years later. Candace, too, became a victim of AIDS medicine. Doctors there prescribed interferon, a powerful anti-metabolic drug that shuts down cell function. They later added AZT to her regimen, a treatment that, unlike in Lindsey's case, would last three and a half years. The constant testing added to the parents' sense of being overwhelmed: X-rays, blood samples, brain scans. For a while, Candace appeared to handle the therapy without too many problems.

Then her condition took a nose dive. Her appetite declined to dangerously low levels. The hospital became almost a second home, and by late 1992 she could no longer leave her bed. A new symptom, hauntingly reminiscent of Lindsey's AZT poisoning, took effect: "When the pain hit she would double over in her bed like a safety pin and, wild-eyed, grab her ankles until it eased."[10] Soon the doctors found cancer—malignant, spreading tumors throughout her stomach area. For the pain they prescribed morphine, then surgically cut the nerves to her intestines. Candace could no longer eat on her own, and the doctors began feeding her through intravenous tubes directly to her blood. Though five years old, she had lost control of her intestines and had to wear diapers.

In June of 1993, only three days before she turned six years old, Candace died painfully. Nearby, Lindsey Nagel had already stopped AZT seven months earlier, and was recovering her health spectacularly. But Candace continued the drug right up to the end. Now both her parents take AZT as well.

The Nagels know of the Simon's situation, and consider themselves lucky for not having followed through on their daughter's AZT treatment.

The death and resurrection of AZT

The virus hunters have always aspired to the glories of their predecessors, the bacteria hunters. Medicine still takes credit, however debatably, for eliminating bacterial diseases with antibiotics such as penicillin. These drugs attacked their bacterial targets with tremendous specificity, meaning they did little direct damage to the host's body. Antibiotics became known as the "magic bullet" for bacterial infections. Fire them into the body, and they only kill invading bacteria.

But for viruses the problem was different. These are nonliving microbes, made of proteins, DNA or RNA, and sometimes even a tiny membrane—molecules no different in principle from the proteins and DNA in a human body. How could any drug possibly discriminate between viruses and their human hosts? The only solution offered has been vaccination. Despite never-ending searches for "magic bullets" against viruses, the efforts have produced little but failure. In principle, such a miracle drug may never be possible.

The 1975 Nobel Prize for Medicine, awarded for Howard Temin's discovery of the protein "reverse transcriptase" (see Chapter Four), popularized this unique retrovirus enzyme. Many virus hunters switched into chasing retroviruses, and the reverse transcriptase protein took on mythic proportions. It did, after all, copy the virus's genetic information from RNA molecules "backward" into DNA, this new copy integrating into the genetic structure of the infected cell. Normally the cell keeps its genetic material in DNA, copying selected genes into RNA as needed. This "reverse" feature of the retrovirus protein inspired virus hunters to make it their key target for "magic bullet" drugs. At least in diseases caused by retroviruses, they speculated, some effective drug could be found. Once AIDS was blamed on HIV, a retrovirus, the race was on to find a drug that could distinguish between reverse transcriptase and the proteins normally found in a human cell.

Drug development since World War II had also been heavily shaped by cancer research. Cancer, too, fueled ambitions among doctors to find "magic bullets" that could destroy the cancer tissue without killing the host. First came surgery, the attempt simply to cut out the tumor; this method has serious limitations. Radiation also became popular, based on the hope that tumors could be burned away by X-rays or other high-energy beams before destroying the body, but radiation therapy has mostly provided disappointment. Chemotherapy, using powerful cell-killing drugs, came into vogue during the 1950s. Starting in the First World War, researchers observed the destruction of blood cells by mustard gas, the chemical warfare agent used to hideous effect in the trenches of Europe's battlefields. A few attempts to use this drug against cancer turned up with minimal results, largely because mustard gas was so toxic to the patient.

Shortly after James Shannon took over the National Institutes of Health (NIH) in 1955, he instituted several major research programs to attract vast new budgets from Congress. The largest of these became the Virus-Cancer Program, which ultimately converted itself into the war on AIDS. The second largest project aimed to develop chemotherapy agents to treat cancer. The 1950s and 1960s therefore saw a proliferation of drugs designed to kill growing cells. At first, the goal seemed straightforward: since cancer is made of persistently dividing cells, find a drug that prefers to kill cells that grow. The biggest problem with this concept lay in the body's own tissues, many of which replenish themselves constantly with rapidly growing cells. Therefore cancer patients undergoing chemotherapy experience the devastating side effects, including hair loss, muscle wasting, severe weight loss, anemia and the need for blood transfusions, and destruction of the immune system, composed mostly of white blood cells. Decades before the appearance of AIDS, chemotherapy patients often died of the same *Pneumocystis carinii* pneumonia that later killed young homosexual men.

AZT was invented under this program in 1964. Jerome Horwitz, heading a lab at the Detroit Cancer Foundation and financed with an NIH grant, created a chemically modified form of a DNA building block. Every time a cell divides, it must copy its complete genetic code, allowing one copy for each new cell. Genetic information is stored as a sequence of "letters" in long chains of DNA, known as chromosomes. Each building block of DNA is linked to the one before it, almost like train cars. But Horwitz's altered DNA building block, azidothymidine (AZT), surreptitiously enters the growing DNA chain while a cell is preparing to divide, and acts as a premature "caboose," blocking further DNA building blocks from being added. In short, the cell cannot copy its DNA sequence, and dies trying. AZT was the perfect killer of dividing cells. However, when he tested the compound on cancer-ridden mice, it failed miserably. Horwitz was so disappointed he never bothered publishing the experiment, and eventually abandoned that line of research. The drug must have killed the tumors, which contain dividing cells, but it so effectively destroyed healthy growing tissues that the mice died of the extreme toxicity. The drug was shelved, and no patent was ever filed.

Twenty years later, Gallo's 1984 press conference announcing HIV as the "AIDS virus" set in motion a new hunt, this time for a "magic bullet" drug to act against the virus. The federal government had promised treatment, and it had to deliver. Some virus hunters, including Jonas Salk, scurried to invent an HIV vaccine. Others searched for an antiviral drug, and turned to the cancer chemotherapy program for already-developed chemicals. The fastest way to put a drug to market would be to select one that had finished some testing in the past.

Burroughs-Wellcome became the pharmaceutical company positioned at the right place and the right time. One of the giants in the industry, the British-based company maintains a relatively unusual corporate structure as a mostly non-profit, charitable institution. Most profits are paid, not to stockholders, but as grants and donations to biomedical research institutions. By throwing so much money around, Burroughs-Wellcome has bought enormous influence throughout government and universities, especially through its American branch. A large number of scientists and physicians had developed informal ties to the company, having been paid to test its pharmaceuticals many times over the years.

The company's head researcher in the United States, David Barry, recognized the opportunity after Gallo's press conference. Barry knew his way around the federal bureaucracy in getting a drug approved. He had originally worked at the Food and Drug Administration (FDA) during the 1970s as a virologist. His research had focused on the flu viruses, occasionally dabbling in retroviruses after they became popular. Upon switching to Burroughs-Wellcome, he paid more attention to herpes viruses, also a hot research item. He brought to his new job a vast network of connections with fellow virus hunters and top FDA people. Upon hearing the official call for anti-HIV drugs, Barry turned to the company shelves for previously rejected substances. If one of these could be approved, the company would save vast sums of research and development money. The political pressure for a quick solution played in his favor.

The key lay in winning FDA approval, which counted for more than mere permission to sell. The agency bans most potential drugs, automatically suppressing the competition and granting treatment monopolies for approved drugs. This monopoly alone can be worth hundreds of millions of dollars to the pharmaceutical company holding the patent. Further, the public knows how difficult the licensing process is, thus magnifying an FDA approval into a virtual certification and endorsement. Back in the days when snake oil could freely be sold as a nostrum, drugs would sell only according to the reputation of the producer. Now the public depends on, and trusts, FDA screening procedures. Burroughs-Wellcome intended to exploit this faith.

Barry selected a handful of drugs and quietly forwarded them to a couple of Burroughs-Wellcome former collaborators. One of them was Dani Bolognesi, a veteran retrovirus hunter and professor at North Carolina's Duke University, who not only knew Barry but was so close to Gallo he belonged to the "Bob Club." Bolognesi tested the substances in his laboratory, checking whether they would prevent HIV from multiplying while infecting cells in the test tube. One of the drugs clearly proved most potent against the virus—compound S, as it was code-named. Its real name was AZT.

Bolognesi then referred Barry to Sam Broder, the man in charge of testing cancer drugs at the National Cancer Institute. Broder had joined the NIH in the early 1970s just as Gallo's star was beginning to rise. Broder made his career testing and developing cancer chemotherapy, but he also allied himself to Gallo and thereby practiced a bit of virus hunting himself, soon becoming a full member of the "Bob Club." Full of political savvy, he could see by the early 1980s that the time had come to switch his emphasis from cancer to AIDS, and immediately after Gallo's press conference he mobilized NIH researchers to find a drug. His tenacity made him a perfect advocate for AZT; Barry realized that Broder, if properly recruited, would aggressively push through the bureaucracy to get AZT approved. So Barry sent compound S to Broder late in 1984, who discovered its powerful effect on HIV and waxed enthusiastic. Broder was hooked.[11]

Barry, Broder, and Bolognesi together published their laboratory experiments on AZT. They reported that only a tiny concentration was needed to block the virus from multiplying. Of course, this would mean nothing if the same dose of AZT would also kill the T cells in which the virus grew, in which case it would destroy the immune system before the virus supposedly could. Further tests gave an answer that sounded too good to be true: at least *one thousand times* as much AZT was needed to kill the T cells as to stop the virus. This theoretically meant doctors could use small doses of the drug to stop HIV without seriously damaging their patients' immune systems. No one bothered checking this fantastic result. The Burroughs-Wellcome and NIH researchers somehow had to explain their success, and billed AZT as a compound that specifically attacked reverse transcriptase, the retrovirus protein. In other words, they breathlessly declared, they had finally found a "magic bullet."

AZT, however, did not really attack reverse transcriptase directly. It only did what it had been designed to do originally—stop the building of DNA. Since reverse transcriptase copies retroviral genes into DNA, the drug certainly interfered with its normal function. But the infected T cell, meanwhile, produces its own DNA. Every time the cell divides, it must copy 100,000 times more DNA than the small virus, giving AZT 100,000 chances to kill the cell for every opportunity to block the virus. The drug could not possibly attack the virus without also killing the cell, casting suspicion on the Bolognesi-Broder experiments. Recent studies conducted by smaller laboratories have tested AZT on other samples of T cells, finding that the same low concentration that stops HIV also kills the cells. According to these studies, the real cell-killing dose is one thousand times lower than reported by Broder and Bolognesi.[12] AZT is definitely toxic, indiscriminately killing the virus and the T cells alike. Barry and his collaborators have never corrected their original reports, nor have they explained the huge discrepancies between their data and the other papers.

They also overlooked a more fundamental problem with their lab experiment. The virus against which they tested AZT was actively growing in the test tube. But in the body of an infected person, antibodies neutralize HIV years before AIDS appears, if it comes at all. Thus AZT in a human being cannot attack the virus anyway, for it has already become dormant.

A toxic chemotherapy was about to be unleashed on AIDS victims, but no one had the time to think twice about its potential to destroy the immune systems of people who might otherwise survive. The pressure was on to find a drug. Barry used this as a bludgeon when he began quiet negotiations with key FDA officials, arguing that AZT should be rushed through the approval process with reduced testing requirements. Broder was doing his bit, championing the drug through every channel of NIH power at his disposal. FDA officials relented and agreed to help the drug through in order to save time. Given the toxicity of AZT, Burroughs-Wellcome would need every break it could get to win approval.

Broder rushed AZT through its Phase I trials, the tests to determine its toxicity in humans. FDA cooperation allowed him to cut corners, making the drug appear to have minimal side effects. Now they were ready for the Phase II study, to see whether the drug would actually fight AIDS symptoms.

The AZT cover-up

Double-blind, placebo-controlled studies form one of the cornerstones of medical science. This rigorous gold standard puts any promising new treatment to the ultimate test: when applied to humans, does it really work? If properly structured, such a study throws out the prejudices of the researchers and yields the bottom line. A group of people with the appropriate disease is carefully selected, then secretly divided into two subgroups matched for every important characteristic. To test a therapy for lung cancer, for example, both groups would contain the same number of heavy smokers, light smokers, and so on. One group is given the treatment, the other a placebo—a "sugar pill," meaning a sham treatment that appears identical to the therapy itself. This removes any interfering effect of patient psychology or actions. And the study is conducted in a double-blind fashion, so that neither the patients nor the doctors know who is receiving treatment and who gets placebo, until the experiment is finished.

Under normal circumstances, AZT's Phase II trial would have been such a controlled study. But the intense political pressure to approve an AIDS drug, enhanced by fast-spreading rumors in the homosexual community of AZT's powerful benefits, forced FDA officials to take short cuts. Although the study was finally published as if a controlled test, a series of protocol violations, sloppy methods, and tampered data betrays its scandalous truth. Even the drug's toxicity necessarily unblinded the study, its effects on patients being painfully obvious.

David Barry structured the entire study from beginning to end. He tapped Burroughs-Wellcome's informal network of scientific collaborators, selecting twelve medical centers around the country for participation. By providing ten thousand dollars per study patient to each clinic involved, he induced a whopping fifty-one researchers to jump on board, a group heavily weighted with old virus-hunting peers of Barry's. Just having that many well-connected medical scientists helped swing the political balance in his favor, and it locked in their own loyalties to AZT. Even Michael Gottlieb, who reported the first five AIDS cases, joined in. Barry chose Margaret Fischl, a virologist at the University of Miami, to head the experiment.

A total of 282 AIDS patients were recruited, roughly half being put on AZT and the other half receiving the placebo. The trial, conducted in 1986, was scheduled to treat each patient for six months. At the end, the announced results seemed stupendous—so amazing, in fact, that the study had to be aborted early. Fischl and her associates decided they could not ethically continue to withhold such a wonderful drug from the placebo group. Nineteen placebo recipients had died during the study, compared to only one member of the AZT group. Forty-five in the placebo group developed opportunistic AIDS diseases, versus only twenty-four in the AZT group. And while the T-cell counts of the placebo patients continued to decline, the AZT group saw a temporary surge in their T cells. Results like these could propel almost any drug to FDA approval.

But even an inspection of the officially published data reveals some grim problems. Fischl and colleagues did not bother sorting their patients according to use of such recreational drugs as heroin or poppers; since most were homosexual men, this could complicate matters if, for example, the placebo group contained more heavy drug users. Fischl herself admitted that an unmentioned number of the patients were allowed to take other medical drugs during the study, a factor that introduced another wild card.

Still, taking the results at face value, a shocking picture of AZT toxicity emerges. Sixty-six AZT recipients suffered "severe" nausea—a category that would only have been mentioned if this was clinically serious—as compared to twenty-five in the placebo group. Eleven AZT users saw their muscles waste away, while only three placebo recipients suffered this symptom. And a full thirty in the AZT group survived only with multiple blood transfusions to replace their poisoned blood cells, compared to five similar cases among the placebo users. The less-publicized "side effects" of AZT more than abolished its presumed benefits.

A follow-up study on those same patients found that Fischl's neat picture mysteriously vanished once everyone was put on AZT. Within months, the death rate of the original AZT test group rapidly caught up to the former placebo group. After a year, one-third of both groups had died. Fischl and her co-workers shrugged off these new results, suggesting that AZT's miraculous effects somehow wore off after a few months.

Or perhaps that the benefits never existed in the first place. A flood of previously concealed information has surfaced since the trial, all showing that it became unblinded from the start. The controls completely broke down.

The doctors certainly found out quickly who took AZT and who did not, because AZT induces serious destruction of blood cells and the bone marrow that produces them. Bruce Nussbaum, in his 1990 book *Good Intentions*, described the mood in the trial's first month:

A move to stop the trial began immediately. The toxicity of AZT was proving to be extremely high, much higher than indicated by Sam Broder's previous safety trials. PIs [Principal Investigators] began to worry that AZT was killing bone marrow cells so fast that patients would quickly come down with aplastic anemia, a murderous disease. This was terrifying to many PIs. "There was enormous pressure to stop," recalls Broder. "People said, 'My god, what's going on, we're getting these anemias, what's going on?' We never saw this level of anemia before."[13]

For those doctors who may have missed AZT patients vomiting up blood, the routine blood tests gave away the secrets. Michael Lange was one of the researchers in the trial, interviewed for a 1992 British television documentary:

> I don't think [the trials] were really blinded, because when you take AZT, your red blood cells increase in size... you can notice that on an ordinary blood count, and since blood counts were monitored and the information fed back to patients, this information was available to the investigators.[14]

The patients, needless to say, often found out what they were taking by such clues. But they had other methods. For one thing, the AZT and placebo pills tasted different at the study's beginning. When doctors finally caught some patients tasting each other's pills, they fixed the problem. This came too late, of course, for full damage control. The patients who missed this opportunity discovered other ways around the controls. According to Christopher Babick, an AIDS activist with the People With AIDS Coalition,

> During the Phase II trials, we received many phone calls in our office from individuals who wanted to determine whether or not they were using the placebo or actually receiving AZT. There were three laboratories in New York which would analyze the medication. We would refer individuals there. If, in fact, they were on placebo, they would make arrangements to acquire the drug AZT. Oftentimes they would share it with individuals who were in the trials, and thus really rendering the Phase II trials unblinded.[15]

The patients had bought the early rumors of AZT's incredible healing powers, and really did not want to take a placebo. Some of the placebo group secretly did use AZT, explaining the presence of its toxic "side effects" among those patients. The AIDS activist group Project Inform, originally an opponent of AZT, tried to dislodge the trial's internal working papers to confirm that the "placebo group" members with toxicity symptoms had used AZT; despite invoking the Freedom of Information Act, they never could get the documents released. In any case, Fischl's pretense of double-blind controls smacks of blatant dishonesty.

Once the controls broke down, the study began to unravel. While some "placebo" recipients were actually taking AZT, some of the "AZT" recipients were being taken off the drug. Many of the patients simply could not tolerate

AZT, and the physicians had to do something to save their lives. "Drug therapy was temporarily discontinued or the frequency of doses decreased... if severe adverse reactions were noted," admitted Fischl in the fine print of her paper. "The study medication was withdrawn if unacceptable toxic effects or a [cancer] requiring therapy developed."[16] This astonishing slip reveals that the doctors did indeed know who was using AZT. But never did Fischl tell how many "AZT" patients were taken off the drug, nor for how long.

Other patients dropped out of the trial altogether. Some fifteen percent of the AZT group disappeared, possibly including patients with the most severe side effects. Fischl and her collaborators never bothered accounting for the loss, fueling the suspicion that they could have even dropped the sickest patients themselves.

This is a likelier possibility than it first sounds. Author John Lauritsen, using documents released under the Freedom of Information Act, found many examples of incomplete or altered data. Causes of death were never verified, as by autopsy, and report forms often listed "suspected" reasons. Naturally, Fischl and colleagues tended to assume that diseases in the placebo group were AIDS-related, while assuming diseases in the AZT group were not. The symptom report forms looked even worse. Mysterious changes appeared, often weeks after the initial report for a given patient, including scratching out the original symptoms. The unexplained tamperings generally had no initials indicating approval by the head researcher. Other symptom reports were copied onto new forms, but often lacked the original form for comparison. And on some forms reporting toxic effects of AZT, the symptoms were crossed out months later.

During the trial, an FDA visit to one of the test hospitals in Boston uncovered suspicious problems. "The FDA inspector found multiple deviations from standard protocol procedure," an FDA official later commented, "and she recommended that data from this center be excluded from the analysis of the multicenter trial."[17] Months after the trial had finished, the FDA finally decided to inspect the other eleven centers. By then much of the evidence had been lost in the confusion. Far too many patients had been affected by test rule violations, and the FDA ultimately chose to use all of the data, good or bad, including from the Boston center. One FDA official let the cat out of the bag on the hopeless mess: "*Whatever the 'real' data may be*, clearly patients in this study, both on AZT and placebo, reported many disease symptom/possible adverse drug experiences." [emphasis added][18]

The trial's organizers pulled one final stunt to help AZT succeed. The original plan had called for each patient to participate for six months, but once it became unblinded, the researchers could constantly monitor the tally of AZT versus placebo. As soon as random chance appeared to favor AZT over placebo, the FDA oversight committee aborted the trial. Insisting they were acting on ethical considerations, rather than political ones, the organizers immediately provided AZT to all patients. As the follow-up study later observed, the death rate among the original AZT group quickly caught up to the former placebo group. Patients spent an average of about four months in the original study, some less than one month. The final analysis included all patients, projecting guesses to fill the gaps in the data. Had the trial not been unblinded, or had the FDA chosen to wait the full six months, the relative death rates would have looked radically different.

Other than allegedly reducing death, the Phase II trial made two other claims on behalf of AZT: it raised the T cell levels of immune-deficient AIDS patients, and reduced the number of opportunistic infections they suffered. All testing violations aside, AZT can temporarily raise T cell counts. So can cyanide and various other poisons. When some tissue is attacked by a toxin, the body tends to over-compensate for the destruction by producing too many replacements—as long as it can. At some point even the ability to replace white blood cells becomes over-taxed, and the T cell counts collapse downward, exactly as observed in the Fischl study. A temporary increase in T cells does not necessarily indicate the patient is improving.

AZT blocks DNA production, not only in human T cells or retroviruses, but also in any bacteria that might exist in the body. Thus it can act as an indiscriminate antibiotic, killing opportunistic infections while destroying the immune system. Even Burroughs-Wellcome had previously billed the drug as an anti-bacterial. This effect could explain the lower number of such infections in the AZT group. But the effect only lasts a short time; once the body's immune system is devastated by AZT, the microbes take over permanently. Ultimately AZT causes AIDS, rather than treating it.

Ignoring all the chaos and dishonesty, the FDA approved the drug on the basis of this experiment. Martin Delaney, founder and head of the AIDS activist group Project Inform, described the irony perfectly:

> The multi-center clinical trials of AZT are perhaps the sloppiest and most poorly controlled trials ever to serve as the basis for an FDA drug licensing approval... Because mortality was not an intended endpoint, causes of death were never verified. Despite this, and a frightening record of toxicity, the FDA approved AZT in record time, granting a treatment IND in less than five days and full pharmaceutical licensing in less than 6 months.[19]

Several leading scientists, even virologists, felt uneasy about the whole affair. Jay Levy, at the University of California at San Francisco, had been one of the first scientists to isolate HIV. A *Newsday* article described his comments on the drug: "'I think AZT can only hasten the demise of the individual. It's an immune disease,' he said, and AZT only further harms an already decimated immune system."[20] Even Jerome Groopman, one of the Phase II participating scientists, harbored serious reservations. The head of a research group at a prominent Boston hospital, he quickly discovered the effects of AZT on his patients. "When Groopman gave it to 14 patients on a compassionate basis, only 2 were still able to take it after 3 months. 'We found it nearly impossible to keep patients on the drug,' Groopman says."[21]

Sam Broder, on the other hand, never entertained a second thought. "When the Wright Brothers took off in their first airplane it probably would have been inappropriate to begin a discussion of airline safety," he nonchalantly told the Presidential HIV Commission in 1988.[22]

David Barry had already negotiated behind closed doors with the FDA for rapid approval. He held a strong bargaining position, given the political climate. But even that took too long for him, and he demanded special permission for Burroughs-Wellcome to sell AZT while waiting for the official approval. FDA officials scrambled for an answer, dredging up a permit known as the Treatment IND (Investigational New Drug). This method had almost never been used. Within days the technicalities were ironed out, and Barry had his permit to sell.

Next he had to get the official permission. He wanted it fast, and based on less scientific data than normally required. Again the FDA complied, cutting the process down to several months. Even AZT studies on mice were dropped from the requirements. The final hurdle lay in a meeting of an advisory committee of scientists and doctors, whose recommendation would likely determine AZT's fate. The panel met for a single day in January of 1987. Barry helped ensure the dice were loaded in his favor, for two of the eleven panel members moonlighted as paid consultants for Burroughs-Wellcome. The FDA granted special permission for those two researchers to remain on the committee with full voting powers.

Dozens of scientists from the Phase II trials showed up to argue their case, packing the room with virtual cheerleaders. They spent hour after hour flashing huge quantities of data past the committee, some of it so new that no one had had the time to review it beforehand. The follow-up results on the patients, showing higher death rates after everyone went on AZT, were cleverly buried in an avalanche of confusing statistics. Dazed, the members of the committee began to feel anxious that something had gone wrong in the testing process. Then Barry played his ace: a high-ranking FDA official, Paul Parkman, showed up and spoke, despite not having been scheduled to do so. After only a minute of suggesting most of the panel's concerns could be addressed, Parkman closed with a dramatic statement: "I think we can probably arrive at a plan that will satisfy people here."[23] Suddenly the arguments stopped, and the mood shifted from opposition to support for AZT. FDA officials had never before interfered in these meetings, and the entire committee was shocked. "Did you hear that?" the panel chairman said to an associate. "He's telling us to approve it."[24]

Few in the room knew that Parkman was a personal friend of Barry's; they had once worked together on virology projects. The panel ended up recommending AZT, with only the chairman voting against it. Burroughs-Wellcome quickly patented the drug, something no one else had ever bothered to do.

The FDA endorsement could seem a cruel joke perpetrated by heartless AIDS scientists. Patients on AZT receive little more than white capsules surrounded by a blue band. But every time lab researchers order another batch for experimentation, they receive a bottle with a special label. A skull-and-crossbones symbol appears on a background of bright orange, signifying an unusual chemical hazard. The label appears on bottles containing as little as 25 milligrams of AZT, a small fraction of a patient's daily prescribed dose.

The adjoining warning on the label reveals secrets not conveyed to the unwitting patient:

> Toxic
> Toxic by inhalation, in contact with skin and if swallowed. Target organ(s):
> Blood   Bone marrow
> If you feel unwell, seek medical advice (show the label where possible).
> Wear suitable protective clothing.[25]

The consensus dissolves

In the years following AZT's approval, a flood of studies on AIDS patients have poured forth illustrating frightening toxicity. None have included placebo groups, an omission rationalized by ethical concerns that patients should not be denied such a miracle drug. But the numbers speak for themselves.

Two years after the end of the Fischl Phase II trial, a group of French physicians working at the Claude Bernard Hospital in Paris published another study on hundreds of AIDS patients. All used high-dose AZT for an average of seven months. One third of the patients experienced a worsening of their AIDS conditions, and a slightly higher percentage developed new AIDS diseases. By nine months, one of every five patients had died, a rate far higher than in the Fischl study, which also used the high dose. "The bone marrow toxicity of AZT and the frequent need for other drugs with haematological [blood] toxicity meant that the scheduled AZT regimen could be maintained in only a few patients," wrote the authors. This has matched other findings; in most studies, half of any group of people suffer an immediate reaction so severe that they must stop. The French doctors cast a cloud of pessimism, noting that "in AIDS and ARC patients, the rationale for adhering to high-dose regimens of AZT, which in many instances leads to toxicity and interruption of treatment, seems questionable."[26]

In England, one group of researchers described the medical consequences of AZT in thirteen patients; all thirteen developed severe anemia. A subsequent Australian study reported the consequences of treating over 300 patients for one to one and a half years. Over half developed a new AIDS disease during the first year, and exactly half needed blood transfusions to survive. Nearly one third died. A Dutch study found still deadlier results: after just more than a year, most of their 91 patients needed blood transfusions and almost three quarters died. The Dutch researchers despaired at prescribing AZT, warning that most of their patients simply could not stay on the drug for loss of blood cells.

A new complication surfaced in 1990. The National Cancer Institute analyzed the status of AIDS patients who had participated in Broder's Phase I trial, and uncovered the fact that of all people using AZT for three years, half were developing lymphoma. This is a deadly cancer of white blood cells, akin to leukemia but forming solid tumors in the body, and also happens to be included on the official list of AIDS diseases blamed on HIV. Since AZT was killing and damaging those same white blood cells, the drug stood out as the likely culprit. Virus hunters rushed to the drug's defense. Some massaged the statistics to lower the lymphoma rate, while others turned the news completely upside-down by claiming AZT actually helped patients live longer— long enough to get lymphoma! Paul Volberding, one of the leading organizers in the Phase II trial, told one interviewer, "So we see the lymphomas as an unfortunate reflection of our success at this point rather than a reason for real caution."[27]

Certainly AIDS officials can hardly be accused of caution when it comes to AZT. Nor does their explanation wash, since AIDS patients tend to get lymphoma as their first disease, or never. AZT survivors, on the other hand, develop lymphoma after a whole series of other AIDS diseases. Even if their lives were prolonged, lymphomas would not have emerged as a late-stage symptom. AZT, furthermore, has given evidence of cancer-causing abilities when tested on cells grown in the laboratory culture dish.

A few small studies have tested the reverse, to see what happens to AIDS patients who stop AZT use. In one group of four patients who developed massive blood cell loss weeks after starting AZT, three recovered after the doctor took all four off the drug. Another group of five patients suffered muscle wasting, a symptom that disappeared in four cases only a couple of weeks after stopping AZT; two of these patients lapsed back into the condition after restarting the drug. In the most dramatic such experiment, a doctor took eleven of his worsening AIDS patients off AZT. The immune systems of ten immediately rebounded, and several continued improving.

Yet no amount of warning data could dissuade AIDS officials from abandoning their "antiviral" compound. Having won approval for treating AIDS patients, Burroughs-Wellcome and the NIH moved to have AZT recommended as a preventive drug, for HIV-positive people without symptoms. This time Anthony Fauci directed the experiment as a project of the National Institute for Allergy and Infectious Diseases (NIAID), the NIH division he headed. Burroughs-Wellcome again financed much of the study, paying hospitals for participating, and several of its consultants again joined in. Margaret Fischl and many other Phase II researchers signed up, and Paul Volberding secured the top position as organizer. But now a stupendous number of scientists were recruited: the final paper mentioned 130 names, which Volberding called "a partial list." The investigators read like a who's who among leading virus hunters and medical doctors involved in AIDS research. With that many prominent researchers involved, few colleagues remained to act as independent reviewers. The study's political success was virtually guaranteed, regardless of its outcome.

Volberding and his colleagues enrolled more than 1300 HIV-positive patients from AIDS risk groups, none of whom had AIDS diseases. The patients were divided into three groups—placebo, high-dose AZT, and, because of growing worries about the drug's toxicity, a low-dose AZT group. Protocol 019, as Fauci designated it, quickly degenerated into a repeat performance of the Phase II trial. More cancers, including Kaposi's sarcoma, occurred in the placebo group, hinting that more users of "poppers" or other recreational drugs may have ended up there (see Chapter Eight), biasing the results in favor of AZT. The double-blind controls broke down again, a fact Volberding covered up publicly. But in the text of his paper, he acknowledged that the drop-out patients tended to come from the AZT treatment groups, removing some of the sickest victims. Having also anticipated sharing of AZT between patients, he had their blood tested for the actual presence of the drug. Nine percent of the "placebo" group were caught with traces of AZT, while almost twenty percent of the AZT groups showed no evidence of ever having used the drug.

The study was terminated early, after patients had been treated for an average of one year. The final analysis showed the AZT groups with fewer AIDS diagnoses than the placebo, but the toxic "side effects" of AZT swamped out this small difference. The low-dose group had as many sick people as the placebo group, although their blood disorders and immune deficiencies were not called "AIDS." The high-dose group suffered by far the most, having dozens of deathly ill patients. By calling diseases in the placebo group AIDS while avoiding that diagnosis for the AZT groups, Volberding successfully won an FDA recommendation for using the drug on healthy HIV-positive people.

Not totally convinced, other researchers put together two long-term studies on AZT's preventive effects. An American research group, sponsored by the Veteran's Administration, ran a two-year trial comparing patients who used AZT before symptoms (the "early" group) to those using it afterwards (the "late" group). These scientists found that the early group actually died slightly more often and a bit faster than the late group, but the differences were small. They concluded AZT showed no survival benefits whatsoever when used for prevention. The news hit the stock market with force, knocking down the value of Burroughs-Wellcome shares some ten percent in one day.

British and French scientists organized a similar study, known as the Concorde trial, while Volberding's Protocol 019 was still in progress. The Concorde study treated two groups with AZT, one before AIDS symptoms and the other after. Only people without AIDS symptoms were recruited into the study, the late group receiving a placebo until after they contracted AIDS. Apparently the researchers were seeing enormous toxicity as the study progressed, for midway through a minor crisis erupted. The scientists became divided over whether to continue, or abort early. At a meeting behind closed doors, an audience member secretly recorded Chairman Ian Weller as he voiced the increasing concerns: "If there is benefit [to AZT therapy], is it maintained, or will it wear off? In which case we may do more harm than good."[28] The study organizers voted to continue, albeit nervously.

After each patient had participated for three years, the researchers came out in 1993 to announce publicly that they could find no difference in survival between the early and late treatment groups. In reality, the early AZT group may have done worse than estimated. The double-blind controls again seem to have dissipated, for symptom-free patients could easily know they were on AZT by its potent toxicity. Many of these AZT patients could no longer tolerate the nausea, vomiting, and anemia, but did not have the courage to confront their doctors. So, according to at least one report, "They have thrown their tablets down the toilet."[29] This would artificially lower some of the apparent toxicity in the early group.

But the news of no positive benefits did stun the AIDS establishments in all countries, sending various officials scrambling for excuses to explain away the Concorde results. This study has provided the heaviest blow yet against AZT, and the first signs of retreat are beginning to emerge. On June 25, 1993, an NIH panel formally announced new guidelines for AZT use, recommending that doctors and patients use more caution. "AZT has benefits, but we are admitting that it is not as good a drug as we thought it was," said the committee chairman sheepishly.[30]

Even Paul Volberding's research team has since published a re-analysis of its original Protocol 019 study, discovering that the patients on AZT actually did worse than the placebo group—when taking into account the toxic "side effects" of the drug. In a dramatic reversal of their earlier position, Volberding and colleagues openly suggested that HIV-positive people without symptoms might do better not to take AZT after all!

AZT, known for decades as a failed and toxic cancer chemotherapy, was resurrected for political reasons and rushed through the FDA's first fast-track approval. By its very nature, such a drug could only cause or worsen AIDS. One experiment after another, despite flaws, has confirmed the drug's toxicity in humans, yet only now is the AIDS establishment slowly backing down. The virus hunters bring tremendous political and financial momentum behind each of their projects, and AIDS treatment is no exception.

Too little, too late?

The recent growth of opposition to AZT may save lives in the future, but it is coming too late for some victims. Feeling giddy with the drug's alleged success, the AIDS establishment has aggressively promoted AZT use wherever it could. Often the treatment is paid for by one federal program or another, creating an indirect subsidy of Burroughs-Wellcome by the taxpayers. Today at least 180,000 people worldwide take the drug every day.

The early months of 1989 brought an unusual notice posted in the buildings of the NIH. Entitled "HIV Safety Notice," it announced a new policy established by the director himself. Any employee of the NIH who underwent accidental exposure to HIV, as for example by a needlestick injury, would be offered preventive AZT. According to the notice, "The advisory group in providing their recommendations emphasized that administration of AZT should be initiated as soon as possible, preferably within hours following the exposure."[31] Only first aid for the injury itself would precede AZT. Numerous medical institutions have since adopted this policy, and a 1993 report in the *Lancet* revealed the practical application. The paper described a doctor accidentally stuck by a needle exposed to HIV-infected blood. The doctor began taking AZT within the hour, and continued for six weeks—too quickly even to do an HIV test.[32] Thus medical workers may use AZT even if they never become infected with HIV.

A second, more disturbing, announcement reached the public in the summer of 1989. NIAID, the NIH division under Anthony Fauci, declared it would be conducting trials of AZT on pregnant mothers infected with HIV. A drug that interferes with growth can only lead to physical deformities in babies developing in the womb. The study, financed through the NIH budget, ironically recruited mothers who had been injection drug addicts. Apparently Fauci believes heroin addiction poses less of a threat to children than HIV; some of their babies, moreover, may never even contract the virus from their mothers, but will receive AZT anyway. Following his lead, the British and French governments in 1993 began organizing a study of AZT effects on HIV-positive babies. But the recent bad news about the drug has caused difficulties in convincing mothers to bring their children.

In February of 1994, Fauci's AZT trial on pregnant women was abruptly terminated. According to the press releases, children born to mothers on AZT had fewer HIV infections than did children born to mothers on placebo; nothing at all was said about the relative sickness in each group. In shades of the Margarate Fischl study that originally led to the approval of AZT, Fauci declared the results to be too spectacular to finish the study. The double-blind controls were officially broken, and AZT was offered to all mothers. At the time of this writing, the toxic "side effects" of the AZT treatment has not yet been reported publicly, nor has a scientific paper on the study been published.

Long-term survivors of AIDS know better than to use AZT. Michael Callen was diagnosed with full-blown AIDS in 1982, before HIV had even been isolated. Given little time to live, he discovered Joe Sonnabend and switched doctors. Callen had participated in the "fast track" homosexual scene for a decade, including sex with over three thousand partners and the attendant drug abuse. His lifestyle changed radically on Sonnabend's advice, although he began taking enormous amounts of antibiotics and sulfa drugs. Because of his cleaned-up lifestyle, and his ongoing refusal to take AZT, Callen lived twelve years with his AIDS diagnosis. He told his story in his 1990 book, *Surviving AIDS*, along with the stories of several other long-term survivors who tend to avoid AZT. For that matter, the CDC estimated that one million Americans had HIV by 1985, but two-thirds of those have not developed AIDS at all in the past nine years. Most HIV positives have never received AZT.

In New York, Michael Ellner has founded a self-help group to help other AIDS patients live. Named HEAL (Health-Education-Action Liaison), it strongly advises members against AZT. And a 1990 article in *Parade* magazine profiled thirteen AIDS cases who had survived their diagnosis for five years. They rejected AZT as counterproductive. "'It's incredible, isn't it, that the drug designed to save you can also kill you,' says Mike Leonard, a survivor. 'It can make you anemic, and you end up having to get blood transfusions.'"[33]

Not all AIDS victims are fortunate enough to hear such advice. The resulting tragedy can sometimes turn into a media circus promoting the HIV hypothesis. Of all the cases hyped up for their AIDS scare value, the Florida woman who supposedly caught AIDS from her dentist has become the most notorious.

The story began in late 1986, in the small town of Stuart on Florida's Atlantic coast. David Acer, a dentist who had begun his private practice five years earlier, felt a bit under the weather and saw a physician. Acer was also an active homosexual, a fact that led him to seek an HIV test. The result came back positive. Although disturbed by the news, he still felt reasonably healthy and saw no reason to stop his dental practice, nor apparently his "fast-track" lifestyle.

One year later he experienced worsening symptoms, and a visit to his doctor confirmed the diagnosis: full-blown AIDS. A Kaposi's sarcoma covered the inside of his throat and his T-cell count had fallen dangerously low. Both symptoms suggested the extensive use of "poppers" and other drugs so common in the homosexual bathhouse scene. Acer could now see his life slowly wasting away. He continued practicing dentistry while remaining discreet about his sexual life and failing health, making sure to follow the standard guidelines for protecting his patients from infection.

That December, in 1987, he pulled two molars from a nineteen-year-old college student, Kimberly Bergalis. At the time he had no idea the business major would one day be touted as his hapless victim.

The story picks up again in May, 1989, when Bergalis developed an oral yeast infection. The disease strikes many women, often chronically, and she thought little more of it. Later that year, during the emotional stress of preparing for an actuarial exam for the state of Florida, she felt some ongoing nausea, and became dizzy during the test itself. Afterwards the symptoms disappeared. But a brief pneumonia that December sent her to the hospital, where the doctor decided out of the blue to test her for HIV. As chance would have it, she had antibodies against the virus.

Up to this point, none of her occasional diseases differed from common health problems many HIV-negative people encounter. But the positive HIV test changed her whole attitude, as well as her medical treatment. Within three months the Centers for Disease Control (CDC) had heard of her case, possibly aided by the presence of several EIS members in the Florida health department, and sent investigators to probe further. The CDC team included such EIS members as Harold Jaffe, Ruth Berkelman, and Carol Ciesielski. Bergalis denied any intravenous drug use or blood transfusions, and insisted she was a virgin. During the prolonged examination, the CDC officers stumbled across David Acer's positive HIV status and made the connection to Bergalis. Before the HIV hypothesis of AIDS, no medical expert in his right mind would ever have entertained the slightest thought that a dentist with a Kaposi's tumor and a patient with a yeast infection had anything in common. But in the era of AIDS, doctors tended to discard common sense. That the dentist and patient both carried a dormant virus was enough.

Excited by its hopeful discovery, the CDC boldly advertised its results in its weekly newsletter, the same one that nine years earlier had broadcast the first five AIDS cases. The July 27, 1990, issue prominently featured their amazing leap of logic—that the dentist must somehow have infected Bergalis.

Naturally, the CDC's speculation leapt straight to the front pages and prime time television news broadcasts.

Acer died in early September. Bergalis meanwhile sought medical care at the University of Miami, where she was treated with an unidentified "experimental" method. Certainly this was the appropriate place for such therapies. Margaret Fischl, the head of the Phase II AZT trial, worked at that medical center, which had served as one of the twelve facilities sponsored by Burroughs-Wellcome for the study. So Bergalis was prescribed AZT.

Suddenly she started a precipitous decline in health. In an angry letter, she partly acknowledged her symptoms resulted from the toxic drug:

> I have lived through the torturous acne that infested my face and neck, brought on by AZT. I have endured trips twice a week to Miami for three months only to receive painful IV injections. I've had blood transfusions. I've had a bone marrow biopsy. I cried my heart out from the pain.[34]

This represented only the beginning. Her yeast infection worsened and became uncontrollable, she lost over thirty pounds, her hair gradually fell out, her blood cells died and had to be replaced with transfusions, and her muscles wasted away. Her fevers hit highs of 103 degrees, and by late 1990 her T cell count had dropped from the average of 1000 to a mere 43. She looked just like a cancer chemotherapy patient—which she now was.

The CDC saw its golden opportunity in the Bergalis case. It publicized a second report on the Bergalis case, announced its belief that four of Dr. Acer's other patients had also been infected by him, and even surveyed the patients of other HIV-positive doctors and dentists—suggesting that all HIV-positive patients had also been infected by their doctors. Such CDC-funded organizations as Americans for a Sound AIDS Policy (see Chapter Ten) aggressively promoted public fear with these speculations. A "media feeding frenzy" resulted, with every major television talk show, and every national magazine, running scare stories.[35] The CDC's relentless publicity had its expected effect: by mid-1991, over ninety percent of the public felt HIV-positive doctors should be forced to inform their patients of their status, and a clear majority favored banning such doctors from medical practice.[36] Many doctors, angered by the publicity campaign, "accused the federal Centers for Disease Control of unduly alarming the public."[37]

The CDC certainly had a political agenda behind its campaign. In July of 1991, the agency issued a set of proposed rules that would require doctors to follow extraordinarily burdensome measures, supposedly to protect their patients from HIV infection. By hyping up the Bergalis case, the CDC had created enough public panic and backlash to favor its proposed regulations. To dramatize the point, Bergalis was brought in to testify before a stunned Senate in October of 1991. Her muscles largely destroyed by AZT, she had to be brought in a wheelchair. Her furious testimony, whispered into the microphone, made a powerful emotional impact on the attentive Congressmen and the television audience.

Congress soon passed a new law requiring the states to adopt the CDC guidelines—or else begin losing federal funds. When the medical profession politically resisted the new rules, the Occupational Safety and Health Administration (OSHA), which works closely with the CDC, stepped in with parallel rules of its own. On threat of criminal prosecution, laboratory and medical workers must now follow incredibly restrictive regulations on their practices and equipment, and must deal with extra bureaucratic red tape.

Blaming her deteriorating condition on the latent virus supposedly passed on by her dentist, Bergalis sued the Acer estate. She received a one million dollar award, plus unannounced compensation from the dentist's insurance company. She parceled out the money to a variety of friends, family members, and AIDS organizations, and told her father to purchase "a new, red Porsche and deliver it to my aunt with a large bow on top."[38] Had she known better, she could have instead sued Burroughs-Wellcome. And she could have discontinued AZT, enjoying the Porsche herself instead of the wheelchair to which she was confined.

Bergalis died that December at twenty-three years of age, having taken AZT for up to two years. Her death became the ultimate symbol of the deadly powers of HIV. No one pointed out that even according to the HIV hypothesis, the virus should take ten years to kill its victims, particularly someone like Bergalis with no other risk factors; she, however, had died within four years of her initial visit to Dr. Acer. As her symptoms would indicate, the AZT must have killed her instead.

The CDC continued to exploit the publicized story as proof of the risk of doctor-to-patient HIV transmission. Some 1100 of Acer's 2000 former clients volunteered for HIV tests. Seven of these were positive, including Bergalis, two of them having standard risk factors for AIDS. That left five people who supposedly caught the virus from Acer. Expanding its search, the CDC tested almost 16,000 total patients of some 32 HIV-positive doctors around the country, finding 84 infected patients. Though admittedly baffled by how HIV could pass from doctors and dentists to their patients, the CDC nonetheless advertised the alleged threat.

Apart from HIV being a harmless virus, the evidence that this virus has even been medically transmitted remains dubious. Based on their own research, insurance companies concluded that the HIV strains in the five patients were different from that in Acer, meaning each caught it from a different source.[39] A study out of Florida State University has backed this conclusion.[40] Even the CDC acknowledged this evidence, though it preferred to believe the dentist had still infected Bergalis. But the CDC's own numbers give away the reality. An estimated one million Americans have HIV, in a total population of 250 million. Thus one in 250 Americans have the virus. Five HIV-infected patients of Dr. Acer, out of 1100 tested, comes to one in 220, virtually identical to the national average. So does the proportion of HIV-positives from the patients of the 32 doctors, which works out to one in 188. These HIV-positive patients merely represent random samples from the general population.

And where did these people get the virus? As we suggested in Chapter Six, HIV is probably transmitted much as other retroviruses, from mother to child during pregnancy. As far as we know, Kimberly Bergalis' mother has never been tested for HIV antibodies, nor have the mothers of Dr. Acer's other patients. Perhaps Kimberly carried the harmless virus for twenty-three years.

In December of 1992, another former patient of Dr. Acer tested positive for HIV, but had no symptoms. Two months later, eighteen-year-old Sherry Johnson began taking AZT. She has since begun wasting away, admitting she periodically feels sick.

While on AZT, Bergalis once told a reporter she hoped also to get dideoxyinosine (ddI), an experimental AIDS drug. This drug, another product of cancer chemotherapy research, works in precisely the same way as AZT. A chemically altered building block of DNA, it enters the growing chain of DNA while a cell is preparing to divide, and aborts the process by preventing new DNA building blocks from adding on. So, like AZT, it kills dividing cells, and has similar toxic effects. It destroys white blood cells, and therefore can cause AIDS. The only difference between ddI and AZT lies in how easily each is absorbed into the body; people who absorb one efficiently may not be equally affected by the other.

A different pharmaceutical giant, Bristol-Myers Squibb, produced ddI. The company sorely wanted to pull this drug off the shelf and into production, hoping to steal a piece of the action from Burroughs-Wellcome. Sam Broder, though working in the mid-1980s to promote AZT, was only too happy to help along any such chemotherapy. He performed lab experiments on cultured cells, again wrongly trying to argue that the drug blocked HIV production more effectively than it killed T cells.

Bristol-Myers began sponsoring research on AIDS patients. But they performed no controlled study, never comparing ddI's effects to placebo in matched groups. The studies did, however, reveal a couple of additional toxic reactions not produced by AZT. It can cause fatal damage to the pancreas, and it can destroy nerves throughout the body. On this experimental basis, a number of doctors began giving ddI to thousands of AIDS patients who could not tolerate AZT. Hundreds of unexplained deaths occurred among these patients, but the FDA managed to quell growing concerns.

The FDA advisory committee meeting to vote on ddI's approval convened in July, 1991. On that day, the panel reviewed the sloppily gathered data on the drug, which was compared to unmatched and untreated AIDS patients from years earlier. On this questionable basis, the committee was told ddI worked as well as AZT. Given the astonishing lack of even a pretense of a controlled study, the panel leaned against approval. That is, until FDA director David Kessler personally intervened on behalf of ddI and pressured the committee to "be creative."[41] The members changed their minds, voting to license the drug, albeit with restrictions. Doctors could only prescribe it for patients they felt did not benefit from AZT, leaving ddI as a secondary treatment, and the second drug ever to win "fast-track" FDA approval.

Since that time, the AIDS establishment has backed yet another DNA chain-terminating chemotherapy, dideoxycytidine (ddC), a drug also developed by Jerome Horwitz in the 1960s and now marketed by Hoffmann-LaRoche. The FDA has approved ddC, but only for use in combination with AZT or ddI.

Both ddI and ddC have begun to claim their victims. In 1988, twenty-two-year-old New York socialite and aspiring graphic artist Alison Gertz entered the hospital for a fever and diarrhea. At some point the doctor decided to test, and found antibodies against HIV. Gertz's transient illness was rediagnosed as AIDS. She had not injected drugs, although her wilder days at Studio 54 bespoke the cocaine and other free drugs available to patrons. A process of elimination traced her infection to a one-night stand with a bisexual male—six years earlier. The announcement left her feeling depressed, but she began a lecture circuit at high schools and colleges, admonishing students that AIDS could come from a single sexual encounter. Television talk shows followed, as did the cover of *People* magazine and Woman of the Year for *Esquire*. Even the World Health Organization circulated a documentary featuring her story.

Gertz started AZT treatment in 1989. The 1990 *People* magazine profile recounted the consequent disaster:

> Last October she was hospitalized with a severe allergic reaction to AZT. When doctors called for a lung biopsy, Ali balked. "I told them if they put me to sleep, I'd never wake up," she says. "My strength was gone." Released after 17 days, she recuperated at home, where her mother and girlfriends took turns nursing her around the clock. "They'd help me to the bathroom, feed me, see that I didn't fall in the shower," says Ali. "My knees were so bony, I had to sleep with a pillow between them."[42]

The doctors switched her to the still-experimental ddI, which Gertz apparently did not absorb as well and thus allowed her partly to recover. She mixed the powder in her drink twice every day. Her immune system and general health declined, though more slowly. "Gertz remains susceptible to infections like thrush, a fungus that frequently affects the mouth," stated the *People* article. "She has lost 30 lbs. since last summer, naps each afternoon and continues to visit her doctor every 10 days."[43] Ultimately, the ravages of the chemotherapy took her life in August, 1992, the news media advertising her death as AIDS-related. She was only twenty-six.

A backlash is now rising against the toxic and irrational treatment approaches to AIDS. In 1993, during the Ninth International AIDS Conference in Berlin, Germany, medical reporter Laurie Garrett was interviewed on the MacNeil-Lehrer News Hour. She described the growing discontent among scientists and patients alike:

> … most drug trials were terminated early. The AZT trial was terminated early, ddI, ddC, and so on, and people were allowed as soon as there was any sign that something showed promise to jump out of the placebo arm and get into the treatment arm…

... Dr. Anthony Pinching, who was really the leader of most of the clinical research related to AIDS in the United Kingdom, gave a very important speech this morning. I think if he had given this precise same speech a year ago, he would have been booed off the stage, and this morning, he was applauded heavily. And what he basically was saying was we have no idea what drugs work. We have no idea what we're doing in treatment, and it's time to return to the use of placebo trials. He went a step further and said that at least in Europe a lot of AIDS activists and patients now agree, because they're shocked to find out that the drugs they've been taking, thinking they would be helpful, might even be hurtful.[44]

This lesson almost saved the life of the late Arthur Ashe, the tennis star and one-time Wimbledon champion who recently died, supposedly of AIDS. Ashe's medical problems surfaced in 1979, despite his young age, with a heart attack. In December he underwent quadruple-bypass surgery. His chronic heart condition continued plaguing him, and by 1983 he had double-bypass surgery. A blood transfusion during either one of the operations may have carried HIV.

His heart condition and its complications kept nagging for several years. Then in 1988 he entered the hospital for toxoplasmosis, a protozoal disease relatively uncommon in humans. The germ resides in cattle and household pets, and in 17 to 50 percent of the U.S. population, but most people never succumb to the disease because of healthy immune systems. This also happens to be one of the many diseases on the AIDS list, so the doctor tested and found Ashe to be HIV-positive. Although his toxoplasmosis soon disappeared, Ashe was pronounced an AIDS victim. His disease was retroactively blamed on HIV, not on his heart condition.

Yet his condition hardly seemed contagious. Neither his wife, nor his daughter born three years after his second transfusion, ever developed any AIDS conditions. Indeed, his immune system must have neutralized HIV quite effectively, as Ashe also never transmitted the virus to his family.

His daily medicine intake expanded to a virtual pharmacy. He continued to take several drugs for his heart problems, one to lower cholesterol by interfering with liver function, another to slow down the heartbeat, and three others, including nitroglycerine, to lower blood pressure. To these his doctors added a spectrum of antibiotics, all with mild to serious side effects, to prevent the possibility of opportunistic infections. Ashe took Cleocin to fight further toxoplasmosis, nystatin to slow down yeast infections, and pentamidine to stave off *Pneumocystis* pneumonia. Two other drugs were prescribed against possible brain seizures. Eventually his daily regimen included some thirty pills, only a few of them vitamins.

But just as soon as Ashe received his AIDS diagnosis in 1988, his doctor pushed him into taking AZT. He started on an unbelievably high dose, nearly double the seriously toxic levels used in the Phase II trial. His doctor only gradually lowered the dose over the next four years. "I refuse to dwell on how much damage I may have done to myself taking the higher dosage," Ashe later admitted.[45]

In early 1992 he established an acquaintance that came close to rescuing him. A close friend arranged a series of meetings with Gary Null, a New York-based radio talk show host and nutritionist. Null introduced Ashe to the evidence of AZT's toxicity and against the HIV-AIDS hypothesis, desperately trying to convince him to halt the therapy. For the next ten months, Ashe "wrestled with the possibility of breaking away from the medical establishment to seek alternative treatment for AIDS," according to one columnist. Ashe never met Peter Duesberg, but became familiar with his arguments. "He read everything; he studied what we gave him and asked lots of questions," recalled Null.[46] In October, Ashe announced the lessons he was learning in a column he wrote for the *Washington Post*: "The confusion for AIDS patients like me is that there is a growing school of thought that HIV may not be the sole cause of AIDS, and that standard treatments such as AZT actually make matters worse. That there may very well be unknown cofactors but that the medical establishment is too rigid to change the direction of basic research and/or clinical trials."[47] But psychological pressure stopped Ashe short from rejecting AZT. As Null stated, "He wanted to do it, but he would say, 'What will I tell my doctors?'."[48]

In his 1993 book, *Days of Grace*, Ashe openly acknowledged his interest in Duesberg's ideas. Ashe faithfully summarized the main points against the HIV hypothesis and for the drug-AIDS hypothesis, and explained the deadly effects of AZT and the flaws of its Phase II trial. "Some tolerate [AZT] for a while, then must give it up. Still others cannot tolerate it at all," wrote Ashe. "To my relief, I tolerate AZT fairly easily."[49] With that rationalization, he sealed his fate.

During 1992, his doctors placed him on ddI. Each morning he sprinkled the powder on his cereal, in addition to the AZT pills he swallowed throughout the day. By this time he was wasting away rapidly, his underweight frame hidden by loose clothes. He began rotating in and out of the hospital. January of the following year brought more bad news: now he had a serious case of *Pneumocystis* pneumonia that his poisoned immune system could no longer fight off. He never recovered. On February sixth, he breathed his last.

As a thoroughly politicized epidemic, AIDS began with a falsehood and ended in tragedy. Virus hunters in the CDC-directed public health movement first made the new syndrome appear contagious. Virus hunters in the NIH-funded research establishment then blamed AIDS on a retrovirus. And virus hunters in the NIH, FDA, and pharmaceutical industry exploited the situation by resurrecting failed cancer chemotherapeutic drugs for AIDS treatment. In the crisis atmosphere created by the CDC, which allowed no time to think before acting, such toxic drugs as AZT, ddI, ddC, and d4T could bypass the normal review procedures and achieve a sanctified monopoly status. The final results have been human death and an artificially expanding AIDS epidemic.

To make all this possible, the virus hunters from all fields first had to join forces. They have used their combined influence, often behind the scenes, to mobilize the government, media, and other institutions behind a global War on AIDS. Few outsiders have realized just how coordinated the whole strategy has been. The story behind this war, and how its leaders are actively suppressing dissent, is told in the next chapter.

Chapter 9 Footnotes

[1] *Physician's Desk Reference.* 1993.

[2] Belani, Medical report on Lindsey Nagel, Park Nicollet Medical Center, Feb. 15, 1991.

[3] Belani, Medical report on Lindsey Nagel, Park Nicollet Medical Center, March 14, 1991.

[4] Hostetter, Letter to Joseph McHugh. Nov. 13, 1991.

[5] Nagel and Nagel, Appeal to the Minnesota Board of Medical Practice, March 31, 1993.

[6] Ibid.

[7] Hostetter, Letter to Joseph McHugh, Dec. 11, 1992.

[8] Hostetter, Letter to Mr. and Mrs. Steve Nagel, Dec. 29, 1992.

[9] Nagel and Nagel, Op cit.

[10] Parsons and Chandler, Girl in family stricken with AIDS virus dies at age 5. *Minneapolis Star/Tribune,* June 28, 1993.

[11] Nussbaum, *Good Intentions: How Big Business and the Medical Establishment Are Corrupting the Fight Against AIDS.* Atlantic Monthly Press, New York, 1990, pp. 23-41.

[12] Duesberg, AIDS acquired by drug consumption and other noncontagious risk factors. *Pharmacology & Therapeutics* 55:201-277, 1992, pp. 249-250.

[13] Nussbaum, Op cit., p. 151.

[14] Meditel. *AZT — Cause for Concern.* Dispatches, Channel Four Television, London, Feb. 12, 1992. Documentary.

[15] Ibid.

[16] Fischl, et al. The efficacy of azidothymidine (AZT) in the treatment of patients with AIDS and AIDS-related complex. *New England Journal of Medicine* 317:185-191, 1987.

[17] Lauritsen, *Poison by Prescription: The AZT Story.* Asklepios, New York, 1990, p. 34.

[18] Ibid., p. 34.

[19] Ibid., p. 27.

[20] Garrett, AIDS: The next decade. *New York Newsday,* June 12, 1990, pp. 1,5.

[21] Kolata, Imminent marketing of AZT raises problems. *Science* 235:1462-3, 1987.

[22] Presidential Commission on the HIV Epidemic. Hearings. Feb. 19, 1988, p. 28.

[23] Nussbaum, Op cit., p. 173.

[24] Ibid., p. 173.

[25] Zidovudine product label, Sigma Chemical Co.

[26] Dournon, et al., Effects of zidovudine in 365 consecutive patients with AIDS or AIDS-related complex. *Lancet* ii:1297-1302, 1988.

[27] Meditel, Op cit.

[28] Ibid.

[29] Hodgkinson, The cure that failed. *London Sunday Times,* April 4, 1993.

[30] Altman. Treatment guidelines for HIV amended. *San Francisco Chronicle,* June 28, 1993.

[31] Office of AIDS Research and Division of Safety, HIV Safety Notice, National Institutes of Health, Feb. 23, 1989.

[32] Anonymous. HIV seroconversion after occupational exposure despite early prophylactic zidovudine therapy. *Lancet* 341:1077-8, 1993.

[33] Gavzer, What we can learn from those who survive AIDS. *Parade*, June 10, 1990, pp. 4-7.

[34] Lauritsen, *The AIDS War: Propaganda, Profiteering and Genocide from the Medical-Industrial Complex.* Asklepios, New York, 1993, p. 324.

[35] Weisberg, The accuser. *The New Republic*, Oct. 21, 1991, pp. 12-14.

[36] Rom, Health-care workers and HIV: Policy choice in a federal system. *Publius*, Summer 1993, pp. 135-153 (p. 138).

[37] Hilton, CDC accused of alarming the public, *San Francisco Examiner*, Feb. 10, 1991, p. B5.

[38] Anonymous. AIDS victim's will is a moving 'good-by.' *San Francisco Chronicle*, Jan. 15, 1992.

[39] Duesberg, AIDS acquired by drug consumption and other noncontagious risk factors, Op cit., p. 234; Palca, The case of the Florida dentist. *Science* 255:392-394, 1992; No trial to come in Florida dentist case, *Science*, Feb. 14, 1992, p. 787.

[40] Study questions whether dentist spread AIDS. *Orange County Register*, Feb. 25, 1993, p. A14, describing a study by Ronald DeBry and colleagues published in the 2-25-93 issue of *Nature*.

[41] Lauritsen, *The AIDS War*, Op cit., p. 335.

[42] McMurran and Neill, One woman's brave battle with AIDS. *People*, July, 1990, pp. 62-5.

[43] Ibid.

[44] *Focus — AIDS Debriefing.* MacNeil-Lehrer NewsHour, June 10, 1993. Television interview.

[45] Ashe and Rampersad, *Days of Grace: A Memoir.* Alfred A. Knopf, New York, 1993, p. 214.

[46] Caldwell, *New York Daily News.* Feb. 10, 1993.

[47] Ashe, More than ever, magical things to learn. *Washington Post*, Oct. 11, 1992.

[48] Caldwell, Op cit.

[49] Ashe and Rampersad, Op cit., p. 213.

Chapter 10

Marching Off to War

The AIDS epidemic had, by the mid-1980s, already become the salvation of the virus hunters. Out of the ruins of the Virus-Cancer Program had emerged the virus-AIDS program of the National Institutes of Health. Cancer chemotherapy research had given birth to the AIDS treatment program, including AZT. The Centers for Disease Control had recovered its shaky reputation after the Swine Flu fiasco, and had won a renewed mandate to pursue contagious diseases. The lay public had bought the entire "slow virus" myth, paradoxes and all. Thus the virologists had maintained their powerful grip on the biomedical research establishment, and the retrovirus hunters had further secured their own envied position at the very top.

But AIDS differed from the fly-by-night episode of Legionnaire's disease or the old, intractable problem of cancer. This syndrome had surfaced recently enough to retain its novelty, while it was definitely growing steadily rather than disappearing. Thus the AIDS epidemic presented the first real opportunity in many years to revive virus hunting on a grand scale. The mystique of infectious diseases had originally spawned microbe-chasing wars, the enemies being invisible but deadly germs whose epidemics fed the public's terrified imaginations. While most people had never gone as far as Howard Hughes in his constant hand-washing paranoia, the fear of germs had sustained the glory days of virus hunting. However, not since polio had the public been so anxious over a "deadly virus," wondering whether it would strike via kisses, one-night stands, mosquito bites, or public toilet seats. For the virus hunters, naming HIV as the cause of AIDS only opened the door. Now the time had come to declare war.

By 1986, one man stood out as the obvious general to lead such a war. The veteran polio virologist who had shared the 1975 Nobel Prize for finding the "reverse transcriptase" protein of retroviruses, David Baltimore had ascended to enormous power among scientists. He had brandished his award to win a large network of allies throughout the research establishment, and even in political and financial arenas. No trend or well-funded scientific program escaped his resourceful opportunism. The War on Cancer during the 1970s, studies on the immune system by the early 1980s, AIDS in the mid-1980s—each allowed Baltimore to enhance his standing as professor at the Massachusetts Institute of Technology (MIT).

Nor did it hurt to establish connections with financial sugar-daddies. When biotechnology mogul Edwin C. "Jack" Whitehead began waving a cool $135 million at universities, Baltimore seized the chance to establish the Whitehead Institute in 1982. Over the furious objections of many faculty members, he rushed the proposal through and managed to affiliate the new research institute with MIT, from which it plundered key professors. Baltimore was named director, and for the next several years harnessed the prestige of the generously-endowed institute to expand his international influence.

Insiders, awed by his enormous influence, referred to him as "the Pope." By the mid-1980s, any ambitious scientist knew the importance of befriending him, and he always reciprocated; those who fell on his bad side faced trouble. Peter Duesberg, for example, publicly raised questions about the scientific validity of cancer genes, and Baltimore retaliated for several years by blocking Duesberg's election to the National Academy of Sciences.[1] Upon hearing that Duesberg had also become a serious candidate for Germany's highest science prize, the Paul Ehrlich Award, Baltimore interceded with an opposing recommendation for his own friends. Whereas a scientist's typical nomination letter includes a few pages of detailed justification, Baltimore's terse letter resounded with his imperial tone:

> Appropriate nominees for the 1988 and 1989 Paul Ehrlich and Ludwig Darmstaedter Award are: Drs. Robert Weinberg of the Whitehead Institute and Michael Bishop of the University of California, San Francisco. Dr. Bishop also worked very closely with Dr. Harold Varmus and they really should be honored together.[2]

Hilary Koprowski, a close ally of both Robert Gallo and Baltimore, sat on the prize committee and made sure the panel quickly changed its opinion.[3] Duesberg was displaced, while his long-time research collaborator, Peter Vogt, alone received the 1988 prize for their joint research on the Rous sarcoma virus. Although Baltimore's nominees did not themselves win the Ehrlich Prize, Weinberg did receive the General Motors Award in 1987, and Bishop and Varmus jointly won the Nobel Prize in 1989. Baltimore's endorsement was widely recognized as a major factor behind those awards.

The blueprint for war

In 1986, Baltimore stood at the apex of biomedical research as the most influential of all retrovirus hunters. Thus when key members of the National Academy of Sciences decided to launch a war on AIDS, they sought him out to lead the charge.

The strategy was simple: a committee of prominent scientific figures would issue a report, which would outline a program of increased funding to win over researchers in almost every field, all under central supervision. It would skillfully exploit public fear of a new, sexually transmitted disease, mobilizing the whole population regardless of political views. It would, in other words, create a national consensus, uniting scientist and non-scientist alike behind the new agenda. Even more ambitious than the wars on polio or cancer, this program would authorize extraordinary measures that might normally meet serious resistance. But such actions would certainly seem justified in light of a looming AIDS pandemic. The research establishment, already by far the largest in history, would expand even more rapidly; federal spending programs, including Medicare, could also grow in size; public health officials could implement emergency controls; and even United Nations agencies and foreign governments could get their share of the largesse. Those scientists not directly benefiting from the war on AIDS could be pressured into silence through the peer review system, and a well-funded propaganda machine would tell the voting public what to believe.

The Institute of Medicine and the National Academy of Engineering co-sponsored the project. Funding came from such notable sources as the Carnegie Corporation of New York, the John D. and Catherine T. MacArthur Foundation, the Andrew W. Mellon Foundation, and the Rockefeller Foundation. Twenty-three prestigious scientists were divided between two panels, David Baltimore chairing the Research Panel and co-chairing the Steering Committee that supervised the whole process. The committee featured such people as Nobel laureate Howard Temin (see Chapter Four) as well as Paul Volberding and Jerome Groopman, two central figures in the AZT Phase II trials. David Fraser, the CDC's Epidemic Intelligence Service (EIS) member who had led the Legionnaire's disease episode in 1976 (see Chapter Five), sat on the Health Care and Public Health Panel. Another EIS graduate, J. Thomas Grayston, sat as chairman of the Epidemiology Working Group. Over one hundred other advisors were listed as participating, reading like a veritable who's who of virus hunting. Robert Gallo and various "Bob Club" members were involved, including Max Essex and William Haseltine. Two major CDC officials participated, as did five graduates of the EIS, including Donald Francis. AZT manufacturer Burroughs-Wellcome and ddC producer Hoffmann-LaRoche each sent a representative.

The committee had been given a sweeping mandate to mobilize the entire nation behind the war. As instructed by the National Academy of Sciences, "The committee shall evaluate methods whereby the ultimate goals of controlling and combating the disease may be achieved... The committee shall prepare a report outlining a strategy (or strategies) whereby these concerns can be addressed. The report shall contain recommendations for its implementation directed to the Executive Branch, the Congress, the research community, those who treat patients, state and local governments, corporate leadership, and the public."[4] Naturally, anyone not cooperating with the committee's goals would be labeled apathetic, irresponsible, or dangerous.

All the key players in the AIDS virus hunt had their hands in the project, whether from the NIH, the CDC, or the politically well-connected pharmaceutical companies. The outcome was predictable. After two public hearings and a series of private meetings, the committee released its report in August, 1986. Entitled *Confronting AIDS*, the book became the "bible" of the entire AIDS establishment, its guidelines universally adopted as a blueprint for war. The report made recommendations in four areas:

1. The committee boasted about the discovery of HIV and "its unambiguous identification as the cause of AIDS" as a supposed triumph of heavily-funded research.[5] Starting with this assumption, the report went on to outline an unrestrained agenda of "future research needs."[6] The plan offered a piece of the pie for virtually everyone. Molecular biologists could study the genetic structure of HIV, while biochemists would analyze viral protein func-

tions and crystallographers would examine protein structures. Virologists would inspect every detail of the infection process and develop more tests for HIV, and animal researchers would experiment with mice and chimpanzees alike. Epidemiologists would not only monitor HIV infection in the population, but would receive vast sums of money to follow cohorts of infected people as they live or die. Pharmacologists would have their hands full developing a spectrum of drugs to attack the virus, the committee specifically suggesting AZT, ddA, and ddC among others. Of course, vaccines against the virus would have to be invented. Even the social scientists could join in, endlessly studying the risk behaviors for transmitting HIV and trying to understand what psychological barriers prevent members of the public from believing the official AIDS doctrine.

The common denominator was that all AIDS research should be predicated entirely on HIV. Even with new money pouring in, no room would be allowed for alternative hypotheses. The committee did hastily list "possible cofactors" that might contribute to AIDS, all implying infectious agents: cytomegalovirus or other microbes, genital ulcers as possible transmission routes for germs, and infection by HIV a second time. Psychological stress and diet were added as possible minor contributors. But drug abuse received no mention at all, effectively blocking any research in that direction.

Every recommendation of *Confronting AIDS* was slavishly followed. Whereas a few scientists privately questioned the HIV hypothesis after Robert Gallo's 1984 press conference, this 1986 report bared enough teeth to squelch most remaining doubts. The report also suggested that drugs being tested for AIDS treatment need not rely on all the proper controls, especially placebo groups, a recommendation later used in approving ddI and ddC. Further, the committee's call for an increase to one billion dollars in federal AIDS research money by 1990 was nearly met by the NIH alone. And, as recommended, much of that money has been used to attract scientists into AIDS research, as well as to train larger numbers of new scientists who add to the growing demand for grant money.

2. As another opportunity to spend large amounts of money, the committee estimated the staggering costs of medical care for each AIDS patient and decided that "it appears likely that future financing of AIDS care will necessarily involve substantial public programs and funds."[7] To make this as open-ended as possible, the report declared that "The committee believes that society has an ethical obligation to ensure that all individuals receive adequate medical care."[8] The meaning of "adequate" was never defined, but since HIV infection was considered inherently fatal and untreatable, this meant providing toxic drugs such as AZT or simply comforting the patient as he died. The suggestion never arose of turning people into long-term survivors by encouraging them to end recreational drug use.

Indeed, spending money seemed to be more important than effective care. The committee wanted "to ensure that all persons at risk of infection, seropositive, or already ill could make provision for or otherwise be assured that their potential health care costs will be covered."[9] The high price of

AZT, in terms of both health and money ($2000 per year wholesale, about $10,000 retail), ultimately weighed heavily in those calculations.

The key to getting AIDS to qualify for such coverage lay in classifying patients as being disabled. This designation has allowed Medicaid to cover forty percent of AIDS patients, and Medicare to pay for a much smaller fraction.

3. The report also placed great emphasis on public health measures—to stop the spread of HIV. Any actions to slow the virus were considered justifiable, even if they caused hysteria, encouraged drug use, or impinged on civil liberties. The public health effort directly conflicted with the medical care program, since AIDS patients had to be classified as disabled to qualify for medical coverage, whereas public health controls depended on classifying patients as infectious and therefore deadly to others. The AIDS establishment was constantly issuing such mixed signals, eroding its public credibility and spawning an enormous diversity of alarmist beliefs.

In the early days of the Public Health Service, decades before the founding of the CDC, federal officers were frequently dispatched to various cities in the midst of disease epidemics. Tuberculosis, bubonic plague, and yellow fever still swept through periodically, but were becoming less common and taking fewer lives as the population became healthier. Hoping to stall epidemics, the federal public health agents tried to seize emergency powers by quarantining patients, restricting travel, and taking control of water supplies. But the local citizens and governments usually disagreed with such tactics, and resisted attempts at control. In time, serious contagious epidemics disappeared altogether, but not because of public health measures. The decline of these epidemics actually occurred during an era of increased nutrition, the construction of plumbing systems, and rising standards of living.[10]

The memories of popular opposition have remained etched in the minds of public health officials, reminding the CDC of its limits. On the other hand, AIDS presented the first opportunity in many years to revive the old public health campaigns. *Confronting AIDS* recognized this potential, recommending a two-step program of "education" and widespread HIV testing.

The committee gave examples of what it meant by "education." This included advocating use of condoms and sterile needles, targeted not only at the AIDS risk groups but at the population as a whole, on the assumption that everyone is endangered by this supposedly infectious disease. Because pregnant mothers can also transmit HIV to their children, the committee noted that "the Centers for Disease Control advises women at risk of HIV infection to consider delaying pregnancy."[11] "Education" also meant damage control—in case anyone began questioning the HIV hypothesis of AIDS. In reviewing a survey of men asked about the HIV test, the report expressed dismay at one of the results. "The most disturbing finding from the survey was the number of subjects (a majority) who believed that a positive antibody test somehow conferred immunity, that they had successfully 'fought off' the virus."[12] A well-funded "education" program would change such common-sense views.

The report recommended easily-available HIV testing on a voluntary basis. It also raised the possibilities of reporting these results to central agencies, tracing the sexual contacts of infected people, and quarantining HIV positives, though it dared not explicitly endorse such measures. But stronger controls were not ruled out. "There may be need, however," the committee stated, "to use compulsory measures, with full due process protection, in the occasional case of a recalcitrant individual who refuses repeatedly to desist from dangerous conduct in the spread of the infection."[13] In other words, infected people who do not willingly follow public health guidelines can be forced to do so.

The committee effectively opened the door to more radical proposals. Donald Francis, the Epidemic Intelligence Service graduate who had played a central role in blaming AIDS on a retrovirus, has formulated such explicit plans. In 1984 he had already summarized the goals of many CDC leaders with a proposal entitled "Operation AIDS Control." He later spelled out these ideas in a 1992 speech to his fellow CDC officials, using the audacious title "Toward a Comprehensive HIV prevention Program for the CDC and the Nation."[14]

Referring directly to the mandate provided by *Confronting AIDS*, Francis called for five major steps to expand CDC authority. First, he wanted the CDC to receive a special status, making it immune from accountability to the voters. "The United States needs to establish a separate line of public health authority that allows for accountability, yet is protected from extremist interference. Perhaps the Federal Reserve is an example to emulate... Specific legislation should be promulgated to protect CDC from political interference with necessary public health practice."

Second, he proposed "guaranteed health care" for HIV positives, mostly to lure infected people out of hiding. "If we are going to be successful in identifying HIV-infected persons through testing programs," he said, "the necessary incentive must be guaranteed health care financing."

His third point called for endorsing drug use, using the logic that providing drugs to addicts would prevent sharing of dirty needles. "Following a more enlightened model for drug treatment, including prescribing heroin, would have dramatic effects on HIV and could eliminate many of the dangerous illegal activities surrounding drugs." Francis even called this "safe injection." But if heroin itself causes AIDS, then taxpayers would be financing the deaths of addicts.

Fourth, he advocated heavier federal intervention in producing vaccines, apparently ignoring the lessons of the 1976 disaster with the swine flu vaccine.

Finally, Francis issued a call to consolidate public health authority in central hands. "Establish clear chains of responsibility," he insisted. "CDC needs to reestablish its leadership role in HIV prevention. Prevention requires close coordination, training, and financial support of state and local health departments." This would subject all public health functions in the country to CDC control.

Francis then revealed how these powers would be used to manage HIV. The CDC would develop a central registry with the identities of all infected people, gathered from every imaginable source. "Whether through hospitals, doctors' offices, sexually transmitted disease clinics, jail health clinics, or whatever, routine testing should be strongly recommended to all patients... the concept of routine voluntary testing for *everyone* should be aggressively promulgated as the standard of medical practice." [emphasis in original] The sexual contacts of all HIV positives would be traced and registered as well—not a simple task, considering that "fast track" homosexuals typically report hundreds or thousands of sexual contacts.

To push CDC "educational" programs in schools, Francis proposed overriding local authority to bypass any resistance from parents. "If, in the opinion of those far more expert than I, schools cannot be expected to provide such programs, then health departments should take over, using as a justification their mandate to protect the public's health."

Little wonder that Francis boasted of "the opportunity that the HIV epidemic provides for public health." Letting down his guard a bit, he revealed the virus hunter within. "The cloistered caution of the past needs to be discarded. The climate and culture must be open ones where old ideas are challenged. Those who desire the status quo should seek employment elsewhere... This is the epidemic of the century, and every qualified person should want to have a piece of the action."[15]

4. The *Confronting AIDS* committee lastly recommended extending parallel efforts to other nations, because "infectious diseases know no national boundaries."[16] This meant scientific research collaborations with foreign scientists as well as public health programs in their countries, including condom distribution. The Agency for International Development (AID) has largely picked up the tab, giving millions of dollars to central African nations to buy their cooperation.

Confronting AIDS specifically called for increased aid to the World Health Organization (WHO) for public health measures. That same year, the WHO released a book outlining its action plan for contagious disease control, *Public Health Action in Emergencies Caused by Epidemics*. This book was considerably more explicit, describing "quarantine," "mass immunization," "restrictions on mass gatherings," and "restrictions on travel" (including the formation of a *cordon sanitaire*) as options when the WHO intervenes in a nation's epidemic—measures that would be more politically ticklish to carry out in the United States.[17] Third World citizens, after all, tend to have less input when objecting to such actions.

The committee proposed that a special commission be established to oversee the implementation of the War on AIDS. This was carried out in the form of the Presidential Commission on the HIV epidemic, established in 1987 and lasting for one year. The President's Commission gathered testimony and issued a report, which merely affirmed the guidelines in *Confronting AIDS*. In 1988 the National Academy of Sciences set up a second committee, including David Baltimore and EIS graduate Donald R. Hopkins as members, which also reiterated the original blueprint and called for yet another permanent commission to supervise the war. Since 1989, the

National Commission on AIDS has been sponsored by Congress and the President, and continues to echo the recommendations of *Confronting AIDS*.

At times these officials of the War on AIDS reveal their intent to manipulate public fear with carefully crafted propaganda. In 1993, when a major scientific report concluded that AIDS was remaining strictly in risk groups and not spreading into the general population, AIDS officials could not deny the clear evidence. Instead, they angrily denounced the report for allowing Americans not to be frightened. David Rogers, vice chairman of the National Commission on AIDS, told a reporter that "his group had worked hard to try to make AIDS a concern to everyone. 'Now to have someone say, 'We can relax',' Rogers said, 'I would much prefer to have them say, 'You should worry about your own son and daughter'.'"[18]

The initial *Confronting AIDS* report has indeed served as the unquestioned standard against which the entire AIDS establishment has measured itself. Virtually all of its recommendations have been carried out enthusiastically, in the spirit of true warfare. But when fighting a war, one has little time to ask questions or indulge in scientific skepticism. Such a war requires immediate action, not careful thought. To prevent any mutiny, the AIDS establishment has made sure to control its potential opposition.

A rigged debate

To prevent serious criticism or opposition from arising against the War on AIDS, whether among scientists or the general public, the entire nation had to be mobilized to participate. Anyone not enthusiastically joining in would be stigmatized with a label of "apathy," and any person raising questions about the HIV hypothesis could be painted as being in a state of "denial."

The NIH carried out its assignment, lavishing billions of dollars on HIV research. Many scientists quickly learned an easy way to tap into this plentiful grant money, while others knew better than to raise questions, an act that peer reviewers could easily punish. Thus virtually all scientists marched along without hesitation.

The CDC, on the other hand, tended to occupy the front lines as the federal government's major publich health agency. Thinking of themselves more as activists than researchers, CDC officers spent much of their time reaching the lay public with prevention measures. Their AIDS activities consisted of more than just HIV testing or distributing condoms and sterile needles; their largest program dealt with mobilizing the public through "education"—indoctrinating the unsuspecting population to join in the war on HIV. The job of inducing the non-scientists to march fell upon the CDC.

Traditionally, the CDC has disseminated its views largely through state and local authorities, whether health departments, school systems, or other government structures. But the new mandate provided by *Confronting AIDS* demanded greater action, much to the CDC's delight. The crux of its mission was to persuade the public "to see HIV-AIDS as an infectious disease," in the words of one CDC official.[19] With large sums of new money appropriated by Congress for the purpose, the agency launched its new initiative.

Only one major obstacle stood in the way. With its messages always attached to the CDC label, the agency would have limited impact on public opinion. So the CDC chose to expand its existing program for buying influence with other organizations. The agency started with its traditional partners, the state governments. Ten million dollars began flowing from the CDC to the states in early 1985, allocated for new HIV testing sites. The money was carefully linked to "appropriate" counseling as defined by the CDC, ensuring that anyone being tested would hear the official line on AIDS.[20] The CDC has continued financing these testing programs.

Looking beyond state and local governments, the CDC also recognized the potential for spreading its views through private groups, which have greater credibility as independent voices for their constituencies. The CDC had already targeted some of these "community-based organizations" and quietly developed ties with them before the publication of *Confronting AIDS*.

It began with the United States Conference of Mayors (USCM), which in 1984 received CDC money for distributing AIDS information. Within months, the CDC began sending increased funding to the USCM, which in turn distributed the new money to private AIDS organizations. Under CDC monitoring, the USCM helped AIDS groups organize and expand their efforts, and even used the money to start new AIDS groups. Eventually the CDC added more funding through state health departments, which also dispersed it to AIDS activists. By the early 1990s, about 300 such groups were funded, directly or indirectly, by the CDC. Under central coordination, these groups became so closely interconnected that they constituted a singular web of activists. Push a button at CDC headquarters in Atlanta, Georgia, and a nationwide network of ostensibly private organizations would act in unison. To the public, the whole thing seemed quite spontaneous.

These organizations, their CDC links invisible to most people, actively spread the ominous message of infectious AIDS. Most of these AIDS activist organizations were homosexual groups, through whom the CDC view quickly permeated the entire homosexual community. This influence became so pervasive that some information, even life-saving messages, were blocked from reaching AIDS patients. Michael Callen, a twelve-year AIDS survivor (until 1994) who worked to give hope to patients, described unexpected opposition from an AIDS activist:

> Once, after giving my "hope speech" during a public forum organized by the Gay Men's Health Crisis, I was angrily pulled aside by a gay man who worked in GMHC's Education Department. He begged me to stop saying that AIDS might not be 100 percent fatal. Shocked that a gay man would make such a request, I asked for reasons. He gave three: (1) efforts to persuade gay men to practice safer sex might be undermined because they would "take AIDS less seriously"; (2) it was bad for fund-raising; and (3) it would make lobbying for increased federal funding more difficult. "After all," he said, "if not everyone who gets it dies, then maybe AIDS isn't *really* the crisis we're being told it is."[21]

After the publication of *Confronting AIDS* in 1986, the CDC started branching out to new types of organizations. While continuing to fund AIDS activists, the agency now also directed its money and influence toward other civic groups that could influence other segments of American society. Tens of millions of dollars, for example, flowed to the American Red Cross in a cooperative agreement that gave the CDC an immense degree of control over the organization. The Red Cross used the money to create and widely distribute many millions of pamphlets, videos, and guides throughout the country, as well as to sponsor uncountable numbers of presentations in local communities. The American branch even pulled influence with international Red Cross and Red Crescent societies to spread the CDC doctrine around the world.

Vast sums of CDC money were allocated to dozens of minority and civil rights organizations ranging from the National Urban League and the Southern Christian Leadership Conference to the National Council of La Raza and the Association of Asian/Pacific Community Health Organizations. Special "partnerships" were also formed between the CDC and powerful lobbies. Elected representatives in state governments were influenced through the National Conference of State Legislatures; unionized workers were reached through funding to the AFL-CIO and some of its affiliated unions, including the American Federation of State, Country, and Municipal Employees (AFSCME) and the Service Employees International Union (SEIU); and school sex education programs were shaped by grants for the Sex Information and Education Council of the U.S. (SIECUS).

CDC influence extended into the schools by funding such organizations as the two major teachers' unions, the National Education Association and the American Federation of Teachers, as well as through the National Parent-Teacher Association, the American Association of School Administrators, the National School Boards Association, the Center for Population Options, and many similar groups.

The CDC even managed to exploit the raging AIDS debate between AIDS activist groups and the religious right. In addition to the funding for AIDS activists mentioned above, the CDC formed a partnership with the National Association for People With AIDS (NAPWA). This group co-sponsored annual conferences for AIDS activist groups, and the 1992 meeting "attracted over 1,000 individuals representing 578 community-based agencies in 189 cities and 46 states as well as Puerto Rico, the Dominican Republic, Japan, Kenya, Ireland and Portugal."[22] The CDC simultaneously became a partner of Americans for a Sound AIDS Policy (ASAP), which "serves as a resource to the religious community and disseminates HIV-AIDS information and publications through 23,000 Christian bookstores."[23] ASAP became the central source of AIDS material for the religious right, and advised Congressman William Dannemeyer.

Funding these two organizations paid off well for the CDC. The AIDS activist movement championed distribution of condoms and sterile needles, while the religious right advocated mandatory HIV testing, tracing of sexual contacts, and sometimes even quarantines. Both sides called for more funding for AIDS research and CDC programs. No matter how much the two movements fought each other, the CDC could never lose.

The CDC was not the only part of the AIDS establishment supporting its ostensible opposition. Burroughs-Wellcome joined the act in 1987, once AZT had been approved and was starting to generate hundreds of millions of dollars in sales, profits that the company certainly wanted to protect. Since the company's market lay disproportionately in the homosexual community, it had to be sure of encountering little criticism from that direction. The homosexual press quickly fell into line as Burroughs-Wellcome began placing high-cost advertising for AZT in virtually every such publication, large or small. Chuck Ortleb's *New York Native* remained stalwart as one of the few holdouts; most others embraced the extra revenue.

Next the company turned to financing AIDS activist groups directly. Some 16,000 such organizations exist in the United States, ranging from relatively mainstream foundations that support research to the more radical groups like ACT UP. Burroughs-Wellcome has given money to most of them, particularly the extremist groups with the strongest reputations for fierce independence. After the money began flowing to AIDS activists, many organizations began blunting their criticisms of AIDS dogma while keeping up the fiery rhetoric. Few constituents of these organizations noticed the change, and HIV-positive people continued relying on their advice.

In the center of the AIDS establishment sits the American Foundation for AIDS Research (AmFAR). It was created in 1985 by Michael Gottlieb, the doctor who reported the first four AIDS cases, and Mathilde Krim, the scientist and socialite who helped launch the War on Cancer and now played a central role in the war on AIDS. AmFAR gained prominence through its Hollywood connections—it recruited such top names as Elizabeth Taylor and Barbra Streisand for fundraising and publicity—and thus came to dominate public relations for the AIDS establishment. The pharmaceutical companies showed their pleasure with generous donations. Burroughs-Wellcome announced a staggering one million dollar donation in 1992, and the Bristol-Myers Squibb Foundation, connected with the company producing ddI, has also provided funds.

Toward the more radical end of the spectrum is Project Inform, a San Francisco-based watchdog group founded by activist Martin Delaney. This group gained its fame as a bulldog fighting the Food and Drug Administration (FDA), based on Delaney's underground testing network that provided various experimental cures to dying AIDS patients. He apparently followed his own medical advice, suffering to this day an irreversible limp from self-medication.[24] Delaney started as one of the angriest critics of AZT as a toxic drug improperly rushed through clinical trials. He also co-authored a book in 1987, *Strategies for Survival*, in which he warned active homosexual men against the disastrous health effects of such recreational drugs as poppers, cocaine, heroin, and amphetamines. In addition to emphasizing "immuno-suppression" among the effects, he and co-author Peter Goldblum admonished their homosexual readers not to ignore the dangers of drug abuse:

And don't get bent out of shape if your favorite "recreational" high gets a bad rap. Maybe your use of the drug is so moderate, so cool, that you never bump into the gremlins lurking within. It's also possible that you haven't been a "user" long enough for the effects to occur. The damage from most drugs is long-term and cumulative... But don't discount the information out of hand simply because it doesn't agree with your own experience or because you don't want to hear it.[25]

But aid from the pharmaceuticals changed all that. Burroughs-Wellcome donated $150,000 for an upgrade and expansion of Project Inform's computer system, and Bristol-Myers Squibb pitched in another $200,000. Suddenly well-funded, prestigious, and personally consulted by Anthony Fauci, Delaney changed his mind. When we heard him give a lecture at Stanford University in 1990, the former nemesis of the FDA now praised that federal agency for its work, and sympathetically described it as "overworked and understaffed."[26] In publicly attacking Duesberg for questioning the HIV hypothesis, he has issued furious monographs and letters to newspaper editors. Delaney has even dropped his former opposition to AZT.

Larry Kramer is another example of a seemingly radical AIDS activist who actually works closely with the establishment. An intensely angry homosexual-rights activist renowned for his bitter language in denouncing AIDS officials, Kramer founded the Gay Men's Health Crisis (GMHC) in 1982. Under his early leadership, GMHC labored to create AIDS activism in a community that did not want to acknowledge the syndrome's existence. Later, after new leaders replaced Kramer and the AIDS epidemic had become institutionalized, GMHC continued spreading the official CDC view of prevention and treatment. This view included endorsing AZT therapy. A former Executive Director of GMHC did admit to writer John Lauritsen that the group had been receiving money from Burroughs-Wellcome, but declined to say just how much.[27]

Kramer went on to found an even more radical group, the AIDS Coalition To Unleash Power (ACT UP), in 1987. Intent on pushing more drugs through FDA approval, ACT UP protesters gained attention by stopping rush-hour traffic on Wall Street, invading corporate and government offices, and disrupting scientific AIDS conferences. Yet very quickly these activists became an integral part of the AIDS establishment. Anthony Fauci, the *de facto* coordinator of the war on AIDS at NIH, began attending ACT UP meetings in 1989 and brought key members (as well as Martin Delaney) into NIH advisory positions. ACT UP members were soon incorporated into AmFAR and other positions of influence.

Burroughs-Wellcome also developed close relations with the group. An editorial note in the San Francisco *Sentinel*, referring to the local ACT UP/Golden Gate, stated that "ACT UP chapters elsewhere have received millions in contributions from Burroughs-Wellcome over the last few years."[28] Certainly the organization has received thousands of dollars. An offshoot group headed by ACT UP/New York member Pete Staley, the Treatment

Action Group (TAG), is funded by the pharmaceutical company, and in 1992 arranged for the one-million-dollar grant from Burroughs-Wellcome to AmFAR. ACT UP is also sponsored as a participant at the annual International AIDS Conferences. According to John Lauritsen, at the Ninth Conference in Berlin in 1993, "Most of the 300 ACT UP members had the 950 DM [*deutschmark*] entrance fee waived by the organizers. Many had travelled to Berlin, staying in hotels with swimming pools, with all expenses paid by Wellcome. An ACT UP representative from London admitted that his group had received £50,000 from Wellcome."[29]

The relationship has paid off for Burroughs-Wellcome and other pharmaceutical companies. Rather than protesting against AZT itself, ACT UP has demonstrated for cheaper AZT. But not only was Burroughs-Wellcome already intending to lower the price, the demonstration itself helped advertise the drug; some of the signs held by activists read, "What good is a cure if you can't afford it?"[30] Only ACT UP demonstrators could get away with calling AZT a "cure." Recently the group has voiced some criticism of AZT, but nothing that will endanger the drug's status. The group also helped Bristol-Myers Squibb win FDA licensing for the toxic drug ddI. Through colorful street actions and high-pressure negotiations, ACT UP maneuvered the FDA into approving ddI on the "fast track," without any controlled studies at all.

ACT UP has also worked to squelch any criticisms of AZT or the HIV hypothesis. John Lauritsen has described his own experiences being "shouted down and silenced" by members when he attended meetings and tried to raise questions, an experience also relayed to us by other AIDS activists.[31] At the 1993 International AIDS Conference in Berlin, ACT UP took direct action against a small contingent of HIV dissenters, whose viewpoint had never previously been represented at such meetings:

> In front of the ICC [the conference center], Christian Joswig and Peter Schmidt were attacked by several dozen members of ACT UP, who destroyed signs, burned leaflets, and attempted to destroy camera equipment. Conference officials witnessed these acts, and then ordered the victims of the assault to stay at least 100 meters from the ICC. Officials took no action against the attackers from ACT UP.
> Also on the 10th [of June], 100 ACT UP members destroyed a booth belonging to AIDS-Information Switzerland. They chanted obscenities, smashed panels, destroyed displays and chairs, and tore up literature, before covering the remains of the booth with 30 rolls of toilet paper. The Swiss group's sin had been to criticize condoms.[32]

With such opposition as Project Inform or ACT UP, AIDS officials need not worry.

The communications media is naturally another target for the war on AIDS. The CDC leads this charge, funding such groups as the National Association of Broadcasters, which is "the broadcasting industry's trade association, representing the major networks and some 6,000 individual radio and television stations."[33] More importantly, the entire network of CDC- and

Burroughs-Wellcome-funded organizations effectively serves as a powerful lobby, both in government and in the media. Politicians and journalists alike, when not consulting the CDC directly, usually get AIDS information from one or more of these many organizations, on the assumption that all these groups function independently.

The CDC can even cultivate relationships with individual journalists. Political writer Michael Fumento wrote the book *The Myth of Heterosexual AIDS* in 1989, arguing accurately that AIDS was not spreading out of its original risk groups and would not explode into a pandemic. The book singled out Harold Jaffe, Rand Stoneburner, and Alexander Langmuir as "the good guys" who provided extraordinary help to Fumento in researching his book.[34] All three were veterans of the Epidemic Intelligence Service (EIS) of the CDC, which Langmuir himself had founded, and Jaffe had managed the KSOI Task Force that had constructed the myth of infectious AIDS. So under this influence, Fumento threw the blame for AIDS alarmism in virtually every direction, to scientists, journalists, and lay people alike, with one exception—the CDC. Many of the groups attacked by Fumento have been quietly funded by the CDC, a delicate point he failed to mention. His book also refused to question the HIV hypothesis itself, and when we have challenged the virus-AIDS dogma, Fumento has sometimes been called in to defend HIV with crafty arguments. Despite his questioning the heterosexual AIDS scare, Fumento has become yet one more advocate for the hypothesis of infectious AIDS.

These avenues give the CDC an impressive hold on the media, allowing it to promote fear of an AIDS explosion while saving the HIV hypothesis from embarrassing public relations disasters. Thus the CDC has been able gradually to lengthen the supposed latent period between HIV infection and AIDS, from ten months to two years, then five, then ten, and now approaching twelve or more years. The agency has also created an illusion of the spread of AIDS, pumping up the number of cases by redefining the syndrome. In 1985, the CDC first expanded the list of diseases officially called AIDS. Again this happened in 1987, artificially increasing the annual case load by fifty percent or more. The definition was expanded again on January 1, 1993, adding such diseases as bacterial pneumonias, tuberculosis, and even low T cells—in healthy people—as AIDS-defining conditions. The increase in AIDS cases has resulted more from this statistical trick than from a genuine rise in sickness. A critical and independent media would have noticed such maneuvers, and would have asked questions.

Stories can also be squelched when they become too embarrassing. The January 20, 1990, issue of the medical journal *The Lancet* contained two adjoining papers on Kaposi's sarcoma. The first, with CDC official Harold Jaffe as senior author, acknowledged that the disease mostly targeted homosexuals with AIDS, consistently avoiding the other risk groups. The second paper reported six HIV-negative homosexuals with Kaposi's sarcoma. We had previously raised these data as arguments against the HIV hypothesis, a fact ignored in these papers. The authors therefore recognized that Kaposi's sarcoma might not be caused by HIV, but they, and presumably the CDC, wanted instead to blame some other undiscovered infectious microbe. The news media gave this story some attention, but during the following weeks this news only helped our case against the virus-AIDS hypothesis. As a result, the CDC dropped the issue and the story died completely.

A more spectacular example briefly stunned the world in July of 1992. We had for some time pointed out the existence of people with AIDS diseases, but no HIV infection. Then, just before the Eighth International AIDS Conference in Amsterdam, *Newsweek* suddenly published an article by reporter Geoffrey Cowley on several HIV-negative AIDS cases. The article mentioned unpublished research by two laboratories suggesting the discovery of a new retrovirus; rumor had it the scientists had leaked the story to *Newsweek* so they could blame HIV-free AIDS cases on a new virus. In any case, one of them had already submitted a paper reporting a new retrovirus to the *Proceedings of the National Academy of Sciences*, which would not be published for several weeks. Anthony Fauci jumped on the potential bandwagon, calling up the editor of the *Proceedings* to pressure him into publishing the paper immediately.

Researchers at the AIDS conference interpreted the *Newsweek* article as a green light, and began unveiling dozens of previously unmentioned HIV-free AIDS cases in the United States and Europe. The situation began reeling out of control. Rather than merely promoting the idea of two AIDS viruses, the media fallout unintentionally started re-opening the question of whether HIV caused AIDS. James Curran of the CDC and Fauci raced to Amsterdam on Air Force Two to take charge of the situation. The best they could do was to listen to all reports of such cases and promise to resolve the situation. In reality, they had decided to drop the whole matter.

Three weeks later, the CDC sponsored a special meeting at its Atlanta headquarters. The scientists reporting HIV-free AIDS cases were invited, as was Cowley, the *Newsweek* reporter who first broke the story. The unexplained AIDS cases were relabeled with an unmemorable name—Idiopathic $CD4^+$ Lymphocytopenia, or ICL—so as to break any connection between these cases and AIDS. The ICL cases were then dismissed as insignificant, and Cowley was apparently persuaded to cooperate more closely with the CDC in the future. His next AIDS article toed the official line perfectly, containing little news, and he never again followed up on the growing list of HIV-free AIDS cases. In February of 1993, a group of papers were published in the *New England Journal of Medicine*, accompanied by an editorial by Fauci. Ironically imitating arguments straight from our own critique of AIDS, he concluded ICL must not be infectious at all. The issue had died, and so had the media coverage.

Lawrence Altman, the EIS alumnus who had become the head medical writer for the *New York Times*, meanwhile admitted to other journalists that "he knew of cases for several months but did not break the story because he didn't think it was his paper's place to announce something the CDC was not confident enough of to publish."[35] No one bothered asking why a top reporter would feel obligated to follow the CDC line so slavishly.

We have personally been informed of at least two scientists in the San Francisco Bay area who work with dozens of HIV-negative AIDS patients, but who, because of CDC hostility to any such reports, have been intimidated into concealing these cases.[36] We suspect this is a nationwide problem, with untold numbers of HIV-free AIDS victims remaining unreported.

By funding AIDS activist groups, the CDC and pharmaceutical companies have created yet another arm of influence over the media. These activists can directly co-opt or intimidate reporters, who often depend on the activists for news stories. Lisa Krieger, medical reporter for the *San Francisco Examiner*, revealed some of the more common tactics:

> I'm often attacked by AIDS activists, whose unspoken assumption is that either I'm on their team, or against them. When I write about the need for reform in San Francisco's AIDS infrastructure, I am called "uninformed," "insensitive" and "racist." When I dare criticize an AIDS organization, I am told I am "writing self-serving drivel" or passing on "rumor, gossip and innuendo."[37]

Though denying she is influenced by such pressure and insisting that her reporting is objective, Krieger nevertheless admitted some of her normally unspoken biases in her attitude toward AIDS reporting:

> How could I resist, in my weaker moments, becoming an AIDS advocate? I want to reach through the newsprint and grab the reader by the collar, as if that would somehow shake the complacency with which the public has come to accept this disease. I want to applaud every new clinical drug trial, elevate AIDS activists to sainthood.[38]

One startling example of such media bias appeared in September, 1993, when a New York City resident who rejects the HIV hypothesis of AIDS wrote a letter to the *New York Times*. Although critical of AZT therapy, the letter was published. However, the newspaper editors actually *added* words; immediately following a reference to HIV, the *Times* inserted the phrase "which causes AIDS."[39] The flabbergasted letter-writer still cannot figure out how to correct this bizarre form of censorship.

Censorship in the media

Aside from funding journalists' associations and AIDS activist groups, influencing individual reporters directly, or having EIS alumni reach high positions, the CDC (and NIH) have one other powerful tool for maintaining media cooperation. Elinor Burkett, a courageous *Miami Herald* reporter who wrote a major article covering the HIV-AIDS debate, explained it best as a question of "access":

> If you have an AIDS beat, you're a beat reporter, your job is everyday to go out there, fill your newspaper with what's new about AIDS. You write a story that questions the truth of the central AIDS hypothesis and what happened to me will happen to you. Nobody's going to talk to you. Now if nobody will talk to you, if nobody at the CDC will ever return your phone call,

you lose your competitive edge as an AIDS reporter. So it always keeps you in the mainstream, because you need those guys to be your buddies...

When you call the CDC on the phone, and I called them certainly on a regular basis when I was writing that piece, they say things to you like "You will be responsible for people in Miami stopping using condoms, if you write that article." Do I want people in Miami to stop using condoms? Of course not!... There's all kinds of blackmail, and I don't mean overt blackmail. It's emotional blackmail of that sort, and it's the fact that exactly what I knew was going to happen, happened, which is, I can't get a phone call returned by any of them.[40]

Faced with growing dissent against the HIV hypothesis since 1987, the generals in the war on AIDS have openly hinted at using such tactics. They have repeatedly made clear their preference that dissidents confine the debate to scientific circles, keeping it out of the public eye. When asked by one reporter to answer Peter Duesberg's challenge, David Baltimore instead condemned the entire viewpoint as "irresponsible and pernicious," and two years later warned in a scientific letter that "Duesberg's continued attempts to persuade the public to doubt the role of HIV in AIDS are not based on facts."[41] Prominent retrovirus hunter Frank Lilly, a member of the original Presidential Commission on the HIV Epidemic, angrily responded to a presentation by Duesberg and declared, "I regret that it has become a public question."[42] Upset by sporadic but growing media coverage of Duesberg, AmFAR sponsored a special scientific meeting in April of 1988. Supposedly the conference would air all views on the cause of AIDS, "but was really an attempt to put Duesberg's theories to rest," admitted one of the many journalists present.[43]

Fauci stated the point more bluntly in 1989, declaring in an editorial that Duesberg's ideas were nonsense and complaining that his views were receiving too much publicity. "Journalists who make too many mistakes, or who are sloppy," he warned, "are going to find that their access to scientists may diminish."[44] And in a 1993 letter to the journal *Nature*, two of the most powerful virologists in Italy bared their teeth:

Your subtitle ends: "He should stop." Or, we submit, "should he be stopped?" For example, should he somehow be prevented from appearing on television to misinform individuals who are at risk from the disease? One approach would be to refuse television confrontations with Duesberg, as Tony Fauci and one of us managed to do at the opening day of the VIIth International Conference on AIDS in Florence. One can't spread misinformation without an audience.[45]

Such threats do work when levelled by the well-funded AIDS establishment, frightening the media and overriding their natural fascination with such a newsworthy story.

Based on internal documents released to us by an anonymous source, we now know that, in 1987, while Duesberg was still on leave at the NIH, key offices of the U.S. government specifically engineered a strategy for suppressing the HIV debate. The operation began on April 28, less than two months after Duesberg's first paper on the HIV question had appeared in *Cancer Research*. Amazingly, government officials had not even heard of the paper until several journalists and homosexual activists began raising questions.

That day, a memo was sent out from the office of the Secretary of Health and Human Services (HHS), headed by the words "MEDIA ALERT." Describing the situation created by Duesberg's paper, the staff member ominously noted that "The article apparently went through the normal pre-publication process and should have been flagged at NIH" (there is no reason any scientific paper should be "flagged" by any government agency). The staffer then pointed out the threat to the government:

> This obviously has the potential to raise a lot of controversy (If this isn't the virus, how do we know the blood supply is safe? How do we know anything about transmission? How could you all be so stupid and why should we ever believe you again?) and we need to be prepared to respond. I have already asked NIH public affairs to start digging into this.[46]

Copies of the memo were addressed to the Secretary, Under Secretary, and Assistant Secretary of HHS, as well as to the "Assistant Secretary for Public Affairs," the "Chief of Staff," the Surgeon General, and "The White House."

A parallel memo was issued by the NIH on the same day. Its author was Florence Karlsberg, the public relations officer interviewed at about that same time by John Lauritsen (see Chapter 7), and the memo was addressed to top NIH officials. "I want to alert you about some incidents that have occurred in the past 24 hours," Karlsberg wrote. She listed several public inquiries about Duesberg. and emphasized, "DHHS is quite anxious and awaiting feedback re NIH/NCI response to and strategy for this provocative situation." Commenting that "Bob Gallo and others have tried to educate Peter [Duesberg] re HTLV-III [HIV] and AIDS—but it's hopeless," Karlsberg recommended creating a response team consisting of NIH epidemiologist William Blattner, Dani Bolognesi, Anthony Fauci, and Robert Gallo to deal with the controversy. "Perhaps the epidemiologic approach might be more productive in countering Peter's assertions," she suggested.[47]

Within two days, Blattner drafted a three-page memo for the sake of damage control. In it he marshaled a list of evasions and pseudo-arguments that would later become the standard defense of the HIV hypothesis used by all scientists and government agencies (see Chapter 6).[48] By June, he had reworked a third draft as a potential press release. But the memo was never released to the public. Instead, NIH and other officials adopted a policy of silence, hoping to discourage further interest by the media.

By December, the strategy was clearly failing. In another internal NIH memo dated December 30, Karlsberg wrote a fellow staffer that the Blattner memo "was not pursued in June because Paul [an NIH staffer] suggested at that time that this project be put aside temporarily—at least until necessary.

Alas—in the past few months, inquiries have been mounting.... The calls and interest are mounting. Perhaps it's time to review and activate the attached statement." On our copy, a hand-written response on the bottom, initialed "PVN," suggests immediate action: "I guess it is time to get off the dime. This isn't going away."[49]

Get off the dime they certainly did. The Blattner memo was apparently revised and expanded, the names of Robert Gallo and Howard Temin were added as co-authors, and it was published in July of 1988 as one-half of the written debate with Duesberg in *Science* magazine (see Chapter 6). Naturally, the piece was not identified as being the product of NIH planning. But that was to be the last time the AIDS establishment would publicly engage Duesberg in debate. Heightened controversy, after all, might backfire on the NIH, attracting attention rather than discouraging media interest.

Indeed, the major media were already learning of the controversy over HIV, and were becoming curious. So the officials of the war on AIDS turned to more covert tactics, quietly yanking the leash of "access" to pull the media into line.

The MacNeil-Lehrer NewsHour sent camera crews to interview Duesberg in early 1988, planning to do a major segment on the controversy. But when the February eighth broadcast date arrived, the feature had been pulled. Apparently AIDS officials had heard of its imminent airing, and intercepted it. A few months later, the program tepidly aired an extremely short segment, with half the time now taken up by Fauci debunking Duesberg.

Meanwhile, the ABC daily program Good Morning America also discovered the story, and arranged to fly Duesberg to New York for an in-studio interview. He arrived Sunday night, February twentieth, and was booked into the Barbizon Hotel. But that very evening he received a call from the studio to announce that something had come up, and the interview was cancelled. Turning on the television the next morning, he saw Fauci connected by satellite, filling Duesberg's time slot and discussing every aspect of AIDS *except* the controversy over HIV. Eventually a Good Morning America film crew did fly to Berkeley, and a short segment was broadcast—again "balanced" with Fauci.

The story repeated itself twice with the Cable News Network (CNN). The second time, for example, a film crew flew out to interview Duesberg, planning to broadcast a half-hour special during the 1991 International AIDS Conference in Italy. Once again, the show was killed at the last minute, and a shorter version, only a couple of minutes long, reached the airwaves long after the conference was over.

The Larry King Live program, carried on CNN, scheduled a half-hour satellite interview with Duesberg for August sixth, 1992. Suspicious that something might again go awry, Duesberg called the producer a few hours before live broadcast. Sorry, she told him, something urgent has just come up regarding the election. Duesberg turned on the television that evening to discover that he had been replaced, not by an election issue, but by Fauci and the president of AmFAR. Neither surprise guest mentioned the controversy over HIV, nor did Larry King.

Duesberg has appeared on major national television only twice. The first was the March 28, 1993, show of the ABC documentary program Day One. Even in this case, we are told by inside sources, Fauci tried to intimidate the producers and get the show cancelled days before broadcast. Day One has never since featured the virus-AIDS controversy. The second appearance took place on the April 4, 1994, show of Nightline, and included Duesberg, Bryan Ellison, and several other dissidents—each being quoted briefly in the recorded segment. However, the broadcast was delayed until Ted Koppel was on vacation, ensuring a smaller audience. The show itself presented the whole issue in a muddled fashion, tending to leave the viewer confused as to what the question really was, and Fauci was brought in to "balance" both the recorded and live segments of the program. Fauci, in fact, was given most of the live air time, while the dissenting voices were represented by Robert Root-Bernstein, who carefully avoided arguing against the HIV hypothesis as such.

Such influence with the media by AIDS officials extends overseas. An award-winning English producer aired a one-hour documentary on Duesberg and the HIV controversy in June of 1990, timed to coincide with the International AIDS Conference in San Francisco. The program, entitled "The AIDS Catch," leaned in Duesberg's favor, and the British press lavished it with advance praise right up to the day of broadcast. But when the British medical and public health establishment retaliated with stern condemnations, the press turned around and began criticizing the program. The Terrence Higgins Trust, an AIDS organization funded mostly by the British government and partly by Burroughs-Wellcome, filed a legal complaint against the program that prevailed on technical grounds.

The long arm of the AIDS establishment reaches even the President of the United States. Jim Warner, a Reagan White House advisor critical of AIDS alarmism, heard about Duesberg and arranged to sponsor a debate in January of 1988. This would have forced the HIV issue into the public spotlight, but was abruptly cancelled days ahead of time, on orders from above.

Nor have the print media been exempt from such pressure. The first national publication to show interest was *Newsweek*, where Duesberg met with a senior writer in March, 1987. However, the magazine had just arranged a special honorary dinner for Robert Gallo, in its Washington, D.C. office, a few days hence. Maybe a story could be done later, the writer told Duesberg. Four years later, that day seemed to arrive shortly after an editorial in *Nature* favorable to Duesberg. Photographers showed up at his laboratory, taking photos for a story to appear immediately. But that article was cancelled within days.

Pulitzer prize-winning journalist John Crewdson, a former *New York Times* writer now on staff with the *Chicago Tribune*, discovered the controversy and became excited at the prospect of breaking a new investigative story. In November of 1987, he took Duesberg to dinner and showed strong interest, and by the following month had written an article on the HIV controversy. But then, as he has since admitted to a mutual contact, he ran into editorial roadblocks, and ended up writing articles on the Gallo virus-stealing scandal. He has expressed to us a genuine desire to cover the debate over HIV, but feared the political pressures.[50] By early 1993, these pressures finally led him to join forces against Duesberg, and he threatened to publish an article refuting our position for good. Nothing has yet happened. But since Robert Gallo's "acquittal" on scientific misconduct charges, Crewdson has once again indicated potential interest in the HIV debate.

The *New York Times* has mentioned Duesberg only four times in seven years, every time attacking him. The *Washington Post* has done likewise, with one hostile article and one small, neutral piece. The *San Francisco Chronicle* intended to cover the story, until it encountered opposition from scientists in the local AIDS establishment. *Harper's* magazine cancelled a major article in 1990 after having commissioned it from a freelance reporter who spent three years on the piece.

The *Los Angeles Times*, unlike other major newspapers, has covered the issue a few times. But each article underwent extraordinary editorial review, even when written by veteran staff reporters, ultimately being framed in terms slightly hostile to Duesberg and always accompanied by a piece openly attacking our position. In June of 1993, its weekly magazine published an article criticizing AZT therapy. The freelance writer told us she had been commissioned for the piece several months earlier, and that it had been subjected to such a gantlet of editors that she had to write nine drafts, many key facts being deleted in the process. She calculated her final pay for that article as three dollars per hour of work—a rate on which she cannot afford to live. The previous year, she had spent many months writing a specially commissioned article for *Esquire* magazine; that story had been killed altogether.

One chemist who wrote to *Time* magazine discovered that they, too, were consciously refusing to cover the sensational HIV debate. In a noncommittal response letter, the editor wrote, "We appreciated your call for coverage of the theories of Peter Duesberg, and have brought your comments to the attention of the appropriate editors. We have been aware of Duesberg's challenge to the mainstream concept of AIDS for several years, and continue to monitor the debate he has set in motion."[51] Then the letter referred to unpublished data supposedly refuting our position.

Again, this censorship extends to other countries. A star reporter for Germany's *Bild der Wissenschaft* was shocked when her article on Duesberg was cancelled without explanation, while *Der Spiegel* went so far as to attack Duesberg without allowing him to respond.

In general, smaller or more local periodicals have proven much more willing to cover the HIV debate than have national publications. After all, the larger media depend more heavily on access to government scientists and public health officials.

Censorship in science

Having averted serious media publicity, the AIDS establishment directed its power toward isolating and neutralizing Duesberg within scientific circles. A scientist's career depends heavily on peer-reviewed grant money, peer-reviewed opportunities to publish in scientific journals, and invitations to conferences. These vulnerabilities became the targets for retaliation by AIDS officials.

Robert Gallo and some other scientists began refusing, for example, to attend scientific conferences if Duesberg would be allowed to make a presentation. So in 1988, when an old colleague and friend of Duesberg's finally arranged a meeting on retroviruses on the Greek island of Crete, he dropped Duesberg's name from the announcement. Incredulous, Duesberg called back only to find that the apologetic long-term collaborator could not allow him to give a lecture, or the meeting would fall apart. Since that time, Duesberg has rarely been invited to retrovirus meetings, and virtually never to AIDS conferences.

Since then, however, Duesberg has received invitations to three major meetings to which Gallo had also been invited. In all three cases, Gallo carried out his threat. These included a retrovirology meeting in New York in 1989, another in Hamburg, Germany, in 1990, and an AIDS meeting in Bonn, Germany, in 1993. Gallo was slated to deliver the opening lecture at the Bonn meeting, but cancelled a mere three hours ahead of his scheduled appearance; the notice was sent from Hamburg, only a few hundred miles away, where Gallo had just lectured the previous day.

After the 1987 paper in *Cancer Research*, publishing suddenly became unbelievably difficult. Papers, especially on AIDS, would constantly run into obstacles at every turn, from hostile peer reviewers to reluctant editors. Even in the *Proceedings of the National Academy of Sciences* (*PNAS*), where Academy members such as Duesberg have an automatic right to publish papers without the standard peer review, he nevertheless encountered serious trouble.

In June of 1988, he submitted a paper to the *Proceedings* providing new arguments and evidence against the HIV hypothesis. The editor promptly rejected it, citing lack of "originality" in the paper's viewpoint.[52] A new editor meanwhile took the helm, and Duesberg invoked his rights as an Academy member and protested. The new editor took up the issue, nervously pointing out the paper was "controversial" and insisting he could not publish it without peer review.[53] The next several months brought three hostile reviewers, dozens of disputed points, and tense negotiations, but finally the paper appeared in February of 1989. The paper hinted at its extraordinary history only with a special disclaimer: "This paper, which reflects the author's views on the causes of AIDS, will be followed in a future issue by a paper presenting a different view of the subject."[54] Robert Gallo was asked to write a rebuttal, but never did.

In August, 1990, Duesberg submitted another paper, this time arguing that drug use is more tightly associated with AIDS than is HIV. Again the editor promptly rejected the paper, without explanation. Forced to split the paper in two, Duesberg submitted a shorter version on HIV. Following two peer reviews and several months of protracted haggling, the editor relented and published the paper.

Duesberg now sent in the other half of the paper—arguing that drug use causes most AIDS. This time his paper was doomed. Although Duesberg had already taken advice from four scientific colleagues in writing it, the paper was subjected to three anonymous reviewers by the editor. Two of the three voted to block publication, one of them calling any questions of the HIV hypothesis "extreme and highly dubious" and warning that the drug-AIDS hypothesis "has a potential for being harmful to the HIV infected segment of the population." This particular reviewer admitted "I am no expert in the fields concerned," and none of the three could point to factual errors in the paper.[55] At this point a new editor replaced the previous one, and Duesberg tried again with a modified paper. The new editor added four new reviewers who, though unable to find serious flaws, all voted to kill the paper. One reviewer even suggested the real reason was that if the paper were published, "one is further tempted to blame the victim."[56]

Trying once more, Duesberg had fellow Academy member Harry Rubin submit the paper after running it by four independent reviewers, all of whom recommended changes but favored its publication. The editor completely ignored those opinions, selecting three more anonymous reviewers who again voted down the paper by late 1991. One year after first being sent to the *Proceedings*, the paper was completely dead. This decision made Duesberg the second member in the 128-year history of the Academy to have a paper rejected from its journal; apparently the other had been Linus Pauling, who had argued vitamin C might prevent cancer.

But the virus hunters made their most effective counterattack by going after Duesberg's funding, the lifeblood of any scientist's laboratory. In 1985 the NIH had awarded him an Outstanding Investigator Grant (OIG), a special seven-year grant designed to give accomplished scientists the freedom to explore new ideas and directions without constantly having to apply for new funding. The time for renewal application arrived in 1990, two years before the grant would finish. But that October, Duesberg received the shocking news: his rating by the peer review committee was so low as to guarantee the grant would be discontinued, whereas two-thirds of the competing OIG applications were approved. Though referring to Duesberg as "one of the pioneers of modern retrovirology," the committee betrayed its real motives by complaining that he had ventured off to question the cause of AIDS. According to the reviewers, "Dr. Duesberg has become sidetracked" and "can no longer be considered at the forefront of his field... More recent years have been less productive, perhaps reflecting a dilution of his efforts with non-scientific issues."[57]

The very fact that a group of top researchers would consider the questioning of orthodox views in science as "non-scientific" comments powerfully on how completely science has been turned upside down since World War II. In this case, moreover, the deck had been deliberately loaded against Duesberg. Of the ten specially selected reviewers, two had severe conflicts of interest. Dani Bolognesi was a Burroughs-Wellcome consultant who tested AZT for the company, and Flossie Wong-Staal was a former researcher working for Robert Gallo—so closely, in fact, that she had born one of his children. And both Bolognesi and Wong-Staal had been involved in the secret NIH strategy to suppress the HIV debate (see above). Of the remaining, less-biased members, Duesberg accidentally discovered that three had never reviewed the grant at all, and a fourth had only given his recommendation by phone—a favorable one. By loading the committee with hostile reviewers and incorporating only the comments of those most opposed to Duesberg, the NIH had rigged the outcome.

Naturally, Duesberg protested vigorously, but received only the brush-off. Throughout the next two years, he waged an unceasing battle to save his grant. At first, the University of California, Berkeley, refused to endorse his appeal to the NIH, without which he could not legally proceed. As with most universities, virtually the largest source of income was from research grants, especially from the NIH, and the university must have feared retaliation. Duesberg also could not get a straight response from NIH. He then turned to his Congressman, Ron Dellums, whose staff aide began writing inquiry letters. The Secretary of Health and Human Services, Louis Sullivan, responded dismissively, admitting familiarity with the Duesberg case but denying any irregularities in procedure. Further correspondence brought equally vague answers from Bernadine Healy, the director of NIH.

This continued for many months, but, after an article in a national academic newspaper embarrassing to the university, Duesberg won university endorsement and the NIH agreed to investigate. After stalling yet another nine months, the NIH announced in early 1993 that the grant proposal would be reviewed from scratch. For a short while, the situation seemed to be improving.

Then in March, while the new committee was reviewing the grant proposal, the journal *Nature* suddenly published a string of articles publicized as definitive proofs of the HIV hypothesis. Michael Ascher and a team of epidemiologists, funded on an NIH contract from Anthony Fauci, wrote a commentary asserting that among a group of a thousand San Francisco men, only those with HIV developed AIDS, regardless of drug abuse. Two weeks later, Fauci himself published a paper boasting that he had found large amounts of HIV hiding in the lymph nodes of infected people. A third article backed up Fauci's claim on the virus detection. At the time, *Nature* issued press releases advertising the papers, and the news media excitedly buzzed with the news that our AIDS viewpoint had finally been disproven. Only months later, when the dust began to settle, did the claims begin to unravel; Ascher and colleagues had used improper and misleading statistical methods on poorly-collected data, and the numbers in Fauci's report actually showed only tiny amounts of dormant HIV, even in the lymph nodes. Ironically, even Ascher and his colleagues later turned on Fauci, criticizing his paper in a letter published in *Nature*.

Duesberg sent in his own letter to *Nature*, trying to point out the logical holes of the Ascher paper. The editor, John Maddox, not only refused to publish the letter, but advertised the censorship in a full-page editorial, boldly entitled "Has Duesberg a right of reply?" The answer, according to Maddox, was no. The editor then revealed the hidden reason behind stifling the response: "Duesberg has made his debating technique thoroughly intolerable by advertising his position to the AIDS community."[58] In other words, this was part of the AIDS establishment's campaign to suppress the HIV debate. This was the editorial to which the prominent Italian virologists gleefully responded, openly calling for further censorship, as mentioned above.

Could Fauci have timed the release of these papers to influence the grant review committee against Duesberg? As director of AIDS research at NIH, Fauci certainly must have known the grant was up for review, and who sat on the committee. More importantly, an NIH staff member in Fauci's institute was caught red-handed circulating preview copies of the Ascher paper. Somehow the unpublished paper ended up at the NIH, and the staffer distributed copies to curious members of the public to discredit Duesberg. All parties have since denied responsibility or kept silent. But given that Fauci's staff was circulating the paper, the possibility remains that it was also given to committee members.

In any case, the review committee again voted down the grant proposal a few months later. This time the rating was low enough to discontinue the grant, but not so startlingly low as to appear abnormal. Nor did any reviewers hold obvious conflicts of interest. They did, however, complain about Duesberg's questioning attitude as the major obstacle to funding him, and singled out his AIDS debate as an example.

Since then, every one of his peer-reviewed grant applications to other federal, state, or private agencies—whether for AIDS research on AZT and other drugs, or for cancer research—has been turned down. The most spectacular example occurred in late 1993, in response to a grant proposal for testing "poppers" in mice. Duesberg had applied with a nationally respected expert in toxicology, and the proposal had been sent to the National Institute on Drug Abuse. Despite having a high-level ally in the federal agency, the bullet-proof proposal was turned down. The review committee acknowledged the proposal's strength, but refused to award it any rating at all.

The chilling effects of silencing tactics extend even onto the campus itself. In March of 1993, Duesberg was scheduled to give a keynote speech on AIDS to a Los Angeles meeting of alumni of the University of California, Berkeley. He flew in the evening before, only to learn that three of his Berkeley colleagues had called up the conference organizers, demanding that he be balanced with an opposing speaker or cancelled. The speech was nevertheless delivered as planned, and received an enthusiastic welcome from the audience. Duesberg did discover the identity of one of the three professors, who turned out to be a member of his same department in charge of advising graduate students.

Several fellow professors hold great personal antagonisms for Duesberg, and vent their anger in various ways. His promotions in pay are blocked, his teaching assignments are restricted to difficult undergraduate laboratory courses rather than the coveted graduate courses, and while other faculty sit on committees governing teaching policies, courses and curricula, speaker invitations, and hiring of faculty, Duesberg is placed in charge of the annual picnic committee.

More importantly, graduate students are discouraged from entering Duesberg's lab during their decision-making first year, advice that can be psychologically intimidating to such inexperienced students. Bryan Ellison himself experienced such pressure more than once, and knows of other examples. Indeed, when he switched from another laboratory to continue his thesis work with Duesberg, Ellison ran into interference from other professors in the department. One tried to dissuade him from working with Duesberg, then later tried to force him to leave the lab. Unable to pull that off, the professor finally imposed restrictions on Ellison's research, preventing him from studying HIV and trying to block experiments on AZT. Even a meeting of Ellison's thesis committee was thrown into disarray, through aggressive intervention by a faculty member not belonging to the committee.

Many of these hostile professors make substantial money on the side by consulting for biotechnology companies involved in HIV business, and virtually all of them are funded by NIH grants. The enormous flow of money into science has reshaped the whole enterprise, creating huge academic bureaucracies with entrenched dogmas and conflicts of interest. Such structures can no longer tolerate independent thinking, and have mobilized the research community in unison behind the war on AIDS.

The changing tide

Although the war on AIDS has almost achieved a life of its own, its original momentum flowed largely from the power of David Baltimore, the co-chairman of the *Confronting AIDS* committee. But despite his many allies, even he ultimately proved to be vulnerable, a victim of his own arrogance.

Baltimore's reign began quietly unraveling in 1986, but few people noticed at the time. An immunology paper he published that year with several colleagues came under fire when one of the authors stepped forward to charge fraudulent research—that some of the reported experiments were never really performed. Baltimore's clout prevented investigations for several months; despite the evidence, both MIT and Tufts Universities cleared the paper of wrongdoing. The NIH spent a full year probing the matter, and also exonerated the authors in January, 1989. Disturbed by this whitewash, Michigan Congressman John Dingell held hearings to revive the case. By May of 1989, Baltimore finally ran into serious problems. Dingell had prodded the Secret Service to investigate the experimental notebooks kept by one of Baltimore's fellow authors, Thereza Imanishi-Kari. She was caught red-handed, having faked her data using ink not in existence when she supposedly carried out the experiments. Now the NIH re-opened its own investigation.

Baltimore's influential friends came to his rescue. Dozens of top scientists campaigned on his behalf, including testifying to Congress. That October, as his reputation was suffering, he even received a career-rescuing offer from the prestigious Rockefeller University in New York. The board of trustees, prodded by wealthy banker and fellow member David Rockefeller, asked Baltimore to serve as president of the university. The faculty opposed the move, embarrassed at the thought of having a fraud-tainted leader:

In fact, said Richard M. Furlaud, chairman of the board, the opposition was so strong that Baltimore "actually withdrew his candidacy because of it." But the board—and David Rockefeller—weren't giving up. Furlaud and Rockefeller flew to Cambridge to persuade him to change his mind. "Mr. Rockefeller said, 'Look, we still think you're the right person to do the job," recalls Furlaud. "And then he accepted [the role of candidate].[59]

Over strenuous objections, the trustees pushed the nomination through and handed the presidency to Baltimore in July, 1990. Rockefeller himself even pulled strings to have Baltimore invited into such exclusive private clubs as the New York-based Council on Foreign Relations. The tensions at the university simmered for another year before the NIH finally released its report on the fraud probe, which after two years of delays concluded that some of the data were indeed faked. Baltimore suddenly had to retract the paper, but dismayed his colleagues by publicly defending it anyway. The controversy erupted into open rebellion as three of the university's top scientists left to take jobs elsewhere. Again Baltimore's friends stepped in, and David Rockefeller donated $20 million to the university as evidence of his "absolute confidence" in Baltimore's presidency.[60] The money briefly held back the opposition, but when yet another leading scientist announced his departure, Baltimore finally had to resign as president. On December 3, 1991, he retreated from the ruins of his former position to continue HIV research in his lab.

Confronting AIDS has not withstood the test of time much better. Even though AIDS officials still refer to its authority, the report has gradually been tarnished by its failures. For example, it predicted a total of over 270,000 American AIDS cases through 1991, including 74,000 new cases during 1991, and a grand total of 179,000 deaths by that time.[61] But using the same 1985 CDC definition of AIDS, only 167,000 AIDS cases had actually been tallied through 1991—a little over half the predicted level. The CDC filled most of the gap by expanding the AIDS definition, but such tricks cannot work forever.

Ultimately, the war on AIDS has failed to save lives, the only test that really counts. Condoms, sterile needles, and widespread HIV testing have made no measurable impact, except to arouse frustration and despair among the HIV positives and fear among the HIV negatives. And such toxic chemotherapies as AZT have been recklessly prescribed to people who might otherwise have lived. The NIH, the CDC, and the virus hunters have been winning this war, but the rest of us have been losing. The next chapter describes imminent signs of change, showing that the truth is finally emerging, and outlines a solution for restoring science to its successful roots.

Chapter 10 Footnotes

[1] Personal communications with Peter Duesberg, from National Academy of Sciences members Harry Rubin and Gunther Stent.

[2] Baltimore, Letter to Prosper Graf zu Castell-Castell, Sept. 9, 1986.

[3] Personal communication with Peter Duesberg from Ehrlich committee member Bernard Witkop.

[4] Institute of Medicine and National Academy of Sciences, *Confronting AIDS: Directions for Public Health, Health Care, and Research*. National Academy Press, Washington, D.C., 1986, p. vi.

[5] Ibid., p. 177.

[6] Ibid., p. 177.

[7] Ibid., p. 172.

[8] Ibid., p. 172.

[9] Ibid., p. 172.

[10] McKeown, *The Role of Medicine: Dream, Mirage, or Nemesis?* Princeton University Press, Princeton, NJ, 1979.

[11] Institute of Medicine and National Academy of Sciences, Op cit., p. 125.

[12] Ibid., p. 124.

[13] Ibid., p. 130.

[14] Francis, Toward a Comprehensive HIV Prevention Program for the CDC and the Nation. *Journal of the American Medical Association* 268:1444-7, 1992.

[15] Ibid., p. 1447.

[16] Institute of Medicine and National Academy of Sciences, Op cit., p. 266.

[17] Brès, *Public Health Action in Emergencies Caused by Epidemics: A Practical Guide*. World Health Organization, Geneva, Switzerland, 1986, pp. 111-12.

[18] New U.S. AIDS study assailed by activists. *San Francisco Chronicle*, Feb. 8, 1993.

[19] Centers for Disease Control. A Comprehensive HIV Prevention Program. *Public Health Reports* 106:601-732, 1991 (p. 699).

[20] Ibid., p. 696.

[21] Callen, *Surviving AIDS*. Harper Perennial, New York, 1990, pp. 61-2.

[22] National Association for People With AIDS. *NAPWA Brochure*, 1993.

[23] Centers for Disease Control, Op cit., p. 676.

[24] Johnson and Neffe, Aufstand der Patienten. *Geo*, March 1993, pp. 12-36 (p. 32).

[25] Delaney, Goldblum, and Brewer, *Strategies for Survival: A Gay Men's Health Manual for the Age of AIDS*. St. Martin's Press, New York, 1987, pp. 137-9.

[26] Delaney, Making Regulatory and Research Programs Work. Speech at Stanford University School of Medicine, Jan. 11, 1990.

[27] Lauritsen, *The AIDS War: Propaganda, Profiteering and Genocide from the Medical-Industrial Complex*. Asklepios, New York, 1993, p. 148.

[28] Ibid., p. 441.

[29] Lauritsen, Dissent at the Berlin AIDS Conference. *Rethinking AIDS*, July, 1993, 7:1-2.

[30] Lauritsen, *The AIDS War*, Op cit., p. 441.

[31] Ibid., p. 442.

32 Lauritsen, Dissent at the Berlin AIDS Conference, Op cit.
33 Centers for Disease Control, Op cit., p. 673.
34 Fumento, *The Myth of Heterosexual AIDS*. Basic Books, New York, 1989, pp. x, 257.
35 Cohen, Doing Science in the Spotlight's Glare. *Science* 257:1033, 1992.
36 Personal communications from Serge Lang (Yale University) and Michelle Cochrane (U.C. Berkeley).
37 Krieger, An AIDS reporter's open letter to the community. *San Francisco Examiner*, March 21, 1993, p. D2.
38 Ibid.
39 Ostrom, *New York Times* inserts propaganda in letter. *New York Native*, Nov. 8, 1993, p. 5.
40 *Hunting the Virus Hunter — Q & A: Part 2* (Interview with Peter Duesberg and Elinor Burkett). Tony Brown's Journal, #1410, June, 1991, PBS. Television interview.
41 Booth, A Rebel Without a Cause of AIDS. *Science* 239:1485-8, 1988; Baltimore and Feinberg, Quantitation of human immunodeficiency virus in the blood. *New England Journal of Medicine* 322:1468-9, 1990.
42 *Hearings*. Presidential Commission on the HIV Epidemic, Feb. 20, 1988, p. 85.
43 Specter, Panel Rebuts Biologist's Claims on Cause of AIDS. *Washington Post*, April 10, 1988.
44 Fauci, Writing for my Sister Denise. *The AAAS Observer*, Sept. 1, 1989, p. 4.
45 Chieco-Bianchi and Rossi, Letter to the editor. *Nature* 364:96, 1993.
46 Kline, Chuck, Media Alert. Memorandum of the Office of the Secretary, Dept. of Health and Human Services, April 28, 1987.
47 Karlsberg, Florence S., Memorandum to Peter Fischinger, Howard Streicher, William Blattner, and Robert Gallo. National Institutes of Health, April 28, 1987.
48 Blattner, William A., Memorandum to Deputy Director, NCI. National Cancer Institute, April 30, 1987; see also Wong-Staal, Flossie, Memorandum to Peter Fischinger, Deputy Director, NCI. National Institutes of Health, May 1, 1987; see also Statement. Office of Cancer Communications, National Cancer Institute, June 1987 (draft #3).
49 Karlsberg, Florence, Memorandum to Linda re: NCI response to Peter Duesberg. National Cancer Institute, Dec. 30, 1987; on the bottom is a hand-written note to Fischinger, dated Jan. 7, 1988, and another handwritten note from "PVN" (Paul van Nevel?) to "Eleanor" and "Pat."
50 Personal communication with Bryan Ellison.
51 Hunter, Letter to David Schryer, Nov. 20, 1992.
52 Singer, Letter to Peter Duesberg, June 30, 1988.
53 Dawid, Letter to Peter Duesberg, July 20, 1988.
54 Duesberg, Human immunodeficiency virus and acquired immunodeficiency syndrome: Correlation but not causation. *Proceedings of the National Academy of Sciences* 86:755-64, 1989.
55 Dawid, Letter to Peter Duesberg, Feb. 12, 1991.
56 Bogorad, Letter to Peter Duesberg, May 13, 1991.
57 Cole, Letter to Peter Duesberg, Oct. 22, 1990.
58 Maddox, Has Duesberg a Right of Reply? *Nature* 363:109, 1993.
59 Hall, David Baltimore's Final Days. *Science* 254:1576-9, 1991.
60 Ibid.
61 Institute of Medicine and National Academy of Sciences, Op cit., p. 86.

Chapter 11

Learning the Lessons

On June 7, 1993, the AIDS establishment descended on Berlin, Germany. Over 15,000 HIV researchers from around the world arrived for the Ninth International AIDS Conference, a four-day meeting at which the latest experimental results would be presented. Such a staggering number of scientists naturally brought with them a comparable volume of data, filling 800 lectures and 4500 poster displays. The one-paragraph summaries of new papers alone filled "two guides the size of telephone directories." No researcher at the conference could possibly review more than a small fraction of the data, a situation described by one reporter as "information overload."[1] But despite being overwhelmed and accomplishing little of substance, AIDS officials previously tended to see such meetings as public relations victories. During the previous eight years, the annual conferences had proven to be gala events, generating week-long, sensational media stories on the frightful AIDS epidemic and the heroic efforts of scientists to stop it.

This time, however, things had changed. An atmosphere of pessimism hung over the Berlin conference, the participants widely acknowledging their confusion and the failures of the war on AIDS. "After more than a decade of struggling in frustration as the epidemic gallops on," wrote one correspondent, "researchers are being forced to reexamine assumptions they once held without question."[2] HIV clearly could not be killing T cells directly, leaving open the question of just how it could cause AIDS. T cell counts, once thought to represent the ultimate measure of the immune system, no longer seemed to diagnose an AIDS patient's condition accurately. AZT treatment was being discredited by the recent Concorde study on nearly 2000 patients, showing that the drug did not prolong life. And when veteran polio virologist Jonas Salk presented the results of his new HIV vaccine, the audience concluded it would not work after all; some listeners even called New York directly on their cellular phones, to dump stock in Salk's biotechnology venture. Every belief and expectation based on the HIV hypothesis was proving false in the face of new evidence. Try as they might, AIDS officials could not prevent the general impression that twelve years of research were falling to pieces.

Although no one in the AIDS establishment questioned the HIV hypothesis itself, clearly the confidence of many scientists was weakening. *Science* magazine had anticipated the negative mood the previous week with a special issue entitled "AIDS: The Unanswered Questions," of which more than forty pages were devoted to the cover story.[3] The Berlin conference also marked the first attendance by dissenters against the HIV hypothesis, who were sur-

256

prised to find serious interest from many conference participants. The mood even affected Robert Gallo, who became touchy with reporters when asked about his conviction on scientific misconduct charges.

The conference, in fact, symbolized the changing tide in the AIDS debate. The Group for the Scientific Reappraisal of the HIV/AIDS Hypothesis has grown from its original two dozen members in 1991 to over four hundred professionals today, including two hundred scientists and medical doctors. The Group's newsletter now reaches over a thousand people. Not only do the growing ranks of dissenting scientists serve as a barometer of frustration among researchers and physicians, but these hundreds of skeptics are beginning to make themselves heard. They are writing books, scientific papers, and popular articles, while giving public lectures and interviews with the media. During the 1992 International AIDS Conference in Amsterdam, they mustered enough support to organize their own parallel AIDS meeting in the same city. By the following year, several dissidents established a high-profile presence at the International AIDS Conference in Berlin.

Though still excluded from powerful virus-hunting circles and largely unable to secure funding for his laboratory research, Peter Duesberg is beginning to find a few open doors. Toxicologists, who work in one of the most neglected and least powerful fields in biomedical research, have become intrigued by the drug hypothesis of AIDS. Several of their leading journals have invited and published Duesberg's papers, including the French journal *Biomedicine and Pharmacotherapy* and the British-based *Pharmacology and Therapeutics*. Even some immunologists and geneticists have now extended publishing invitations to him.

Duesberg's speaking invitations have also increased, including some prestigious scientific meetings. American universities ranging from Tulane to the University of North Texas have sponsored his lectures on AIDS, as have the Universities of Köln and Dortmund in Germany, among others. Major hospitals and medical centers have also decided to open the debate by inviting him. And now scientific conferences around the world, often out of curiosity or expecting to refute Duesberg easily, are featuring his speeches— only to discover that good reasons do exist for doubting the HIV hypothesis. In 1992, the American Association for Adolescent Psychiatry sponsored a keynote speech by Duesberg and covered him extensively in their Washington, D.C newsletter. Later that year, he gave another featured talk at the Third International Austrian AIDS Conference, attended by some of the most prominent retrovirus hunters from around the world. And in October, 1993, he gave an invited lecture at an international conference on AIDS and cancer in Pavia, Italy, which sparked news coverage and debate in the wide-circulation newspaper *Corriere de la Sera*. Such opportunities are growing each year.

Of course, the virologists are not delighted at this increasing attention given the dissenting viewpoint. When Duesberg spoke at a meeting of the New York Academy of Sciences in 1989, Robert Gallo had a last-minute change of heart and failed to show up to deliver his own talk. Again this occurred at the 1990 National Hematology meeting in Germany, with Gallo

cancelling his speech upon learning of Duesberg's lecture at the same conference. In 1992, both Gallo and Duesberg were scheduled to speak at a student-
sponsored meeting at the University of Calgary in Canada, but Gallo asked
for a raincheck and bowed out. Most recently, the International Academy of
Tumor Marker Oncology invited Gallo to give the opening speech at its 1993
conference in Germany, and asked Duesberg to close the meeting with another lecture. This time all parties believed Gallo would show, but just three
hours before his scheduled appearance, he sent a fax from another part of
Germany claiming that he could not attend because of a "disease" in the family. Thus Gallo has completely avoided any public confrontation with
Duesberg or other AIDS dissidents.

The lay public is also beginning to hear more of the HIV debate, despite
the general blackout on the issue. Duesberg has spoken to such prestigious
forums as the Commonwealth Club, and radio and magazine interviews are
becoming a regular fact of life for Duesberg, Bryan Ellison, and other dissidents. The top-rated German talk show *Zeil um Zehn* hosted Duesberg on one
of its shows, and the ABC television program Day One has aired a segment
featuring Duesberg and other scientists critical of the HIV hypothesis, as well
as another segment critical of AZT therapy. Even the legal profession has
taken an interest: Duesberg's information and testimony has been used in the
courtroom defenses of two HIV-positive men, both accused of assault with a
deadly weapon for having sexual intercourse with women. Other defense attorneys have sought similar information. And a group named Project AIDS
International has formed in Los Angeles, preparing materials and talking with
interested attorneys over the possibility of suing Burroughs-Wellcome for the
production of AZT.

Such a lawsuit has already become reality in England, the world headquarters of Burroughs-Wellcome. Sue Threakall is a school teacher whose
husband, a hemophiliac, tested positive for HIV in 1985. He remained basically healthy until he began taking AZT in 1989. From that point forward,
Bob Threakall's life went downhill. One year later he had to quit his job, suffering "severe weight loss, thrush, stomach upsets, poor sleep patterns, sore
mouth, continued sinus infections, weakness, breathlessness, loss of appetite,
etc." Early in 1991 he died, "confused, delirious, wasted, constant diarrhea,
unable to swallow, and with hardly any normal lung tissue left."[4] After con-
tacting Peter Duesberg and absorbing the information refuting the HIV hypothesis, an angry Sue Threakall turned to the courts. In January, 1994, she
won a government commitment to finance her lawsuit—guaranteeing her
case will proceed regardless of her own financial condition—and she filed for
damages against Burroughs-Wellcome. Several more people, including
hemophiliacs, have joined the growing list of plaintiffs.

The absence of an AIDS explosion has helped create skepticism toward
the HIV establishment, causing, for example, serious changes in the British
AIDS program. Referring to English statistics, the London *Sunday Telegraph*
noted in late 1992 that

The initial official estimates that the disease will cut a swathe throught the nation with an estimated 100,000 new cases a year by the mid-Nineties had to be revised downwards to 30,000 and downwards again to 13,000. Then the Government Actuary looked at the figures and suggested they be reduced downwards yet again to 6,500, but even this has proved to be a six-fold over-estimate of the number of new cases this year.

    ... By this summer when these results were published it had become apparent that with such a low prevalence rate there was no "heterosexual Aids epidemic," nor was there likely to be one.[5]

As a result, the British government has decided to cut out AIDS "education" programs aimed at the general public, focusing instead on the risk groups.

England, for that matter, has recently witnessed the most spectacular crack in the official wall of silence on HIV. It began largely with ongoing coverage of the HIV controversy by the *Sunday Times* of London in 1992, spearheaded by medical writer Neville Hodgkinson. Gradually, other major British newspapers were drawn into the fray: the *Independent*, the *Financial Times*, the *Sunday Express*, the *Telegraph*, and the *Daily Mail*. As both sides argued the issue more openly, the London-based scientific journal *Nature* finally decided it had had enough—and issued an editorial blast condemning the *Sunday Times* on December 9, 1993. The *Times* fired back, the fight becoming louder and harder to ignore over the next few months. Charge followed furious countercharge. Even the *New York Times* was forced, for a single day, to break silence on the issue and publish an article on the spectacular British feud. In the meantime, this heated HIV controversy has spread to Canada. The open debate in the British press shows no signs of abating, and is becoming a major problem for AIDS officials trying to maintain their War on AIDS.

But despite these openings, the AIDS establishment still retains its full grip on power. The many billions of dollars spent each year by the U.S. federal government on biomedical research, and especially those billions devoted to HIV research and control, have purchased enormous influence with every significant interest group involved in AIDS. Scientists, as frustrated or uncertain as they may become over their lack of progress, can never afford to destroy their careers by turning against the peer-enforced dogma. The pharmaceutical industry, particularly Burroughs-Wellcome, Bristol-Myers Squibb, and Hoffmann-LaRoche—the producers of AZT, ddI, and ddC, respectively—cannot afford to lose their profitable AIDS drugs. AIDS activist groups would hardly want to lose favor with their pharmaceutical patrons or the Centers for Disease Control. The communications media also will not endanger its cozy relationship with the CDC, National Institutes of Health, and other key agencies. All these groups must continue to support the war on HIV, ignoring or suppressing all genuine debate.

Thus the Group for the Scientific Reappraisal of the HIV/AIDS Hypothesis still cannot publish its short statement of skepticism in any major biomedical research journal. Duesberg has lost his NIH grant, and faces the threat of losing his laboratory if more funds do not arrive from somewhere. Most importantly, the great majority of the public at large have had little or no opportunity to find out that questions exist about the HIV hypothesis, much less to hear a fair presentation of the arguments. If the public were to discover the facts, and how the debate had been hidden from them, they would likely demand an end to the war on AIDS.

Taxpayers, and HIV-positives and their relatives, potentially constitute the most explosive opposition to the AIDS establishment. As the failures of the war on AIDS mount up, the size of the imminent backlash grows; the longer AIDS officials resist the inevitable, the harder they will fall. Time, therefore, has become our most valuable ally. Unfortunately, the history of virus hunting seems to teach that the biomedical research establishment is also becoming more intransigent with time.

Science grown out of control

"Germs are back," declared one newspaper article ominously in July of 1993. "Those who track trends in advertising and who sell disinfecting products confirm that today's Americans are acutely attuned to the invisible, microbial world and its potential hazards. Rebounding tuberculosis, undercooked fast-food burgers in Seattle, tainted tap water in Milwaukee and the mystery disease in the Southwest serves [*sic*] only to encourage our concern about microscopic invaders, it seems." Quoting journalism professor Gail Baker Woods on this rising public fear, the article then noted its biggest cause. "The trend—which Woods says includes not only disinfecting products but also newly introduced clear products with their aura of purity— is in part a response to fear of AIDS and a need to feel immune from such invisible threats."[6]

The fear of microbes is resurging at a most ironic time. Infectious diseases, which once were the leading killers, have stopped killing people in the industrial world. Today, less than one percent of all death in the First World results from contagion; heart disease has become the major cause, followed by cancer, and life expectancies have grown nearly to eighty years. The polio epidemic marked the end of the era of infectious disease for industrial societies. Yet by blaming AIDS, cancer, and other modern, non-contagious diseases on microbes, the virus-hunting research establishment has pointlessly resurrected this old anxiety.

That modern science could so effectively terrify the public of a long-vanished threat testifies to its enormous power. But to some extent, the fear of catching disease has always helped medical authorities, making the lay public more willing to yield money and freedoms for the sake of an answer. Researchers discovered this gold mine of popularity once Robert Koch had proved in 1882 that a bacterium caused tuberculosis. Soon newly graduated medical doctors scurried to find the bacteria causing every conceivable disease. Once blamed, the right germ could open the door to a vaccine or public health measures to control the disease—and to a place in the textbooks, a secure career, and perhaps even a Nobel Prize. Certainly microbes were easier to blame for a disease than spending years of frustrating effort in search of complex or unfamiliar causes. Microbes were tangible, a well-defined target at which to aim.

Enthusiasm turned to fashion, and fashion to a stampede. Bacteria were being found even in non-contagious diseases. Scurvy, pellagra, and beriberi, among others, were each in turn blamed on a series of microbes, sometimes leading to control measures that only exacerbated these epidemics, and always delaying the search for missing vitamins in the diet. Merely isolating a germ often served to implicate it as being guilty for some disease. Few people stopped to consider the possibility that most germs were simply harmless.

Bacteria hunting temporarily disappeared with the end of contagious epidemics. Virus hunting meanwhile arrived on the scene, seeing its heyday primarily in the polio epidemic. Once polio disappeared, however, the microbe hunters should have dropped their outmoded specialty, developing new methods and ideas for studying other types of disease. But because of a series of political decisions during the 1950s, they did not.

In 1951, Alexander Langmuir founded the Epidemic Intelligence Service of the CDC, intended to act as an early warning detection and control system for contagious epidemics. The EIS, and the CDC, would go on during the next several decades to ring nationwide alarm bells over minor disease outbreaks, while falsely labeling leukemia, Legionnaire's disease, and AIDS as infectious. The NIH, the other federal cornerstone of modern biomedical research, underwent radical restructuring after James Shannon took over in 1955. Determined to create the largest scientific research establishment in world history, Shannon milked Congress for exponentially increasing budgets by launching massive new programs, most notably the war on polio and the Virus-Cancer Program. The new NIH monies went to purchase greater quantities of data gathering, and to recruit enormous numbers of new people into the swelling ranks of researchers.

The outcome of these two changes was predictable. Microbe hunting reappeared with a vengeance, seizing every available disease to blame on a germ; NIH funding patterns ensured that the virus hunters would predominate over the others. In trying to explain the slow, degenerative diseases of nerve and brain tissues, or of cancer, the virus hunters were forced to improvise. Carleton Gajdusek, who performed questionable research in which he could never even isolate a virus from kuru disease, nevertheless became known as the father of the "slow virus" idea and received the 1976 Nobel Prize for the notion. According to this hypothesis, a virus could infect a host one day and, despite being permanently neutralized by the immune system, could somehow cause a fatal disease years later. Although a blatant violation of the logic behind Koch's postulates and the germ theory, Gajdusek's "slow virus" hypothesis captured the imagination of scientists and reshaped their whole approach to medicine. Hilary Koprowski, Robert Gallo, and David Baltimore numbered among the converts who searched avidly for "slow viruses," and eventually led AIDS research.

By the time the AIDS epidemic surfaced, the outcome of research on the new syndrome had been predetermined. AIDS in the United States and Europe fits the pattern of non-infectious diseases, and for several reasons is likely to be a product of the drug abuse epidemic of recent years. Nevertheless, virus hunters jumped on the new opportunity, the retrovirologists being in the right position to have a retrovirus, HIV, officially declared the cause. As with so many products of modern virus hunting, HIV completely failed the test of Koch's postulates. But just finding it was all the evidence the virologists needed. Eventually, the microbe hunters in research and public health teamed up to declare war on AIDS, a daring move given the thin scientific ice upon which they stood.

But the wars on cancer and AIDS have proven to be dismal failures. Despite glorious promises of a cancer cure by 1976, no such thing materialized. Cancer death rates have remained completely unaffected to this day, and many scientists now acknowledge defeat. Nor has a cancer vaccine emerged, a paradox if one believes the official doctrine that several human cancers are caused by viruses.

AIDS research has likewise turned embarrassingly futile. The promises of a vaccine and a therapy remain unfulfilled. Public health officials cannot demonstrate they have saved any lives by controlling the blood supply, nor through their programs for promoting and distributing condoms and sterile injection needles. Worst of all, none of the virus-based predictions has been borne out: AIDS has not exploded into the heterosexual population, as do all other sexually-transmitted diseases, nor can doctors predict the course of illness in any given patient, which can involve any combination of some thirty unrelated diseases. And in contrast to the official prediction that HIV would kill virtually all infected people, some two-thirds of the HIV positives have remained AIDS-free for nearly a decade. AIDS officials can neither control nor predict the epidemic, leaving AZT therapy as their only consistent answer—a drug originally developed for cancer chemotherapy that efficiently destroys the immune system and causes symptoms largely indistinguishable from AIDS itself.

As the pinnacle of power in biomedical research, microbe hunting typifies the collapse of true science since World War II. On the surface, this seems incredible. Modern American science was designed to be the best ever, and it now carries that reputation around the world. How could it have gone so wrong, and yet create the illusion of glorious success?

The answer lies in the money. Simply put, science has grown vastly too large, employing far too many researchers generating overwhelming amounts of data. Daniel S. Greenberg, editor of the widely respected newsletter *Science & Government Report*, has referred to biomedical science as "one of the most swollen, overindulged, underexamined, and self-pitying public enterprises on the national landscape."[7] In a stinging indictment of the NIH-funded establishment, Greenberg aired the dirty laundry that is common knowledge among scientists today:

> Now, it may be that NIH's political success is fueled by calamitous rhetoric, that the budget soars on doomsday prophecies, and without them, biomedical science would not have attained today's financial heights. That's probably the case, for the NIH establishment has become skilled in exploiting the health fears and expectations of the Congress, while eluding White

House control. The lobbying works, but the eventual prices could be high: the credibility of science.

... No amount of money within political attainability can quell the clamor. That's because the NIH constituency is both infinitely expansible and intrinsically insatiable. It possesses those dual characteristics because, first, NIH gives high priority to training programs that produce new customers for its grants; and, second, the world abounds with fascinating scientific questions—and salesmen of the costly equipment needed for attempts to answer them.

... Even so, the faithful will respond, biomedical research is a societal good of which there cannot be too much. That foolishness, which flies in the face of Economics 1, is actually the intellectual underpinning of the unceasing demands for more and still more for NIH.

... The biomedical-research enterprise has developed a pathological appetite for expansion that bears little relation to scientific productivity. It has become a welfare system for multitudes of mediocre timeservers posing as scientists.[8]

The explosion in biomedical funding since the mid-1950s, when James Shannon took over at NIH, has completely inverted science from the brilliantly successful pursuit it once was. The drive to expand science was rooted in the fallacy that more money means better and faster science, that quantity is identical to quality. In reality, this bloated size destroys genuine science through several direct consequences:

1. <u>An explosion of useless data</u>. Science, by definition, is primarily a process of interpreting, rather than gathering, data. Although a few technicians are needed to carry out limited experiments under the supervision of scientists, the accumulation of data becomes aimless and burdensome when conducted for its own sake. Yet precisely such gathering of throw-away data overruns research as funding increases. More money, in the end, adds up to larger piles of raw data, not a better understanding of it. As Greenberg pointed out, "In private conversations, many scientists will declare their specialty is crowded with hacks who litter the journals with material of little or no consequence."[9]

The sheer quantity of data actually makes the job of interpretation exceedingly difficult. Unable to sort through the mountains of experimental information, most of which serves no purpose, scientists are forced to specialize in ever-narrower fields of study. The interpretation and understanding of the data thereby becomes fragmented, bringing the whole effort under collective control. In such an atmosphere, the individual scientist who challenges majority wisdom is crowded out. Each researcher begins to protect his own turf, resenting interference by someone with a different interpretation. The official doctrine becomes rigidified.

So who decides which data is important for scientists to know? Surprisingly, researchers have admitted to us that they absorb their scientific views on such subjects as cancer or AIDS from the *New York Times*! As a rule, press releases now have more influence on scientific opinion than do the unreadably massive volume of professional papers. One recent sociology study confirmed that "researchers use newspapers as a 'filter' to help them decide which scientific article is worth reading."[10]

2. <u>Enforced consensus through peer review</u>. Under the peer review system, a scientist's access to funding, publication in journals, ability to win prizes, and invitations to conferences are controlled by his peers. This absurd situation puts one's competitors in charge of one's career, a direct conflict of interest. Imagine if every new automobile or new computer had to be approved by competing corporations before being released to the market: products would cease improving, and the market would experience a steady decline in quality. Innovation and competition would die. Such inherent problems have led to public criticisms of peer review over the last twenty years, with various congressmen and even the Office of Management and Budget voicing objections to the system.

The stifling effect of peer review becomes worse as the number of peers increases, one of the direct effects of overfunded science. The growing number of researchers creates a herd effect, drowning out the voice of the lone scientist who questions official wisdom. Researchers begin spending more time networking and seeking to build coalitions of allies than stepping on toes by raising unpopular questions, which threaten the career investments of the crowd. When the number of scientists in a field is small, they all feel more free to break into conflicting factions with different opinions; a field crowded with peers quickly stifles all such independent thinking, imposing a consensus on the group as a whole.

As a result, biomedical research has gradually squeezed out the practice of interpreting information, substituting for it an inoffensive, mechanical process of grinding out ever-larger quantities of raw data. David Horrobin, a biologist and editor of the journal *Medical Hypotheses*, has explained how peer review has stamped out individual theorizing in science:

> [One] possibility is that most established scientists do not actually want to make rapid progress. A state of atheoretical confusion is agreeable to them because in that state almost nothing can ever be shown to be wrong. Atheoretical biomedicine is a relatively risk-free world because its absence of precision ensures an absence of real failure. Related to this fear of failure is the fact that what most scientists want out of life is to be hailed as the originator of a new scientific concept. But most biomedical scientists are simply incapable of generating new ideas and feel threatened by those who can. They feel more comfortable in a world in which theory and hypothesis are not respected because the development of concepts is an ability they do not have.[11]

Former NIH director Bernadine Healy, when questioned during her confirmation hearings before the Senate in 1991, brought up this same problem. She referred to the competition between Mozart and his less competent but more popular rival, Salieri. One journalist summarized her point: "Salieri would probably have fared better than Mozart in the equivalent of today's peer review system, Healy said, but if medicine is to succeed, 'the Mozarts must be allowed to flourish' as well."[12]

As long as a scientist's work is reviewed by competitors within his own field, peer review will crush genuine science. At a minimum, a scientist should only be reviewed by researchers outside his field, those without such direct conflicts of interest. The further removed from the grant applicant's field, the less biased the reviewers will be. However, no reform of peer review can ever possibly succeed until science itself shrinks, removing that majority of researchers who pursue science less for the love of knowledge than for the sake of career opportunities. The peer review system, moreover, may be so inherently flawed that other review mechanisms might have to replace it altogether.

3. <u>Centralization of science policy</u>. By lavishing vast sums of money on science, and particularly on biomedical research, the federal government has attained a near-monopoly on science. A handful of federal agencies, primarily the NIH, dominate research policies and effectively dictate the official dogma. HIV research provides a case in point: by declaring the virus the cause of AIDS at a press conference sponsored by the Department of Health and Human Services, NIH researcher Robert Gallo swung the entire medical establishment, and even the rest of the world, behind his hypothesis. If the federal government spent much less on research, then state, local, and private agencies would carry more weight within science and could support a more diverse set of opinions in any controversy. As the situation stands now, scientists who sit as peer reviewers for non-federal granting agencies generally receive NIH funding themselves, and thus merely enforce the federal dogma through other organizations.

4. <u>Commercial conflicts of interest</u>. The biotechnology industry arose mainly to supply equipment and reagents to NIH-funded laboratories. As the NIH budget has increased, so has the subsidized market for biotechnology products. The pharmaceutical industry, likewise, has profited from monopolies granted by the Food and Drug Administration, which bans competing therapies. Both the biotechnology and pharmaceutical industries feed opportunistically off the NIH largesse.

Naturally, some of these federally-provided corporate profits find their way back to scientists in the form of patent royalties, consultantships, paid board positions, and stock ownership. These same scientists often sit in judgment of their fellow researchers as peer reviewers, deciding whether a competitor should be funded or allowed to publish. Such commercial conflicts of interest have almost totally permeated scientific institutions today, whether universities or the NIH or FDA. Researchers have made a regular policy of looking the other way, or even rewriting the rules to allow such behavior.

Conflicts of interest must inevitably arise when huge sums of money are poured into science. With all that money available, people will always find clever ways to pocket some for personal use. The only workable solution lies in greatly reducing NIH funding for research, which would cut out most of the graft and restore ethics to their status of forty years ago.

5. <u>Misconduct and fraud</u>. Overfunded science turns the enterprise into a high-stakes, publish-or-perish game. Since scientists have less room to question each other's interpretations, the competition degenerates into a rat race to

find the data first. This has spawned a growing list of fraud cases among researchers, who resort under pressure to fabricating or altering their experimental results. AIDS research, which is proportionally the most heavily funded area of all, has generated a startling number of fraud or misconduct investigations. The cases of Robert Gallo, David Baltimore, and others have been reviewed in this book.

Serious cuts in science funding would not only slow the pace of data collection, but would allow scientists to ponder their data more carefully. The motive for cheating would be minimized. Fraud, moreover, has no meaning in the realm of ideas and interpretation, which all individuals are free to examine and question for themselves.

As the NIH budget continues to increase, the science lobby becomes ever more entrenched and the oversized research structure continues to magnify disasters. Nor have politicians learned the lessons of overfunded science, still believing that the war on AIDS remains on the right course. President Clinton, for example, has now maneuvered legislation through Congress to escalate spending on AIDS research and prevention to $2.5 billion for 1994, a total larger than for all cancer research, and has expanded total federal AIDS spending in 1994 to $6 billion. This new funding will ensure the absolute dominance of HIV research within medicine, adding thousands of new data collectors to the ranks of science. He has also established the post of an AIDS "czar." And he has appointed the retrovirologist Harold Varmus, a close ally of David Baltimore, as director of NIH; under Varmus remain retrovirologist Samuel Broder as head of the National Cancer Institute (NCI), retrovirologist Anthony Fauci as head of the National Institute of Allergy and Infectious Disease (NIAID), and Robert Gallo, who heads the largest retrovirology lab at NCI. Rather than effecting long-needed reform, Clinton is merely raising the stakes by expanding the failed war on AIDS. In the end, this stubborn resistance will severely damage or destroy the reputation of science.

The bloated science bureaucracy, and particularly the virus hunting program, have succeeded for decades mostly by using the war motif. James Shannon first squeezed extra money out of Congress by declaring war on polio. Richard Nixon mobilized researchers behind the War on Cancer. David Baltimore and his allies engineered the war on AIDS. Now the NIH is declaring a war on breast cancer, which is doomed to finish on the same trash heap as the other wars; scientific fashion today blames breast cancer on specific genetic mutations, which hard evidence proves harmless and irrelevant to the cause of the tumor. Increased monies for breast cancer research will lock into place the scientific mistakes and stifle all attempts to discover the real causes of the disease. Progress will be delayed and lives will be lost from too much funding, all in the name of war. But while a state of war can mobilize public support for a time, the tactic eventually backfires, creating public opposition once defeat becomes obvious. The wars on cancer and AIDS have produced nothing but tragedy.

Last stand of the microbe hunters

The AIDS explosion finally struck at midnight, January 1, 1993. "As many as 40,000 Americans who are HIV-positive will wake up on New Year's Day with a diagnosis of AIDS," announced the *Los Angeles Times* on the last day of 1992.[13] The prophecy came true: during the first three months of 1993, the number of new AIDS cases was 204 percent higher than for the same months of the previous year.

Although AIDS officials, activists, and the news media will be trumpeting these new figures to exploit public fear, this pandemic is actually the artificial product of a new clinical definition of AIDS. Periodically, as the public loses interest waiting for an AIDS explosion, the CDC has added more diseases to the diagnostic list, thus classifying more HIV-positives as having AIDS and pumping up the official numbers. The CDC pulled this trick in 1985, in 1987, and now at the beginning of 1993. Previously including about two dozen diseases, the AIDS list was again expanded with somewhat milder conditions than in the past, such as tuberculosis in the lungs, any repeated bacterial pneumonia, a blood platelet disorder, and even low T cell counts in a healthy person. To inflate the percentage of women with AIDS, the CDC also added cervical cancer—the first AIDS disease than can only affect one sex.

The new definition will produce major consequences. For one thing, it "is likely to place a strain on already strapped social service agencies and add to the emotional trauma of many who are infected... Legal advisers say that as more people are diagnosed as having AIDS, more will face discrimination by their employers and by health insurance providers. Counselors warn that the sudden switch in diagnosis may cause psychological trauma for patients."[14]

Not to mention, of course, renewed public hysteria over AIDS. Such tactics had induced widespread fear, even panic, during the mid-1980s. One news article described it in 1987:

> Fear of acquired immune deficiency syndrome is sweeping heterosexual society on both coasts.
>
> ... Restaurants in gay districts of San Francisco, New York and the Los Angeles area are shunned by many people, and the Bon Appetit restaurant in suburban Sacramento lost numerous customers after the January AIDS death of a chef who worked there five years earlier.
>
> ... At Gay Men's Health Crisis Inc., which helps AIDS patients in New York, "we consistently have television crews who will not come inside our building," said spokeswoman Lori Behrman.
>
> About half the 4,000 calls received monthly by the center's AIDS hotline are from "worried well" people, half of whom are needlessly concerned about getting AIDS from swimming pools, insects or non-risky sex practices, said hotline coordinator Jerry Johnson.[15]

But while such fear can ruin lives, a few people know how to take advantage of anxiety resulting from the expanded AIDS definition. "The updated definition is a victory for AIDS activists," noted the *Los Angeles*

Times, because they "will use the bigger numbers to clamor for additional funding, arguing that the crisis is more acute than previously believed." This should have appeased the activists. "But many say the expansion does not go far enough; at a news conference Wednesday in Los Angeles, representatives of the AIDS Healthcare Foundation and other local groups decried the new definition as inadequate and said it must be broadened further still."[16]

This cynical manipulation of public fear may bring in the money for the AIDS lobby, but it creates human tragedy for everyone else. From Miami, Florida, comes the personal account of some real victims of the War on AIDS—Cesar and Teresa Schmitz, and their baby daughter Louise—whose lives were nearly destroyed by the "AIDS virus" propaganda. Teresa herself related the story in December of 1993:

> January 1992 we found out my husband was HIV+. I will never forget that morning. I will never forget the first three or four days after that test result. It was, surely the most devastating experience I ever had in my entire life. Abruptly, it was all gone. No more future. No more nothing. From that moment on life would be waiting for death.
>
> The [worst] part was to face my beautiful and adorable one year old little girl. She was condemned to die.
>
> Out of my despair I did anything I could to get an answer tabout the chances of my baby surviving. The "trained professionals" at the 800 numbers that I called gave me answers like: "Oh my God," after I said that my husband was HIV+ and I had a baby. They even asked me: "Is her hair falling?", "Is she losing weight?"
>
> I could not allow my beautfiul and precious baby to go through all that suffering. I could not imagine her going from hospital to hospital, having needles stuck in her little arm, seeing her going skinnier and skinnier. I could not take that....
>
> The only way out of that despair, of that suffering, was to kill ourselves. There was no other solution for us but this one. It would end the pain and the nightmare right at the beginning....
>
> ...Two weeks later my test result came out: I WAS NEGATIVE! So, it meant that Louise was negative too....Now Cesar was the only of us condemned to die....
>
> March 1992 (not even two months after the results) Cesar started with the symptoms of AIDS: diarrhea, nausea, weight loss, and so on. The strange thing was that the symptoms began right after he started taking AZT.
>
> He was feeling so bad, so sick, he decided, against his doctor's will, to stop taking AZT. All of a sudden, like magic, no more symptoms. He was healthy and normal again and remains so, since then. He goes regularly to a clinic for lab tests. The doctor thinks he is doing very well, but insists and pressures him to take AZT or its similars because "it is the only way." The doctor's faith... is so strong that he does not listen to Cesar....
>
> Our marriage was falling apart: no sex life for two years. He did not want to take any chances of contaminating me. The only sure way was abstinence....
>
> About a month ago I decided to write to Dr. Peter Duesberg....
>
> After talking to him my life changed, everything went back to normal. Cesar and I are having a really normal life. We are planning our second

child. We got to the conclusion this whole HIV hypothesis is a mistake, a tragic hoax.[17]

While hundreds of thousands of people die of heavy drug abuse, or from their AZT prescriptions, AIDS officials insist on pushing condoms, sterile needles, and HIV testing on a terrified population. "'AIDS' propaganda is ubiquitous," observes Charles Ortleb, publisher of the homosexual-interest *New York Native*. "Ten percent of every brain in America must be filled with posters, news items, condom warnings, etc., etc. The iconography of 'AIDS' is everywhere. Part of the Big Lie that some activists promote over and over in an Orwellian way is that 'AIDS' is somehow not on the front burner of America. 'AIDS' propaganda has become part of the very air that Americans breathe."[18] All of this based on a war against a harmless virus, waged with deadly "treatments" and misleading public health advice.

This is truly a medical disaster on an unprecedented scale.

Ironically, HIV positives actually have no reason to fear. As with uninfected people, those who stay off of recreational drugs and avoid AZT will never die of "AIDS." Antibody-positive people can live absolutely normal lives. Worldwide, 12 of the 13 million HIV positives certainly do.

When the public finally catches on to these deceptive tactics, the HIV hypothesis of AIDS and its proponents will find harsh judgment. AIDS researchers will do their best to control the downfall, accepting the idea of co-factors and gradually relegating HIV to a less important role in the syndrome. They will probably even try to take credit themselves for discovering the unimportance of HIV, disguising the reversal as further "progress" in AIDS research. But the fact that they are stubbornly fighting such change, and even accelerating the war on AIDS, indicates they may learn only too late.

For this time the public may hold biomedical researchers and public health experts accountable, and misguided microbe hunting will meet its long-overdue judgment.

Chapter 11 Footnotes

[1] Cohen, Special News Report. *Science* 260:1253-1293, 1993, p. 1262.

[2] Ibid., p. 1254.

[3] AIDS: The Unanswered Questions. *Science* 260:1253-1293, 1993.

[4] Sue Threakall, Letter to Peter Duesberg, May 31, 1992; additional information in Hodgkinson, Court battles launched over anti-Aids drug, *Sunday Times* (London), Jan. 30, 1994.

[5] LeFanu, Telescope. *London Sunday Telegraph*, Nov. 29, 1992.

[6] Condon, The Assault on Germs. *San Francisco Chronicle*, July 28, 1993, pp. C3-C4.

[7] Greenberg, What Ails NIH? *Journal of NIH Research* 2, 1990, p. 29.

[8] Ibid., pp. 29-30.

[9] Ibid., p. 30.

[10] All the [Science] that's fit to print. *Science* 254:649, 1991.

[11] Horrobin, Discouraging Hypotheses Slows Progress. *The Scientist*, Nov. 26, 1990, pp. 13, 15.

[12] Marshall, Committee Treats Healy Gently. *Science* 251:1423, 1991.

[13] Stolberg, AIDS Tally to Increase Due to New Definition. *Los Angeles Times*, Dec. 31, 1992, pp. A3, A29.

[14] Ibid.

[15] Siegel, AIDS fear manifesting itself in irrational ways. *Daily Recorder*, March 23, 1987, p. 4.

[16] Stolberg, Op cit.

[17] Teresa Schmitz, A personal experience (an open letter, unpublished), Dec. 8, 1993.

[18] Ortleb, The Chanterelle syndrome, *New York Native*, Jan. 17, 1994, pp. 4-5.

Selected Bibliography

Zidovudine product label, Sigma Chemical Co.

Report. Pellagra Commission of the State of Illinois, November, 1911.

Central Dogma Reversed. *Nature* **226**:1198-9, 1970.

The Paris Fashions. *Nature* **228**:609-610, 1970.

Legionnaires' Disease. House Subcommittee on Consumer Protection and Finance, November 23 & 24, 1976.

Legionnaires' Disease, 1977. Senate Subcommittee on Health and Scientific Research, November 9, 1977.

Postdoctoral Appointments and Disappointments. National Research Council, 1981.

NIH Almanac: 1985. Division of Public Information, National Institutes of Health, Bethesda, MD, 1985.

Doctoral Scientists and Engineers: A Decade of Change. National Science Foundation, March, 1988.

Hearings. Presidential Commission on the HIV Epidemic, Feb. 20, 1988. p. 85.

Science & Engineering Indicators—1989. National Science Board, December 1, 1989.

Interview with Dr. Root-Bernstein. Meditel Ltd., April, 1990. Transcript.

The Ph.D. Shortage: The Federal Role. Association of American Universities, January 11, 1990.

All the [Science] that's fit to print. *Science* **254**:649, 1991.

Hunting the Virus Hunter—Q & A: Part 2 (Interview with Peter Duesberg and Elinor Burkett). Tony Brown's Journal, June, 1991. Television interview, PBS.

AIDS victim's will is a moving 'good-by'. *San Francisco Chronicle*, Jan. 15, 1992.

EIS Directory. Epidemic Intelligence Service, Centers for Disease Control, September, 1992.

AIDS: The Unanswered Questions. *Science* **260**:1253-1293, 1993.

Focus - AIDS Debriefing. MacNeil-Lehrer News Hour, June 10, 1993. Television interview.

HIV seroconversion after occupational exposure despite early prophylactic zidovudine therapy. *Lancet* **341**:1077-8, 1993.

Physician's Desk Reference. 1993.

Adams, J. *AIDS: the HIV Myth.* St. Martin's Press, New York, 1989.

Altman, L. K. Treatment guidelines for HIV amended. *San Francisco Chronicle*, June 28, 1993.

Antonio, G. *The AIDS Cover-up?* Ignatius Press, San Francisco, 1986.

Aoun, H. When a house officer gets AIDS. *New England Journal of Medicine* **321**:693-6, 1989.

Ashe, A. and Rampersad, A. *Days of Grace: A Memoir.* Alfred A. Knopf, New York, 1993.

Astor, G. *The Disease Detectives.* The New American Library, New York, 1983.

Bailey, H. *The Vitamin Pioneers.* Rodale Books, Emmaus, Pennsylvania, 1968.

Balter, M. Montagnier Pursues the Mycoplasma-AIDS Link. *Science* **251**:271, 1991.

Baltimore, D., letter to Prosper Graf zu Castell-Castell, Sep. 9, 1986.

Baltimore, D. and Feinberg, M. B. Quantitation of human immunodeficieny virus in the blood. *NEJM* **322**:1468-1469, 1990.

272   *Selected Bibliography*

Belani, K. K., Medical report on Lindsey Nagel, Park Nicollet Medical Center, March 14, 1991.

Belani, K. K., Medical report on Lindsey Nagel, Park Nicollet Medical Center, Feb. 15, 1991.

Bergel, M. *Leprosy as a Metabolic Disease.* Meny Bergel, Buenos Aires, Argentina, 1988.

Bergel, M. *Leprosy: Etiology, Pathogenesis, Treatment.* Instituto de Investigaciones Leprologicas, Rosario, Argentina, 1990.

Blattner, W., Gallo, R. C. and Temin, H. M. HIV causes AIDS. *Science* **241**:515-516, 1988.

Bogorad, L., letter to Peter Duesberg, May 13, 1991.

Booth, W. A Rebel Without a Cause of AIDS. *Science* **239**:1485-8, 1988.

Brandt, A. M. *No Magic Bullet: A Social History of Venereal Disease in the United States Since 1880.* Oxford University Press, New York, 1985.

Brès, P. *Public Health Action in Emergencies Caused by Epidemics: A Practical Guide.* World Health Organization, Geneva, Switzerland, 1986.

Brock, T. D. *Robert Koch: A Life in Medicine and Bacteriology.* Science Tech Publishers, Madison, WI, 1988.

Brock, T. D. *The Emergence of Bacterial Genetics.* Cold Spring Harbor Laboratory, Cold Spring Harbor, NY, 1990.

Buianouckas, F. R., Letter to Peter Duesberg, April 29, 1993.

Caiazza, S. S. *AIDS: One Doctor's Personal Struggle.* Stephen S. Caiazza, New York, 1989.

Caldwell, E. *New York Daily News*, Feb. 10, 1993.

Callen, M. *Surviving AIDS.* Harper Perennial, New York, 1990.

Callen, M. A dangerous talk with Dr. Sonnabend. *QW*, Sep. 27: 42-6, 71-2, 1992.

Carpenter, K. J. (eds). *Pellagra.* Hutchinson Ross Publishing, Stroudsburg, Pennsylvania, 1981.

Carpenter, K. J. *The History of Scurvy and Vitamin C.* Cambridge University Press, Cambridge, England, 1986.

Centers for Disease Control. A Comprehensive HIV Prevention Program. *Public Health Reports* **106**:601-732, 1991.

Chieco-Bianchi, L. and Rossi, G. B. Duesberg: rights and wrongs. *Nature* **364**:96, 1993.

Cochrane, M. Deconstructing 'African AIDS': an analysis of the production of scientific knowledge. 1991.

Cohen, J. Doing Science in the Spotlight's Glare. *Science* **257**:1033, 1992.

Cohen, J. Special News Report. *Science* **260**:1253-1265, 1993.

Cole, J. S., letter to Peter Duesberg, Oct. 22, 1990.

Condon, G. The Assault on Germs. *San Francisco Chronicle*, July 28, 1993.

Connor, S. AIDS: Science Stands on Trial. *New Scientist*, Feb. 12: 49-58, 1987.

Cotton, P. Cofactor Question Divides Codiscoverers of HIV. *Medical News & Perspectives* **264**:3111-2, 1990.

Coulter, H. L. *AIDS and Syphilis: The Hidden Link.* North Atlantic Books, Berkeley, CA, 1987.

Coyle, W. B., "In memory of... The way it was" (an open letter, unpublished), Jan. 14, 1992.

Cramer, R., letter to Peter Duesberg, July 8, 1991.

Crewdson, J. The Great AIDS Quest. *Chicago Chicago Tribune*, Nov. 19, 1989.

Crewdson, J. Burden of Proof. *Chicago Chicago Tribune*, Dec. 6, 1992.

Culliton, B. J. Legion Fever: Postmortem on an Investigation That Failed. *Science* **194**:1025-1027, 1976.

Culliton, B. J. Gallo Reports Mystery Break-in. *Science* **250**:502, 1990.

Culliton, B. J. Inside the Gallo Probe. *Science* **248**:1494-1498, 1990.

D'Arcy, P. F. and Griffin, J. P. (eds). *Iatrogenic Diseases*. Oxford University Press, Oxford, 1986.

Dawid, I., letter to Peter Duesberg, July 20, 1988.

Dawid, I., letter to Peter Duesberg, Feb. 12, 1991.

Delaney, M., Making Regulatory and Research Programs Work, speech at Stanford University School of Medicine, Jan. 11, 1990.

Delaney, M., Goldblum, P. and Brewer, J. *Strategies for Survival: A Gay Men's Health Manual for the Age of AIDS*. St. Martin's Press, New York, 1987.

Dingell, J., *AIDS Prevention Act of 1990*. Committee on Energy and Commerce, May 31, 1990.

Dingell, J. D. Shattuck Lecture—Misconduct in medical research. *New England Journal of Medicine* **328**:1610-1615, 1993.

Duesberg, P. HIV is not the cause of AIDS. *Science* **241**:514-517, 1988.

Duesberg, P. Bookshelf: The Enigma of Slow Viruses. *Lancet* **342**:729, 1993.

Duesberg, P. The HIV Gap in National AIDS Statistics. *Bio/Technology* **11**:955-956, 1993.

Duesberg, P. H. Retroviruses as Carcinogens and Pathogens: Expectations and Reality. *Cancer Research* **47**:1199-1220, 1987.

Duesberg, P. H. Human immunodeficiency virus and acquired immunodeficiency syndrome: Correlation but not causation. *Proc. Nat. Acad. Sci.* **86**:755-764, 1989.

Duesberg, P. H. Responding to "The AIDS Debate". *Naturwissenschaften* **77**:97-102, 1990.

Duesberg, P. H. AIDS epidemiology: Inconsistencies with human immunodeficiency virus and with infectious disease. *Proc. Nat. Acad. Sci.* **88**:1575-1579, 1991.

Duesberg, P. H. AIDS acquired by drug consumption and other noncontagious risk factors. *Pharmacology & Therapeutics* **55**:201-277, 1992.

Duesberg, P. H. The role of drugs in the origin of AIDS. *Biomedicine & Pharmacotherapy* **46**:3-15, 1992.

Duesberg, P. H. and Ellison, B. J. Is HIV the Cause of AIDS? *Policy Review*, Fall: 70-83, 1990.

Duesberg, P. H. and Ellison, B. J. Is the AIDS virus a science fiction? *Policy Review*, Summer: 40-51, 1990.

Duesberg, P. H. and Schwartz, J. R. Latent Viruses and Mutated Oncogenes: No Evidence for Pathogenicity. *Progress in Nucleic Acid Research and Molecular Biology* **43**:135-204, 1992.

Eigen, M. The AIDS Debate. *Naturwissenschaften* **76**:341-50, 1989.

Ellison, B., Interview with Etsuro Totsuka, May 1, 1992.

Ellison, B. J., Interview with Stephen S. Caiazza, Dec. 13, 1989.

Ellison, B. J., Interview with John Lauritsen, April 21, 1993.

Epstein, S. S., Bingham, E., Rall, D. and Bross, I. D. Losing the "war against cancer": a need for public policy reforms. *International Journal of Health Services* **22**:455-469, 1992.

Etheridge, E. W. *The Butterfly Caste: A Social History of Pellagra in the South*. Greenwood Publishing Co., Westport, Connecticut, 1972.

Etheridge, E. W. *Sentinel for Health: A History of the Centers for Disease Control*. University of California Press, Berkeley, CA, 1992.

Evans, A. S. (eds). *Viral Infections of Humans: Epidemiology and Control*. Plenum Medical Book Co., New York, 1989.

Farber, C. AIDS: Words from the Front. *Spin*, Sept.: 97, 120, 1992.

Farber, C. Out of Africa, part I. *Spin*, March: 61-3, 86-7, 1993.

Fauci, A. Writing for my Sister Denise. *The AAAS Observer*, Sep. 1: 4, 1989.

Fenner, F. and White, D. O. *Medical Virology*. Academic Press, New York, 1970.

Fischl, M. A., Richman, D. D., Grieco, M. H. and the AZT Collaborative Working Group. The efficacy of azidothymidine (AZT) in the treatment of patients with AIDS and AIDS-related complex. *New England Journal of Medicine* **317**:185-191, 1987.

Francis, D. P. Toward a Comprehensive HIV Prevention Program for the CDC and the Nation. *Journal of the American Medical Association* **268**:1444-7, 1992.

Freeman, B. A. *Textbook of Microbiology*. W.B. Saunders Co., Philadelphia, 1979.

Fumento, M. *The Myth of Heterosexual AIDS*. Basic Books, New York, 1989.

Gajdusek, D. C. Unconventional Viruses and the Origin and Disappearance of Kuru. *Science* **197**:943-960, 1977.

Gajdusek, D. C., Clarence J. Gibbs, J. and Alpers, M. (eds). *Slow, Latent, and Temperate Virus Infections*. Government Printing Office, Washington, DC, 1965.

Gallo, R. *Virus Hunting—AIDS, Cancer, & the Human Retrovirus: a Story of Human Discovery*. Basic Books, New York, 1991.

Gallo, R. C. and Montagnier, L. AIDS in 1988. *Sci. Am.* **259**:40-48, 1988.

Garrett, L. AIDS: The next decade. *New York Newsday*, June 12: 1,5, 1990.

Gavzer, B. What we can learn from those who survive AIDS. *Parade*, June 10: 4-7, 1990.

Gent, M. and Shigematsu, I. (eds). *Epidemiological Issues in Reported Drug-induced Illnesses—S.M.O.N. and Other Examples*. McMaster University Library Press, Hamilton, Ontario, Canada, 1978.

Greenberg, D. S. What Ever Happened to the War on Cancer? *Discover*, March: 47-64, 1986.

Greenberg, D. S. What Ails NIH? *Journal of NIH Research* **2**:29-30, 1990.

Greenwood, D. C. *Solving the Scientist Shortage*. Public Affairs Press, Washington, DC, 1958.

Griffin, B. E. Burden of Proof. *Nature* **338**:670, 1989.

Gunby, P. Battles against many malignancies lie ahead as federal 'war on cancer' enters third decade. *JAMA* **267**:1891, 1992.

Hall, S. S. Gadfly in the Ointment. *Hippocrates*, Sep./Oct.: 76-82, 1988.

Hall, S. S. David Baltimore's Final Days. *Science* **254**:1576-9, 1991.

Harris, H. F. *Pellagra*. MacMillan Co., New York, 1919.

Haverkos, H. W. and Dougherty, J. A. (eds). *Health Hazards of Nitrite Inhalants*. National Institute on Drug Abuse, Rockville, MD, 1988.

Hess, A. F. *Scurvy Past and Present*. J.B. Lippincott Co., Philadelphia, 1920.

Hill, C. A., Letter to Peter Duesberg, June 4, 1992.

Hilts, P. J. Federal inquiry finds misconduct by a discoverer of the AIDS virus. *New York Times*, Dec. 31, 1992.

Hodgkinson, N. Experts mount startling challenge to Aids orthodoxy. *London The Sunday Times*, April 26, 1992.

Hodgkinson, N. The cure that failed. *London Sunday Times*, April 4, 1993.

Hopkins, D. Dr. Joseph Sonnabend. *Interview Magazine*, Dec.: 124-6,142-3, 1992.

Horrobin, D. Discouraging Hypotheses Slows Progress. *The Scientist*, Nov. 26: 13, 15, 1990.

Hostetter, M., Letter to Joseph McHugh, Dec. 11, 1992.

Hostetter, M. K., Letter to Joseph McHugh, Nov. 13, 1991.

Hostetter, M. K., Letter to Mr. and Mrs. Steve Nagel, Dec. 29, 1992.

Humphrey, L. C. (ed.). *America Living With AIDS.* National Commission on AIDS, 1991.

Hunter, W., letter to David Schryer, Nov. 20, 1992.

Institute of Medicine and National Academy of Sciences. *Confronting AIDS: Directions for Public Health, Health Care, and Research.* National Academy Press, Washington, D.C., 1986.

Jawetz, E., Melnick, J. L. and Adelberg, E. A. *Review of Medical Microbiology.* Lange Medical Publications, Los Altos, California, 1976.

Kaplan, M. Three decades of collaboration with Hilary Koprowski. *Journal of Cellular Physiology* 2 (**Suppl.**):1-6, 1982.

Karpas, A., letter to Serge Lang, Feb. 3, 1993.

Kidd, C. V. *American Universities and Federal Research.* Belknap Press, Harvard University Press, Cambridge, Mass., 1959.

Klaw, S. *The New Brahmins: Scientific Life in America.* William Morrow & Co., New York, 1968.

Kolata, G. Anthropologists Suggest Cannibalism Is a Myth. *Science* 232:1497-1500, 1986.

Kolata, G. Imminent marketing of AZT raises problems. *Science* 235:1462-3, 1987.

Kono, R. The SMON virus theory. *Lancet* II:370-371, 1975.

Konotey-Ahulu, F. I. D. AIDS in Africa: Misinformation and disinformation. *The Lancet*, July 25: 206-7, 1987.

Konotey-Ahulu, F. I. D. *What Is AIDS?* Tetteh—A'Domeno Company, Watford, England, 1989.

Koshland, D. E., Letter to Charles A. Thomas, June 11, 1991.

Krieger, T. and Caceres, C. A. The Unnoticed Link in AIDS Cases. *The Wall Street Journal*, Oct. 24: 1985.

Kruif, P. d. *Microbe Hunters.* Blue Ribbon Books, New York, 1926.

Langmuir, A. D. Biological Warfare Defense. *American Journal of Public Health* 42:235-8, 1952.

Langmuir, A. D. The Epidemic Intelligence Service of the Center for Disease Control. *Public Health Reports* 95:470-477, 1980.

Lapp, R. E. *The New Priesthood: The Scientific Elite and the Uses of Power.* Harper & Row, New York, 1965.

Lauritsen, J., Notes on conversations with CDC/NCI people (unpublished), June 11-12, 1987.

Lauritsen, J. AZT: Iatrogenic Genocide. *New York Native*, March 28: 13-17, 1988.

Lauritsen, J. *Poison by Prescription: The AZT Story.* Asklepios, New York, 1990.

Lauritsen, J. *The AIDS War: Propaganda, Profiteering and Genocide from the Medical-Industrial Complex.* Asklepios, New York, 1993.

Lauritsen, J. Dissent at the Berlin AIDS Conference. *Rethinking AIDS*, July: 7:1-2, 1993.

Lauritsen, J., Letter to Bryan Ellison, May 28, 1993.

Lauritsen, J. and Wilson, H. *Death Rush: Poppers and AIDS.* Pagan Press, New York, 1986.

LeFanu, J. Telescope. *London Sunday Telegraph*, Nov. 29, 1992.

Leiphart, J., Mann, C., Farber, C., Buianouckas, F. B., Schildwaechter, D., Verney-Elliott, M., Ellner, M., Gilliland, D., Owen, B. L., Missen, D., Michel, F., Shenton, J., Bixley, C. and Lauritsen, J., *Press Release.* International Symposium: AIDS—A Different View, May 16, 1992.

Lemaitre, M., Guetard, D., Henin, Y., Montagnier, L. and Zerial, A. Protective activity of tetracycline analogs against the cytopathic effect of the Human Immunodeficiency Viruses in CEM cells. *Research in Virology* 141:5-16, 1990.

Lenderking, W. R., Gelber, R. D., Cotton, D. J., Cole, B. F., Goldhirsch, A., Volberding, P. A. and Testa, M. A. Evaluation of the quality of life associated with zidovudine treatment in asymptomatic human immunodeficiency virus infection. *New England Journal of Medicine* **330**:738-743, 1994.

Lindenbaum, S. *Kuru Sorcery: Disease and Danger in the New Guinea Highlands.* Mayfield Publishing, Palo Alto, CA, 1979.

Liversidge, A. Heresy! Modern Galileos. *Omni*, June: 43-51, 1993.

Lwoff, A. Introduction. In: *RNA Viruses and Host Genome in Oncogenesis*, pp. 1-11, Emmelot, P. and Bentvelzen, P. (eds.) American Elsevier Publishing, New York, 1972.

Maddox, J. Has Duesberg a right of reply? *Nature* **363**:109, 1993.

Marshall, E. Committee Treats Healy Gently. *Science* **251**:1423, 1991.

McKeown, T. *The Role of Medicine: Dream, Mirage, or Nemesis?* Princeton University Press, Princeton, NJ, 1979.

McMurran, K. and Neill, M. One woman's brave battle with AIDS. *People*, July: 62-5, 1990.

McNamee, L. J. and McNamee, B. F. *AIDS: the Nation's First Politically Protected Disease.* National Medical Legal Publishing House, La Habra, California, 1988.

Meditel, *The AIDS Catch.* Dispatches, Channel Four Television, London, June 13, 1990. Documentary.

Meditel, *AZT—Cause For Concern.* Dispatches, Channel Four Television, London, Feb. 12, 1992. Documentary.

Meditel, *AIDS and Africa.* Dispatches, Channel Four Television, London, March 24, 1993. Documentary.

Miller, J. AIDS Heresy. *Discover*, June: 63-68, 1988.

Mims, C. A. and White, D. O. *Viral Pathogenesis and Immunology.* Blackwell Scientific Publications, Oxford, 1984.

Moseley, B. Interview: D. Carleton Gajdusek. *Omni*, March: 62-68, 104-106, 1986.

Nagel, S. and Nagel, C., Appeal to the Minnesota Board of Medical Practice, March 31, 1993.

National Association for People With AIDS, *NAPWA brochure.* 1993.

Nussbaum, B. *Good Intentions: How Big Business and the Medical Establishment Are Corrupting the Fight Against AIDS.* Atlantic Monthly Press, New York, 1990.

Office of AIDS Research and Division of Safety, HIV Safety Notice, National Institutes of Health, Feb. 23, 1989.

Ostrom, N. *What Really Killed Gilda Radner? Frontline Reports on the Chronic Fatigue Syndrome Epidemic.* That New Magazine, New York, 1991.

Ostrom, N. *50 Things You Should Know about the Chronic Fatigue Syndrome Epidemic.* TNM, New York, 1992.

Parsons, J. and Chandler, K. Girl in family stricken with AIDS virus dies at age 5. *Minneapolis Star/Tribune*, June 28, 1993.

R. Kono et al. Reviews on SMON. *Japanese Journal of Medical Science and Biology* **28 (supplement)**:1-293, 1975.

Radetsky, P. *The Invisible Invaders: The Story of the Emerging Age of Viruses.* Little, Brown & Co., Boston, 1991.

Rapoport, R. Dissident scientist's AIDS theory angers colleagues. *Oakland Tribune*, Jan. 31, 1988.

Rapoport, R. AIDS: The Unanswered Questions. *Oakland Tribune*, May 21, 1989.

Rappoport, J. *AIDS, Inc.* Human Energy Press, San Bruno, California, 1988.

Reagan, M. D. *Science and the Federal Patron.* Oxford University Press, New York, 1969.

Regush, N. AIDS risk limited, studies suggest. *Montreal Gazette*, Aug. 15, 1987.

Relman, A. S., Letter to John Lauritsen, July 11, 1988.

Rettig, R. A. *Cancer Crusade: The Story of the National Cancer Act of 1971.* Princeton University Press, Princeton, New Jersey, 1977.

Roe, D. A. *A Plague of Corn: The Social History of Pellagra.* Cornell University Press, Ithaca, NY, 1973.

Root-Bernstein, R. S. Do we know the cause(s) of AIDS? *Persp. Biol. Med.* **33**:480-500, 1990.

Root-Bernstein, R. S. Non-HIV immunosuppressive factors in AIDS: a multifactorial, synergistic theory of AIDS aetiology. *Res. Immunol.* **141**:815-838, 1990.

Root-Bernstein, R. S. *Rethinking AIDS: The Tragic Cost of Premature Consensus.* The Free Press, New York, 1993.

Rous, P. The Challenge to Man of the Neoplastic Cell. *Science* **157**:24-28, 1967.

Rubinstein, E. The untold story of HUT78. *Science* **248**:1499-1507, 1990.

Sadownick, D. Kneeling at the crystal cathedral. *Genre*, January: 40-45, 86-90, 1994.

Schmitz, T., A Personal Experience (an open letter, unpublished), Dec. 8, 1993.

Scott, J. Dangerous Liaisons. *Los Angeles Times Magazine*, March 11: 10-19, 37, 1990.

Shannon, J. A. The National Institutes of Health: Some Critical Years, 1955-1957. *Science* **237**:865-868, 1987.

Shilts, R. *And the Band Played On.* St. Martin's Press, New York, 1987.

Shodel, M. NIH Overview. *Journal of NIH Research* **2**:19-24, 1990.

Shorter, E. *The Health Century.* Doubleday, New York, 1987.

Siegel, L. AIDS fear manifesting itself in irrational ways. *Daily Recorder*, March 23, 1987.

Singer, M., letter to Peter Duesberg, June 30, 1988.

Smith, J. S. *Patenting the Sun: Polio and the Salk Vaccine.* Anchor Books/Doubleday, New York, 1990.

Soda, T. (eds). *Drug-Induced Sufferings: Medical, Pharmaceutical, and Legal Aspects.* Excerpta Medica, Amsterdam, 1980.

Sonnabend, J., Letter to Peter Duesberg, May 24, 1988.

Sonnabend, J., Witkin, S. S. and Purtilo, D. T. Acquired Immunodeficiency Syndrome, Opportunistic Infections, and Malignancies in Male Homosexuals. *Journal of the American Medical Association* **249**:2370-4, 1983.

Sonnabend, J. A. The Etiology of AIDS. *AIDS Research* **1**:1-12, 1983.

Sonnabend, J. A. Caution on AIDS viruses. *Nature* **310**:103, 1984.

Sonnabend, J. A. Letter to the editor. *Wall Street Journal*, Nov. 18: 1985.

Sonnabend, J. A. and Lauritsen, J. Letters to the Editor. *New York Native*, June 29: 4, 1992.

Specter, M. Panel Rebuts Biologist's Claims on Cause of AIDS. *Washington Post*, Apr. 10, 1988.

Stetten, D. and Carrigan, W. T. (eds). *NIH: An Account of Research in Its Laboratories and Clinics.* Academic Press (Harcourt Brace Jovanovich), New York, 1984.

Stewart, C. P. and Guthrie, D. (eds). *Lind's Treatise on Scurvy.* Edinburgh University Press, Edinburgh, 1953.

Stewart, G., Root-Bernstein, Luca-Moretti, Brands, M., Callen, M., Sonnabend, J. A., Eleopolis, Bastide, M. and Leiphart, J., *Press Release*. International Symposium: AIDS—A Different View, May 16, 1992.

Stolberg, S. AIDS Tally to Increase Due to New Definition. *Los Angeles Times*, Dec. 31, 1992.

Studer, K. E. and Chubin, D. E. *The Cancer Mission: Social Contexts of Biomedical Research.* Sage Publications, Beverly Hills, 1980.

Terris, M. (eds). *Goldberger on Pellagra.* Louisiana State University Press, Baton Rouge, LA, 1964.

Thomas, G. and Morgan-Witts, M. *Anatomy of an Epidemic.* Doubleday & Co., Garden City, NY, 1982.

Threakall, S. E., Letter to Peter Duesberg, May 31, 1992.

Tokyo District Court. *Decision of the Tokyo District Court, August 3, 1978.* Kyoto International Conference Against Drug Induced Sufferings, Tokyo, Japan, 1979.

Tooze, J. (eds). *The Molecular Biology of Tumour Viruses.* Cold Spring Harbor Laboratory, Cold Spring Harbor, NY, 1973.

Wade, N. Scientists and the press: Cancer scare story that wasn't. *Science* **174**:679-80, 1971.

Wecht, C. H. The swine flu immunization program: Scientific venture or political folly? In: *Legal Medicine Annual*, pp. 227-244, Wecht, C. H. (ed.) 1978.

Weiss, R., Teich, N., Varmus, H. and Coffin, J. (eds). *RNA Tumor Viruses.* Cold Spring Harbor Laboratory, Cold Spring Harbor, NY, 1982.

Weiss, R. A. and Jaffe, H. W. Duesberg, HIV and AIDS. *Nature* **345**:659-660, 1990.

Werth, B. By AIDS Obsessed. *GQ*, August: 145-151, 205-208, 1991.

Williams, A. O. *AIDS: An African Perspective.* CRC Press, Boca Raton, Florida, 1992.

Williams, G. *Virus Hunters.* Alfred A. Knopf, New York, 1959.

Williams, R. R. *Toward the Conquest of Beriberi.* Harvard University Press, Cambridge, MA, 1961.

Winn, W. C. Legionnaires Disease: Historical Perspective. *Clinical Microbiology Reviews* **1**:60-81, 1988.

Wright, K. Mycoplasmas in the AIDS Spotlight. *Science* **248**:682-3, 1990.

Wyngaarden, J. B. The National Institutes of Health in Its Centennial Year. *Science* **237**:869-874, 1987.

Yuan, R. and Hsu, M. Vaccines in Asia. *Genetic Engineering News*, Oct. 1: 14, 1992.

Index

Abelson, Philip, 44
Ablashi, Dharam, 113
Acer, David, 217, 219-220
acquired immune deficiency syndrome (AIDS)
  African swine fever virus hypothesis, 152
  autoimmunity hypothesis, 167
  cancer, 121
  candidiasis, 1, 103, 121, 138, 141, 173, 192, 194, 217, 221
  cervical cancer, 129, 138, 174, 267
  clinical definition, 105, 135, 138, 140, 240, 253, 267- 268
  cofactors, 116, 131, 154, 162-164, 223, 230, 269
  cytomegalovirus, 138, 166, 173
  cytomegalovirus hypothesis, 16, 106, 107, 146, 230
  dementia, 121, 124-125, 129, 135, 138, 141, 174, 187-188
  drug hypothesis, 143, 148-149, 152-154, 249, 257, Chapter 8 *passim*
  Epstein-Barr virus hypothesis, 107, 146
  first cases, 15-16, 102-103, 108, 146-147, 150, 173-174, 207, 237
  hepatitis, 194
  herpes, 138, 141
  HIV hypothesis, v, 3, 16, 110, 116-117, 183, 188, 194, 200, 216-217, 223, 256-258, 260, 265, 269, Chapters 6, 7, & 10 *passim*
  HIV-negative cases, 125, 128, 141, 164, 183, 191-193, 240-242
  HTLV-I hypothesis, 109, 146, 148
  HTLV-II infection, 149
  Kaposi's sarcoma, 104, 124-125, 129, 135, 138, 140-141, 166, 173-174, 180, 182, 187-188, 194, 217, 240
  long-term survivors, 216
  low T-cell counts (new clinical definition), 240, 267
  lymphoma, 1, 129, 138, 174, 180, 188, 212
  malnutrition, 185, 193
  multifactorial hypothesis, 147-149, 154, 166, 168, 177
  mycoplasma hypothesis, 157, 162-164
  named, 105
  Pneumocystis carinii pneumonia, 103, 105, 138, 147, 149, 166, 173-174, 180, 185, 203, 222-223
  pneumonia, 1, 121, 140-141, 183, 187-189, 194, 240, 267
  public health measures, 1, 3, 17, 120, 122, 149, 156, 176, 182-183, 186, 194, 229, 231-233, 269
  semen hypothesis, 147-148
  "slim disease", 140, 141, 191
  syphilis hypothesis, 35, 152, 155-156, 179
  thrombocytopenia, 267
  toxoplasmosis, 140, 166, 222
  tuberculosis, 138, 140-141, 173-174, 183-184, 189, 191, 194, 240, 267
  "voodoo death" syndrome, 193
  wasting disease, 121, 129, 138, 141, 173-174, 183-184, 188, 268
  zinc deficiency, 169, 185
acyclovir, 177
Adams, Jad, 179
Addison-Wesley publishing, vii
Adult T-Cell Leukemia (ATL), 86, 109
Adult T-Cell Leukemia Virus (ATLV), 111
Advocate, The, 176
AFL-CIO, 236
Africa, 1-2, 55, 69-71, 86, 107, 113, 120, 123, 140, 142, 148, 173-174, 233
  AIDS epidemic, 16, 189-194

HIV infection, 140
African Medical Research Foundation, 191
African swine fever virus, 152
Agency for International Development (AID), 233
AIDS. *See* acquired immune deficiency syndrome
AIDS Coalition To Unleash Power (ACT UP), 121, 179, 237-9
AIDS Healthcare Foundation, 268
AIDS Prevention Act of 1980, 122
AIDS Research, 147-148, 150
AIDS Research and Human Retroviruses, 150
AIDS War: Propaganda, Profiteering, and Genocide from the Medical-Industrial Complex, The, 154
Alaska, 71, 100
Altman, Lawrence, 96, 101, 241
Alzheimer's disease, 17, 53
American Association for Adolescent Psychiatry, 257
American Association for the Advancement of Science (AAAS), 43
American Association of Blood Banks, 59, 87
American Association of School Administrators, 236
American Broadcasting Company (ABC), 96, 258
American Cancer Society (ACS), 89
American Federation of State, Country, and Municipal Employees (AFSCME), 236
American Federation of Teachers, 236
American Foundation for AIDS Research (AmFAR), 167, 237-238, 243, 245
American Laboratory, 169
American Legion, 35, 100
American Medical Foundation (AMF), 149-150
American Pediatric Association, 24
Americans for a Sound AIDS Policy (ASAP), 218, 236
And the Band Played On, 103, 180
Andrews, Justin, 94
anthrax, 20
antibiotics, 47, 129, 147, 156, 177, 185, 202, 216, 222
    Cleocin, 222
    diiodohydroxyquin, 185
    flagyl, 185
    nystatin, 222
    penicillin, 156, 185, 198, 202
    pentamidine, 149, 222
    sulfa drugs, 198-200, 216
    sulfa drugs (bactrim, septra), 185
    tetracycline, 163-164, 185
antibodies, 13, 34, 47-48, 54-56, 58, 70-71, 78, 83, 86, 88, 115, 125-128, 130, 134-135, 138, 148
antimony, 155
Antonio, Gene, 122
Argentina
    Institute for Leprological Investigation, 34
Arizona State University, 53
Armed Forces Institute of Pathology, 157
arsenic, 27, 28, 30, 35, 155
artificial bleeding, 28
Ascher, Michael, 250, 251
Ashe, Arthur, v, 222-223
Asia, 78-79, 107
Asian flu, 98, 99
Association of American Universities, 44
Association of Asian/Pacific Community Health Organizations, 236
Atomic Energy Commission, 41-42
Australia, 51, 53, 165, 212
azidothymidine (AZT), vii, 1, 123, 128, 153-154, 156, 177-178, 188, 194, 227, 229, 230, 237-239, 247, 249, 251-253, 258-259, 262, and Chapter 9 *passim*
    approval for AIDS prevention, 214
    approval for AIDS therapy, 198, 211
    as cause of AIDS, 16, 212, 213, 218, 269
    chemistry, 198, 203, 205, 210
    compound S, 205
    Concorde trial, 214-215, 256
    for medical workers, 215
    invention, 203
    laboratory testing, 205-206
    Phase I trials, 206, 212
    Phase II trials, 206-213, 216, 218, 222, 229

Protocol 019 trial, 213-215
"side effects", 198-200, 207-209,
212, 214-215, 218, 220, 222-
223, 258, 268
trial on pregnant mothers, 216
Veteran's Administration study,
214

B cells, 130
Babick, Christopher, 208
bacteria hunters, vi, 17, 23, 26, 28, 33,
38, 46, 49, 62-63, 75, 97, 123, 202,
261
Baltimore, David, vii, 3, 49, 81, 111,
115, 227-229, 233, 243, 252-253,
261, 266
Bang, Oluf, 63
Barbizon Hotel, 245
Barr, Yvonne, 69
Barry, David, 204-206, 211
Beecham, Jim, 100
Behrman, Lori, 267
Beijerinck, Martinus Willem, 46
Bellevue Stratford Hotel, 35, 37
Beppu, Dr., 9
Bergalis, Kimberly, v, 217-220
Bergel, Meny, 34-35
beriberi, 25-27, 169, 175, 261
Berkelman, Ruth, 217
Bialy, Harvey, 168-169
Bild der Wissenschaft, 247
Bio/Technology, 132, 168-169
Biomedicine and Pharmacotherapy, 257
Bishop, J. Michael, vii, 228
Black Plague. *See* bubonic plague
Blattner, William, 132, 135-137, 168,
244
"Bob Club", 114, 150, 205, 229
Bolognesi, Dani, 150, 204-205, 244, 249
Brazil, 22
breast cancer, 64, 82-83, 266
Bristol-Myers Squibb, 220, 238, 239,
259
Bristol-Myers Squibb Foundation, 237
British Medical Journal, 168
Broder, Sam, 150, 205-206, 208, 210,
212, 220, 266
bubonic plague, 120, 122, 231
Bureau of Justice Statistics, 175
Burkett, Elinor, 242
Burkitt's lymphoma, 8, 69-71, 75, 88,
107

Burkitt, Dennis, 69
Burnet, Sir Frank Macfarlane, 51
Burroughs-Wellcome, 198, 201, 204,
206, 210-211, 213-215, 218, 220,
229, 237-240, 246, 249, 258-259
Burton, Phillip, 105
Bush, George, 121

Cable News Network (CNN), 245
Caceres, Cesar, 179
Caiazza, Stephen, 156-157
California, 155, 164, 173, 186
California Institute of Technology,
Pasadena, 80
Callen, Michael, 216, 235
Cambridge Bioscience Corporation, 84
Canada, 163, 259
University of Calgary, 258
cancer, vii, 19, 49, 53, 93, 102, 130-131,
181, 192, 202, 227, 249, 251, 260,
262, and Chapter 4 *passim*
chemotherapy, 64, 71, 103, 107,
203-204, 218, 220, 223, 227,
262
interferon treatment, 147
oncogenes, 131, 228, 266
therapy, 64, 203
Cancer Research, 131, 153, 158-159,
165, 168, 244, 248
cannibalism, 51-53
carbon monoxide, 181
Caribbean, 86
Carnegie Corporation, 229
Cararoli, 28-29
Carter, Jimmy, 150
Carter, Rosalynn, 150
CBS Nightly News, 106
Ceni, 29
Center for Disease Control. *See* Centers
for Disease Control
Center for Population Options, 236
Centers for Disease Control (CDC), v,
vii, 88, 98-102, 116, 120, 125, 127-
128, 133, 135, 138-141, 146-149,
152-153, 156, 173, 176, 179, 184,
187, 189, 194, 216, 223, 227, 229,
253, 259, 261, 267
Auditorium A, 99
Communicable Disease Center,
95, 99

control over media & AIDS
  activists, 96, 217-219, 235-237,
  239-243, 260
creation of virus-AIDS
  hypothesis, 102-110, 181-182
Epidemic Intelligence Service
  (EIS), 95-101, 103-107, 217,
  229, 232, 240-241, 261
Hepatitis Laboratories Division,
  108
KSOI Task Force, 104-106, 108,
  149, 187, 240
Malaria Control in War Areas
  (MCWA), 94-95
political agenda, 95, 97-98, 121,
  218-219, 231-234
Special Pathogens Branch, 100
Venereal Disease Division, 103
Centocor, 115
cervical cancer, 17, 74-79, 86, 133
Cetus, 59
Chicago Tribune, 112, 113, 246
chickenpox, 127, 133
Children's Hospital, Minneapolis, 197,
  201
China, 71
Chirac, Jacque, 114
Chiron Corporation, 57, 58, 59
chlamydia, 75, 143
cholera, 21, 148
Christopher Street, 165
Chronic Fatigue Syndrome (CFS), 17,
  87-89
Ciba-Geigy, 11, 14
Ciesielski, Carol, 217
Clinton, Bill, 266
clioquinol, 6, 9-15, 185
  England (documentary), 15
  Germany (documentary), 15
cod liver oil, 34
cofactors, 29-31, 70, 78, 116, 131, 154,
  162-164, 223, 230, 269
Cold Spring Harbor, 73, 160-161
Cold Spring Harbor Symposium, 73
Cold War, 42, 49
Colorado, 105, 139
Columbia University, 150
Committee to Monitor Poppers, 152
common cold, 56, 66, 127
Commonwealth Club, 258
Communicable Disease Center. *See*
  Centers for Disease Control

Community Research Initiative, 150
Community Research Initiative on AIDS
  (CRIA), 151
compound S. *See* azidothymidine
Confronting AIDS, 229-234, 236, 252-
  253
Connolly, Louise, 75
Connor, Steve, 111-112, 115
Cook, James, 23
Copernicus, 41
coronavirus, 56
Corriere de la Sera (Italy), 257
corticosteroids, 185
Council on Foreign Relations, 253
Cowley, Geoffrey, 241
cowpox, 46
coxsackie viruses, 7, 54, 73
Coyle, William Bryan, 178
Creutzfeldt-Jakob disease, 53
Crewdson, John, 112-113, 115, 246
Crick, Francis, 41
Crimea, 24
Cuba, 122
Curran, James, 103-104, 108, 149, 241
cytomegalovirus, 106, 110, 129, 148
Czechoslovakia
  University of Prague, 20

d4T, 123, 177, 223
Daily Mail (London), 259
Dan, Bruce, 96
Dannemeyer, William, 122, 236
Davaine, Casimir Joseph, 20
Day One (ABC television), 246, 258
Days of Grace, 223
ddA. *See* dideoxyadenosine
ddC. *See* dideoxycytidine
ddI. *See* dideoxyinosine
Death Rush: Poppers & AIDS, 153
Delaney, Martin, 210, 237-238
Dellums, Ron, 250
Democratic Party, 149
dendritic cells, 125
Denmark, 63
deoxyribonucleic acid (DNA), 45, 70,
  73, 76, 79, 81, 126, 159-161, 181,
  202-203, 205, 210, 220
Department of Agriculture, 31, 42
Department of Defense, 45, 95
Department of Health and Human
  Services (HHS), 110, 115, 266

Department of Health, Education, and Welfare (HEW), 48, 90
Der Spiegel (Germany), 247
Detroit Cancer Foundation, 203
diabetes, 54, 192
dideoxyadenosine (ddA), 230
dideoxycytidine (ddC), 1, 123, 177, 221, 223, 229-230, 259
dideoxyinosine (ddI), 1, 123, 177, 199, 220-221, 223, 230, 237, 239, 259
Digene Diagnostics, 78
Dingell, John, 122, 252
diphtheria, 21, 97
Discovering, 166
DNA. *See* deoxyribonucleic acid
Dominican Republic, 236
Drug Enforcement Administration (DEA), 175
Duesberg, Peter H., vi, vii, 59, 135-136, 149-151, 153-154, 158-169, 177-178, 200, 223, 228, 257-259, 268
    censorship, 243-252
    early virology, 47, 81-82, 85
    HIV/AIDS debate, 130-132
Duke University, 150, 204
Dutch Colonial Administration, 26
dysplasia, 77

E. coli, 22, 185
Early Homosexual Rights Movement (1864-1935), The, 151
East Indies, 23
Ebola Fever, 107
echovirus, 6
Echthius, 22
Edwards, Charles, 90
Ehrlich, Paul, 35
Ehrlich, Paul, Award, 228
Eigen, Manfred, 162
Eijkman, Christiaan, 26
Einstein, Albert, 41
Eisenhower, Dwight, 43, 49, 98
Ellermann, Vilhelm, 63
Ellison, Bryan J., 153, 156, 162, 188, 246, 252, 258
Ellner, Michael, 216
Enders, John, 47
Epidemic Intelligence Service (EIS). *See* Centers for Disease Control
Epstein, M. Anthony, 69-71
Epstein-Barr virus, 70-72, 75, 88, 107, 110, 129, 148

erythromycin, 185
"ESP virus", 66
Esquire, 221, 247
Essex, Myron "Max", vii, 84, 85, 108-109, 114, 150, 229
Etheridge, Elizabeth, 104, 108
Europe, 1, 16, 19, 30, 98, 115, 123, 125, 141, 143, 155-156, 165, 175, 186, 189, 193, 197, 203, 222, 241, 261
Evatt, Bruce, 106

Factor VIII, 188-189
Faggots, 179
Family Account for the Education of the Sarin children, 113
Farber, Celia, 190
Farr's Law, 141
Fauci, Anthony, 3, 106, 150, 213, 216, 238, 241, 243-246, 250-251, 266
Feline AIDS (FAIDS), 116
Feline Leukemia Virus (FeLV), 84, 108, 116, 133
Financial Times (London), 259
First World, 260
Fischl, Margaret, 207-208, 210, 213, 216, 218
Florida, 105, 216, 268
Florida State University, 219
Fogarty fellowship, 158
Fogarty, John, 49
Food and Drug Administration (FDA), 58, 59, 149, 199, 204, 206-207, 209-211, 214, 220-221, 223, 237, 239, 265
food poisoning, 21
foot-and-mouth disease, 46
Ford, Gerald, 99, 101
Fore tribe, 51
Fort Dix, 99
France, 20, 84, 112, 114, 116, 128, 163, 166, 183-184, 190, 214, 216, 257
    Claude Bernard Hospital, 212
    Paris Academy of Medicine, 23-24
    Pasteur Institute, 67, 85, 109, 112, 114, 163
Francis, Donald, viii, 107-108, 114, 229, 232-233
Fraser, David, 100, 229
Freedom of Information Act, 208, 209
French Revolution, 25
Fumento, Michael, 139, 240
Furlaud, Richard M., 253

284   *Index*

Gajdusek, D. Carleton, viii, 50-54, 56,
    67, 261
Galileo, 41
Gallo, Robert, viii, 3, 56, 93, 109, 113,
    123, 126, 128, 130-137, 141, 146,
    148-151, 158, 162, 165, 168, 186,
    204-205, 228-230, 244-249, 257, 261,
    265
        early virology, 84-88, 99, 107,
            110-111
        stolen virus controversy, 111-112,
            114-116, 149, 266
gancyclovir, 177
Gann, Paul, vi, 186-187
Garrett, Laurie, 221
Gay Men's Health Crisis (GMHC), 235,
    238, 267
General Motors Award, 228
Georgia, 95, 235
germ theory, 20, 23-24, 261
Germany, 46, 113, 156-157, 183, 221,
    228, 247-248, 256-258
        Cancer Research Center, 76
        Göttingen University, 20
        Imperial Health Office, 22
        Max Planck Institute, 82
        public health, 94
        University of Dortmund, 257
        University of Köln, 257
Gertz, Alison, 221
Ghana, 190, 192
Gilbert, Walter, 159-160
Glaser, Donald, 59
Goldberger, Joseph, 17, 32, 47
Goldblum, Peter, 237
gonorrhea, 75, 143
Good Intentions, 207
Good Morning America (ABC
    television), 245
Gottlieb, Michael, 15-16, 103, 105-106,
    108, 146-147, 150, 173-174, 207, 237
Grayston, J. Thomas, 229
Great Britain, 23, 51, 71, 111, 114, 146,
    167, 204, 208, 212, 214, 216, 222,
    246, 257-259
        Cromwell Hospital, 190
        London University, 24
        Middlesex Hospital, 8, 69
        Royal Postgraduate Medical
            School, 169
        Royal Society of London, 24

University of Edinburgh, 25
Greece, 248
Greek philosophers, 41
Greenberg, Daniel S., 72, 89, 116, 262-
    263
Griffin, Beverly, 169
Groopman, Jerome, 210, 229
Gross National Product, 43
Gross, Ludwik, 65-66, 68, 73
Group for the Scientific Reappraisal of
    the HIV/AIDS Hypothesis, 165-166,
    168-169, 257, 259
Guinan, Mary, 104

H. Claude Hudson Comprehensive
    Health Center, 74
H9 cell line, 112
Haiti, 2, 105, 140, 148, 193
Hameau, Jean-Marie, 28
Hansen, Gerhard Armauer, 33
Harper's, 247
Harvard University, 84, 108, 151, 159-
    160, 164
Haseltine, William, 114, 229
Haverkos, Harry, 105
Hawkins, Sir Richard, 22
HEAL (Health-Education-Action
    Liaison), 216
Health Century, The, 93
Healy, Bernadine, 250, 264
heart disease, 19, 49, 62, 260
Heckler, Margaret, 110
Helicon Foundation, 164
Henle, Jakob, 20
hepatitis, 50, 57, 93, 102, 127, 147
        hepatitis A, 57, 133
        hepatitis B, 57, 78-79, 105, 108,
            124, 133, 139, 143, 177
        hepatitis C, 17, 57-59
        hepatitis, non-A, non-B, 57
herpes, 50, 75-76, 125, 129, 133-134,
    193, 204
herpes simplex virus, 76, 78, 107, 127,
    134
Hill, Lister, 49
Hirohito, Emperor, 59
hit-and-run hypothesis, 76
HIV. *See* human immunodeficiency
    virus
Hodgkinson, Neville, 259
Hoffmann-LaRoche, 221, 229, 259
Holland, 46, 150, 183, 212

Hopkins, Donald R., 233
Horrobin, David, 264
Horwitz, Jerome, 203, 221
Hostetter, Margaret, 199-201
HTLV-Associated Myelopathy (HAM), 87
HTLV-I. *See* human T-cell lymphotropic virus
HTLV-II. *See* human T-cell lymphotropic virus II
HTLV-III. *See* human immunodeficiency virus
Hudson, Rock, vi
Huebner, Robert J., 66, 73
Hughes, Howard, 227
human genome project, 161
Human Herpes Virus-type 6 (HHV-6), 88
human immunodeficiency virus (HIV)
    antibodies, 110, 121, 125-129, 136-138, 141, 153, 169, 174, 186, 193, 206, 217, 220-221, 231, 270
    as cause of SSPE, 56
    discovery, vi, 3, 109-112
    epidemiology, 125, 137-142, 174, 189, 219-220
    healthy positives, vii, 139-140, 189-190, 262, 269
    in lymph nodes, 125, 250
    latent period, 1, 104, 108-109, 120, 127, 130-131, 134-135, 140, 143, 163-164, 167, 182, 187, 240
    lymphadenopathy-associated virus (LAV), 109-112, 114
    named, 115
    test, 2, 110, 114, 122-123, 125, 127, 129-130, 134, 138-142, 159, 164, 174, 184, 186, 191, 193, 197, 215, 217-218, 220-222, 230-236, 253, 258, 268-269
    vaccine, 1, 113, 120, 123, 136, 204, 230, 232, 256, 262
    viral properties, 124-129, 136, 142
human papilloma virus, 74, 76-78, 129, 133
human T-cell leukemia virus. *See* human T-cell lymphotropic virus I

human T-cell lymphotropic virus I (HTLV-I), 86-87, 107, 109-111, 116, 133
    as cause of AIDS, 16
human T-cell lymphotropic virus II (HTLV-II), 87-88, 109, 114
HUT78 cell line, 112
Hygienic Laboratory. *See* National Institutes of Health
hyperplasia, 77

Idiopathic CD4+ Lymphocytopenia (ICL), 241
Imanishi-Kari, Thereza, 252
Independent, The (London), 259
India, 71
Indiana, 188
Indiana Hemophilia Foundation, 188
influenza, 19, 46, 55, 57, 67, 87, 98-99, 124, 127, 133, 135, 148, 177, 204
Inoue, Shigeyuki, 13-14
Inside Story Communications, ix
Institute for Thermobaric Studies, 155
Institute of Medicine, 229
interferon, 146, 201
International Academy of Tumor Marker Oncology (IATMO), 258
International AIDS Conferences
    3rd (1987), 159
    6th (1990), 162, 246
    7th (1991), 243, 245
    8th (1992), 165, 241, 257
    9th (1993), 221, 239, 256-257
International Austrian AIDS Conference, Third, 257
Ireland, 236
Italy, 243, 245, 251, 257
    cervical cancer, 75
Ivory Coast, 193
Iwanowski, Dmitri, 46

Jackson, Frederick, 24
Jackson, Michael, 188
Jaffe, Harold, viii, 104, 133-137, 217, 240
Japan, 3-5, 8-9, 11, 14-15, 26, 42, 54, 59, 111, 114, 236
    Institute of Public Health, 7
    Japanese Society of Internal Medicine, 5
    Kanazawa District Court, 15
    Kurume University, 6

Kyoto University, 5, 13
Kyushu, 86
Mie University, 4
Ministry of Health and Welfare, 5, 7, 11
National Institute of Health, 7
Niigata University, 10
Tokyo District Court, 14
University of Tokyo, 7
Jarvis, Howard, 186
Jenner, Edward, 46-47
Johns Hopkins University, 95
Johnson, "Magic", vi
Johnson, Jerry, 267
Johnson, Sherry, 220
Joswig, Christian, 239
Journal of AIDS Research, 132
Journal of Infectious Diseases, 96
Journal of NIH Research, 45
Journal of the American Medical Association (JAMA), 89, 96, 139, 148

Karlsberg, Florence, 244
Karpas, Abraham, 111, 114
Kenya, 173, 236
Kessler, David, 220
King, Larry, 245
Klebs, Edwin, 20
Koch's postulates, 20-22, 25, 28, 33, 35-36, 38, 46, 50, 54, 58, 60, 63, 66, 68-70, 77, 79, 84, 101, 123-129, 133, 135, 142, 153, 157, 159, 261-262
Koch, Robert, 12, 20-23, 26-28, 41, 62, 124, 133-134, 260
Kono, Reisaku, 4-8, 12-13, 15-17
Konotey-Ahulu, Felix, 190, 192-194
Koop, C. Everett, 69, 120
Koppel, Ted, 246
Koprowski, Hilary, viii, 54-56, 88, 115, 228, 261
Korean War, 95
Kramer, Larry, 179, 238
Krieger, Lisa, 242
Krim, Mathilde, 149-150, 167, 237
Krynen, Evelyne, 190
Krynen, Philippe, 190
KSOI Task Force. *See* Centers for Disease Control
kuru, 8, 51-53, 55-56, 87, 261
Kusui, Kenzo, 4-5

Lancet, The, 14, 26, 165-166, 168, 190, 192, 215, 240
Landers, Ann, 72
Lange, Michael, 208
Langmuir, Alexander, viii, 95-96, 98, 240, 261
Lapp, Ralph E., 41
LaRouche, Lyndon, 122
Larry King Live (CNN), 245
Lasker Prize, 114, 167
Lasker, Mary, 72
latent period, 50-52, 54-56, 58-59, 68-71, 73, 77, 79, 86, 108-109, 127, 135, 155-157
Lauritsen, John, 151-154, 165, 179, 181, 185, 209, 238-239, 244
LAV. *See* human immunodeficiency virus
Lavinder, Claude, 30-31
Lederle pharmaceutical company, 54
Leeuwenhoek, Antony, 19, 22
Legionella pneumophila, 36-38
Legionnaire's disease, 35-38, 101-103, 227, 229, 261
Leonard, Mike, 216
leprosy, 33-34, 133
leukemia, 53, 63-68, 71, 82, 84-87, 99, 107-108, 111, 133, 261
Levy, Jay, 111, 210
Lilly, Frank, 243
Lind, James, 23
Lister, Joseph, 19, 24
liver cancer, 78-80, 86
liver cirrhosis, 175
Lo, Shyh-Ching, 157, 162, 164
Long, John D., 30
Los Angeles Times, 247, 267
Los Angeles Times Magazine, 74
lung cancer, 104, 175, 206
Lwoff, André, 67-68, 73, 77, 85, 115
lymphadenopathy-associated virus (LAV). *See* human immunodeficiency virus
lymphoma, 88

MacArthur, John D. and Catherine T., Foundation, 229
MacArthur Prize, 165
MacNeil-Lehrer News Hour, 221, 245
macrophage cells, 125
Maddox, John, 250
Maekawa, Magojiro, 5

Majocchi, 28
malaria, 19, 27, 30, 70, 94-95, 191, 193
Malaria Control in War Areas (MCWA)
  See Centers for Disease Control
Manhattan Beach Women's Health
  Center, 75
Manhattan Project, 41-42, 49, 123
Mann, Jonathan, 96
Marine Hospital Service, 47
Maryland, 51, 55, 78, 131
Massachusetts Institute of Technology
  (MIT), 81, 227, 252
Max Planck Institute, 162
McClintock, Barbara, 160-161
McCloskey, John, 113
McCormick, Douglas, 169
McKenna, Joan, 155-156, 179, 185
measles, 55-56, 127, 133
Medicaid, 231
Medical Hypotheses, 264
Medicare, 229, 231
Mellon, Andrew W., Foundation, 229
mercury, 30, 35, 155
Merson, Michael, 96
Mexico, 80, 100
Miami Herald, 242
Michigan, 252
Michigan State University, 165
Middle Ages, 122
Milstein, Cesar, 115
monoclonal antibody, 115
mononucleosis, 70, 87-88, 107, 129
Montagnier, Luc, 109111, 114115, 126,
  128, 134, 149, 157, 162-164
Morbidity and Mortality Weekly Report
  (MMWR), 103
Mouse AIDS (MAIDS), 116
Mozart, Wolfgang Amadeus, 155, 264
Mullis, Kary, 169
multiple sclerosis, viii, 53, 56, 130, 147
mumps, 54-56
Murphy, John, 37-38, 101
mycoplasma, 75
Mycoplasma incognitus, 157, 164
Myth of Heterosexual AIDS, The, 139,
  240
myxoviruses, 55

Nagel, Cheryl, 197-201
Nagel, Lindsey, 197-202
Nagel, Steve, 197-201
Nasopharyngeal carcinoma, 71

National Academy of Engineering, 229
National Academy of Sciences, vii, 43,
  45, 57, 83, 112, 115, 153, 158, 167,
  228-229, 233, 248-249
National Aeronautics and Space
  Administration (NASA), 45
National Association for People With
  AIDS (NAPWA), 236
National Association of Broadcasters,
  239
National Cancer Act, 72, 82
National Cancer Conference (Third) 66
National Commission on AIDS, 121,
  234
National Conference of State
  Legislatures, 236
National Council of La Raza, 236
National Education Association (NEA),
  236
National Foundation for Infantile
  Paralysis (NFIP), 47-49, 51
National Institute on Drug Abuse
  (NIDA), 175, 251
National Institutes of Health (NIH),
  passim, except Chapters 2 and 6
    Foundation for the Advancement
      of Education in the Sciences,
      113
    Hygienic Laboratory, 47
    Laboratory of Central Nervous
      System Studies, 53
    National Cancer Institute (NCI),
      64-66, 68, 71-73, 84, 89, 99,
      106, 109, 135, 150, 153, 157,
      205, 212, 244, 266
        Acute Leukemia Task
          Force, 71
        Laboratory of Tumor Cell
          Biology, 85
    National Institute of Allergy and
      Infectious Diseases (NIAID),
      73, 106, 150, 213, 216, 266
    Office of Research Integrity
      (ORI), 112, 115
National Panel of Consultants on the
  Conquest of Cancer, 72
National Parent-Teacher Association,
  236
National School Boards Association,
  236
National Science Foundation (NSF), 42
National Urban League, 236

288   *Index*

Nature, 76, 81-82, 115, 132, 148, 162-163, 165, 167-169, 243, 246, 250, 259
   New Biology, 82
Naturwissenschaften, 162
neoplasia, 77
New England Journal of Medicine, 103, 128, 132, 153, 165, 241
New Guinea, 8, 27, 51, 53
New Scientist, 111
New York, 54, 73, 101, 176, 248
New York Academy of Medicine, 152
New York Academy of Sciences, 67, 257
New York City Department of Health, 147
New York Native, 152-154, 165, 237, 269
New York Safer Sex Committee, 152
New York Times, 32, 96, 101, 241-242, 246-247, 259, 263
news media, vi, 13, 30, 32, 35, 82, 85, 96, 101, 106, 110, 120, 187-190, 221, 239-240, 250, 256, 259, 267
   censorship, 165, 169, 240-247
Newsday, 210
Newsweek, 106, 241, 246
Newton, Isaac, 41
niacin, 33
Nigeria, 192
nitroglycerine, 222
Nixon, Richard, 72, 82, 89, 149, 266
Nobel Prize, vii-viii, 46-47, 53, 73, 81, 85, 111, 115, 159-161, 169, 202, 227-228, 260-261
Null, Gary, 223
Nureyev, Rudolf, 154
Nussbaum, Bruce, 207

Occupational Safety and Health Administration (OSHA), 219
Office of Management and Budget, 264
Office of Naval Research, 41
Olympic Games, 5
"Operation AIDS Control", 232
Orion Pictures, 149
orphan viruses, 50
Ortleb, Charles, 152-153, 165, 237, 269
Osler's Modern Medicine, 24
Outstanding Investigator Grant (OIG), vii, 249-251

Pan Data Systems Inc., 113

Parade, 216
Parkinson's disease, 184
Parkman, Paul, 211
Partage, 191
Pasteur Institute. *See* France
Pasteur, Louis, 12, 19, 24, 27-28, 46, 62
pasteurization, 24
Pauling, Linus, 249
peer review, vii, 44, 264-265
Pekelharing, Dr., 26
Pellagra, 17, 27, 29-32, 47, 97, 116, 169, 175, 261
   1st National Conference on Pellagra, 30
   2nd National Conference on Pellagra, 31
   Thompson-McFadden Commission, 31, 32
Penhoet, Edward, 58-59
Pennsylvania, 55
People, 221
People With AIDS Coalition (PWAC), 208
Petri plate, 21
Pharmacology and Therapeutics, 257
Philadelphia Gay News, 152
Physician's Desk Reference, 198
Pinching, Anthony, 222
pneumonia, 19, 21, 36-38, 97, 103
Poison by Prescription: The AZT Story, 154
Policy Review, 156, 158
polio, 2, 97, 127, 133, 159
   epidemic, viii, 1, 3, 17, 47, 49, 50, 53, 62, 98, 110, 130, 260
   vaccine, 158
   virus, 4, 47-48, 50
   war on polio, viii, 3, 12, 45, 47-50, 54, 65-66, 73, 81, 228, 261, 266
polymerase chain reaction (PCR), 126, 169
polyoma virus, 65-66, 69, 73
Popovic, Mikulas, 112
Portugal, 236
Presidential Commission on the HIV epidemic, 210, 233, 243
prions, 57
Priori, Elizabeth S., 66
Proceedings of the National Academy of Sciences (PNAS), 132, 161, 241, 248-249

Project AIDS International, 258
Project Inform, 210, 237, 239
Proposition 102, 186
Proposition 13, 186
Prusiner, Stanley, 56-57
ptomaines, 24
Public Health Action in Emergencies Caused by Epidemics, 233
Public Health Service, (PHS) 30, 31, 45, 47, 94-96, 231
Puerto Rico, 236
Pulitzer prize, 246
Purtilo, David, 148
Pyrard, Francois, 23

quarantine, vi, 24, 31, 33, 35, 94, 122, 231-233, 236
quinine, 27-28

rabies, 46, 55, 95
Rather, Dan, 106
Rauscher, Frank, 73
Reagan, Ronald, 114, 246
recreational drugs, 177-180, 184, 207, 230, 237, 251, 269
    amphetamines, 175, 178-180, 184, 237
    cocaine, 157, 175, 177-180, 184, 193, 221, 237
    drug epidemic, 175-176
    ethylene chloride, 178-180
    heroin, 2, 16, 57, 78, 93, 105, 121, 125, 140-142, 175-176, 180, 182-184, 187-188, 193, 207, 216, 232, 237
    marijuana, 175, 177-179
    methamphetamine, 177, 184
    nitrites, 104, 106, 110, 148, 152-153, 173, 175-184, 207, 213, 217, 237, 251
    psychedelics, 175
Red Crescent, 236
Red Cross, 86, 105, 191, 236
Reed, Walter, 46
Research in Immunology, 132, 163
Research in Virology, 163
Rethinking AIDS, 166
Retrovir. *See* azidothymidine
retroviruses, 80-82, 84-87, 93, 107-109, 111, 116, 123, 125, 129, 131, 142
reverse transcriptase, 81, 83, 85, 110, 202, 205, 227

Review of Medical Microbiology, 14
rhinovirus, 124
ribonucleic acid (RNA), 45, 58, 81, 202
rifampicin, 34
risk groups (AIDS), 142-143, 155, 174, 176, 182, 187-189
    Africans, 173-174
    Haitians, 105
    hemophiliacs, vi, 1, 2, 16, 105-106, 120, 128, 140, 161, 174, 176, 180, 187-189
    homosexuals, vi-vii, 2, 16, 93, 103-106, 120, 125, 128, 139-140, 146, 148, 152, 173-174, 176-185, 189, 216-217, 237, 240
    intravenous drug users, vi-vii, 2, 16, 93, 105, 120, 125, 128, 140, 174, 176, 180, 183-184, 189, 216
    transfusion recipients, 1, 16, 105-106, 128, 174, 186-187, 197
RNA. *See* ribonucleic acid
Rockefeller Foundation, 229
Rockefeller Institute, 54, 63-64
Rockefeller University, 252-253
Rockefeller, David, 252-253
Rogers, David, 234
Romania, 197
Ronsseus, 22
Roosevelt, Franklin, 47, 64
Root-Bernstein, Robert S., 165-167, 246
rotavirus, 124
Rous sarcoma virus, 64, 73, 80, 82, 228
Rous, Peyton, 63-64, 73, 80
rubella, 127
Rubin, Harry, vii-viii, 80, 82, 167, 249
Russia, 46

Sabin, Albert, 1, 55, 65-66, 158-159
"safe sex", v, 1, 121, 123, 136, 149, 151, 156, 194, 231, 234, 236, 243, 253, 262, 269
Salahuddin, Syed Zaki, 113
Salieri, 264
Salk, Jonas, 1, 48-49, 55, 65, 98, 115, 159, 165, 204, 256
Sambon, Louis, 30-31
San Francisco Chronicle, 247
San Francisco Examiner, 242
Sarin, Prem, 113
Schmidt, Peter, 239

Schmitz, Cesar, 268
Schmitz, Louise, 268
Schmitz, Teresa, 268
Science, 44, 53, 110, 113, 132, 162-163, 165, 167-168, 183, 245, 256
Science & Government Report, 72, 262
Scott, Frederick, 169
scrapie, 53, 56
scurvy, 22-25, 97, 116, 169, 175, 261
Secret Service, 252
Secretary of Health and Human Services, 244, 250
Sencer, David, 99, 101-102
Sentinel, The, 238
Service Employees International Union (SEIU), 236
Sex Information and Education Council of the U.S. (SIECUS), 236
Shandera, Wayne, 103
Shannon, James, 48-49, 65, 71-72, 94, 98, 203, 261, 263, 266
Sharrar, Robert, 101
Shigematsu, Itsuzo, 7
Shilts, Randy, 103, 107-108, 180
Shingu, Masahisa, 6
Shorter, Edward, 93
simian AIDS (SAIDS), 116
simian immunodeficiency virus (SIV), 116, 134
simian virus 40 (SV40), 65-66, 69, 73
Simon, Candace, 201-202
Simon, Doug, 201-202
Simon, Nancy, 201-202
Singer, "Nan", 75
slow viruses, 8, 51-52, 54-55, 67, 87, 123, 134, 227, 261
smallpox, 2, 46
Sonnabend, Joseph, 146-152, 154, 166, 177, 216
South Africa, 146
Southern Christian Leadership Conference, 236
Southern Medical Association, 32
Soviet Union, 42
Spiegelman, Sol, 83, 85
SPIN, 156, 190
Sputnik, 42
St. Martin's Press, ix
Staley, Pete, 238
Stanford University, 238
Stanley, Wendell M., 46-47, 66, 73, 80-81

Steadman, Lyle, 53
sterile needles, vi, 1, 121, 123, 183, 231, 234, 236, 253, 262, 269
steroid hormones, 78
Stewart, C.P., 25
Stewart, Gordon, 168
Stewart, Sarah, 65
Stewart, William, 96
Stoneburner, Rand, 240
Strategies for Survival, 237
Straus, Stephen, 88
Streisand, Barbra, 237
strychnine, 27, 179
Studio 54 (New York), 221
subacute myelo-optic neuropathy (SMON), 54, 97, 116, 175, 185, Chapter 1 *passim*
    Australia, 11
    bacteria, 8
    coxsackie virus, 7
    epidemic, 3-4, 6, 8, 11, 12, 14
    Europe, 11
    Great Britain, 11
    India, 11
    Inoue virus, 13-15
    Maekawa Commission, 5-6, 9, 12
    mycoplasma, 8
    named, 5
    Okayama outbreak, 6-7, 9
    Pseudomonas bacteria, 9
    Shingu virus, 6
    SMON Research Commission, 7-9, 11-12, 14-15
    Sweden, 11
    Toda outbreak, 5
    virus (unnamed), 7
Subacute sclerosing panencephalitis (SSPE), 55-56, 133
    caused by HIV, 56
sulfones, 34
Sullivan, Louis, 250
Sunday Express (London), 259
Sunday Telegraph (London), 258
Sunday Times (London), 168, 259
Surgeon General, vi, 69, 94, 96, 120, 244
Surviving AIDS, 216
Sweden, 183
swine flu, 99-102, 227, 232
Switzerland, 156, 183, 239
Symonds, John Addington, 151
syphilis, 21, 25, 29, 35, 75, 143, 155

neurosyphilis, 35, 130, 155
treatment, 155-156
treatments, 35

T cells, 93, 103, 108-109, 112, 116, 121,
124-125, 128-131, 138, 183-184, 198-
200, 205, 207, 210, 217-218, 220,
240, 256, 267
Taiwan, 80
Takaki, Kanehiro, 25-26
Takasaki, Hiroshi, 4
Tanabe Seiyaku, Ltd., 15
Tanzania, 191-193
tapeworms, 95
Taylor, Elizabeth, 188, 237
Telegraph, The (London), 259
Temin, Howard, viii, 80-85, 110, 115,
132, 135-137, 167-168, 202, 229, 245
Tennessee, 185
Terrence Higgins Trust, 246
tetanus, 21
Texas, 178
Thailand, 80, 123, 193
AIDS epidemic, 189
Third World, 19, 47, 57, 78-79, 107,
189-191, 193, 233
Thomas, Charles, 164-165, 169
Threakall, Bob, 258
Threakall, Sue, 258
Time, 106, 247
Titius, 28
Tizzoni, 29
tobacco mosaic disease, 46, 50
Todaro, George, 81
Totsuka, Etsuro, 5, 7, 9-10, 13-14
transposons, 160
Treatment Action Group (TAG), 238
trichomonas, 75
Tsubaki, Tadao, 10
Tsugane, Dr., 12
tuberculosis, 2, 19, 21, 23, 26, 33-34,
97, 184, 190, 192, 231, 260
Tufts University, 252
Tulane University, 257
Turck, Marvin, 96
Tylenol, 199
typhus, 23, 95

UCLA Medical Center, 147
Uganda, 69, 140, 190, 194
unconventional viruses, 52-53, 55-56,
67

United Nations, 229
UN Development Programme
(UNDP), 191
United States, 51, 68, 80, 85, 94, 96,
100, 155, 165, 175, 189-190, 197,
204, 232-233, 237, 241, 261
AIDS epidemic, 139, 143
Congress, 37, 44, 47, 49, 71-72,
89, 95, 98-99, 105, 122, 152,
203, 219, 229, 234, 252, 261-
262, 266
President, 234, 246
restrictions on HIV positives, 122
science spending, 43-45, 49, 72,
82, 88, 105, 234, 259, 266
Senate, 218, 264
United States Conference of Mayors
(USCM), 235
University of California
Berkeley, vii, 47, 80, 250-251
Los Angeles, 15, 103
San Francisco, 56, 210, 228
University of Miami, 207, 218
University of Minnesota, 199
University of North Texas, 257
University of Washington, 96
University of Wisconsin, 81
US Labor Party, 122

Varmus, Harold, viii, 228, 266
Veteran's Administration, 214
VA Hospital, 65
Vietnam War, 107, 175
Villemin, Jean-Antoine, 23-24
virus hunters, vii, viii, 3, 12, 15-17, 33,
39, 45, 47, 50, 53-57, 63-64, 66, 71-
72, 74-78, 83, 86, 88, 90, 93-94, 97,
102, 106-107, 109-111, 116, 127,
130, 133, 146, 159, 167-168, 202,
204, 207, 213, 215, 223, 227-228,
249, 253, 257, 260-262
Virus-Cancer Program, 71, 73, 85, 87,
99, 203, 227, 261
vitamin B1 (thiamin), 25, 27
vitamin C, 22, 23, 24, 25, 249
Vogt, Peter, 82, 228
Volberding, Paul, 213-215, 229
Voyage des Krynen en Tanzanie, 190
Vurpillat, Patty, 74-75
Vurpillat, Victor, 74

Wall Street Journal, 149, 179

war on AIDS, vii-ix, 1, 16, 45, 50, 54,
    60, 90, 121, 146, 174, 203, 223, 256,
    259-260, 262, 266, 268-269, Chapter
    10 *passim*
war on cancer, 45, 49, 60, 93, 102, 107,
    116, 129-130, 149, 161, 227-228,
    237, 262, 266, Chapter 4 *passim*
Warner, Jim, 246
warts, 64, 74, 76-78, 129, 143
Washington Post, 223, 247
Watson, James, 41, 73, 160-162
Waxman, Henry, 105
Wecht, Cyril H., 102
Weinberg, Alvin, 45
Weinberg, Robert, viii, 228
Weiss, Robin, 114, 133-137
Weller, Ian, 214
White House, 244, 246, 262
White, Ryan, vi, 188-189
Whitehead Institute, 227
Whitehead, Edwin C., 227
Williams, Louis, 94
Williams, Robert, 27
Wilson, Hank, 152-153, 179, 181
Wimbledon, 222

Wistar Institute, 55, 88, 115
Witkin, Steven, 148
Wong-Staal, Flossie, 249
Woods, Gail Baker, 260
World Bank, 191
World Health Organization (WHO), 35,
    55, 80, 96, 107, 120, 140, 190-191,
    221, 233
    Global Program on AIDS, 96
World War I, 94, 203
World War II, 41-43, 47, 49, 65, 68, 94,
    160, 186, 203, 249, 262
Wright Brothers, 210
Wylie, Catherine, 74

yellow fever, 46, 133, 231

Zagury, Daniel, 113
Zaire, 107, 140, 173-174, 190
Zeil um Zehn, 258
zidovudine. *See* azidothymidine
zur Hausen, Harald, 76-77

———————— Order Form ————————

Get your own copy now!

Why We Will Never Win the War on AIDS
by Bryan J. Ellison and Peter H. Duesberg

Copies are $19.95 each plus $3.00 shipping & handling
($9.00 s&h outside US)
—California residents, please add 8.25% sales tax

No.   Amount

_____ quality paperback copies at $19.95 each _____

sales tax (if applicable)   _____

shipping   _____

Total   US$ _____

(*please print*)

Name: _____

Address: _____

City: _____ State: ____ Zip: _____

Send check or money order to:

Inside Story Communications
1525 E. Noble, #102
Visalia, CA 93292

(Ask about volume discounts, including wholesale prices, and
about promotional arrangements)

———————— Order Form ————————

Get your own copy now!

Why We Will Never Win the War on AIDS
by Bryan J. Ellison and Peter H. Duesberg

Copies are $19.95 each plus $3.00 shipping & handling
($9.00 s&h outside US)
—California residents, please add 8.25% sales tax

No.   Amount

_____ quality paperback copies at $19.95 each _____

                              sales tax (if applicable)   _____

                                        shipping   _____

                              Total   US$_____

(please print)

Name: _____

Address: _____

City: _____ State: _____ Zip: _____

Send check or money order to:

Inside Story Communications
1525 E. Noble, #102
Visalia, CA 93292

(Ask about volume discounts, including wholesale prices, and
about promotional arrangements)

———————— Order Form ————————

Get your own copy now!

Why We Will Never Win the War on AIDS
by Bryan J. Ellison and Peter H. Duesberg

Copies are $19.95 each plus $3.00 shipping & handling
($9.00 s&h outside US)
—California residents, please add 8.25% sales tax

No.   Amount

_____ quality paperback copies at $19.95 each _____

                              sales tax (if applicable) _____

                                        shipping _____

                              Total   US$_____

(*please print*)

Name: _____

Address: _____

City: _____ State: _____ Zip: _____

Send check or money order to:

Inside Story Communications
1525 E. Noble, #102
Visalia, CA 93292

(Ask about volume discounts, including wholesale prices, and
about promotional arrangements)

Do today's news headlines confuse you?
That's because the media doesn't tell you the real story—
The INSIDE STORY

These days, just about everyone realizes that the news media is so biased in its "coverage" that you can no longer make sense of the world. But that bias isn't in what the media reports. It's in what the media <u>doesn't</u> report—or else <u>buries</u> on the back pages.

And without the real news, you can't possibly make sensible decisions to protect your family, your investments, your career... or your future as a free citizen. Powerful events are about to take place throughout the world, events that will disrupt the way you live. Unless you prepare yourself now, you'll be taken totally by surprise.

Author **Bryan J. Ellison** brings you the hard information you need in the form of a monthly, 8-page newsletter called **The Inside Story: World Report**. He and his research team of well-informed conservatives fill each issue with startling facts, opening your eyes to issues you didn't even know existed. We answer the questions you never even thought to ask, and expose the hidden forces behind fast-moving events:

• Why terrorism is on the rise, and will soon explode in America.

• How, and why, the State Department is betraying such allies as Israel, South Africa, the Philippines, and El Salvador.

• The Clintons' links to the PLO and other terrorists.

• What the New World Order <u>really</u> means, and why you will want to help stop it.

• Who's behind the gun control movement, and why they plan to disarm <u>you</u>.

• The shocking evidence that Communism <u>never died</u>—and that the "former" Soviet Union is about to re-emerge as a superpower.

• And much, much more.

How do we uncover these stories? We're not prophets. But we do know the background to the headlines, as found in many thousands of books, reports, and other published sources. By digging up the complete news from hundreds of publications and placing it <u>back</u> into context, we can bring you hard-hitting, information-packed analysis every month—and give you amazingly accurate insight into the future. We even break the cardinal rule of newsletter publication: we publish footnotes, showing you where to find the original sources.

You simply <u>can't</u> find this full information anywhere else today. Parts of it can be found in high-priced financial publications. But because we want <u>you</u> to have access to this knowledge, we're making the <u>whole</u> story available to you <u>for only $48.00 per year</u> (US$60.00 foreign). So take us up on this fantastic deal—before you find yourself on the wrong side of world events.

For a subscription to *The Inside Story: World Report*, send a check or money order to

Inside Story Communications
190 El Cerrito Plaza, #201
El Cerrito, CA 94530

Do today's news headlines confuse you?
That's because the media doesn't tell you the real story—
The INSIDE STORY

These days, just about everyone realizes that the news media is so biased in its "coverage" that you can no longer make sense of the world. But that bias isn't in what the media reports. It's in what the media doesn't report—or else buries on the back pages.

And without the real news, you can't possibly make sensible decisions to protect your family, your investments, your career... or your future as a free citizen. Powerful events are about to take place throughout the world, events that will disrupt the way you live. Unless you prepare yourself now, you'll be taken totally by surprise.

Author **Bryan J. Ellison** brings you the hard information you need in the form of a monthly, 8-page newsletter called **The Inside Story: World Report**. He and his research team of well-informed conservatives fill each issue with startling facts, opening your eyes to issues you didn't even know existed. We answer the questions you never even thought to ask, and expose the hidden forces behind fast-moving events:

• Why terrorism is on the rise, and will soon explode in America.

• How, and why, the State Department is betraying such allies as Israel, South Africa, the Philippines, and El Salvador.

• The Clintons' links to the PLO and other terrorists.

• What the New World Order really means, and why you will want to help stop it.

• Who's behind the gun control movement, and why they plan to disarm you.

• The shocking evidence that Communism never died—and that the "former" Soviet Union is about to re-emerge as a superpower.

• And much, much more.

How do we uncover these stories? We're not prophets. But we do know the background to the headlines, as found in many thousands of books, reports, and other published sources. By digging up the complete news from hundreds of publications and placing it back into context, we can bring you hard-hitting, information-packed analysis every month—and give you amazingly accurate insight into the future. We even break the cardinal rule of newsletter publication: we publish footnotes, showing you where to find the original sources.

You simply can't find this full information anywhere else today. Parts of it can be found in high-priced financial publications. But because we want you to have access to this knowledge, we're making the whole story available to you for only $48.00 per year (US$60.00 foreign). So take us up on this fantastic deal—before you find yourself on the wrong side of world events.

For a subscription to *The Inside Story: World Report*, send a check or money order to

Inside Story Communications
190 El Cerrito Plaza, #201
El Cerrito, CA 94530